CS NOW! 11-14

02/089

~~RYAN MOORE~~
~~7 GREEN~~

~~James Buckle~~
~~8 Pn~~

~~George Coombes~~

Ezra Charles
7Blue

~~Jack Perrin~~
~~8 Green~~

Physics NOW!

11–14

Peter D Riley

JOHN MURRAY

Titles in this series:
Biology Now! 11–14 Pupil's Book ISBN 0 7195 7548 6
Biology Now! 11–14 Teacher's Resource Book ISBN 0 7195 7549 4
Chemistry Now! 11–14 Pupil's Book ISBN 0 7195 7546 X
Chemistry Now! 11–14 Teacher's Resource Book ISBN 0 7195 7547 8
Physics Now! 11–14 Pupil's Book ISBN 0 7195 7544 3
Physics Now! 11–14 Teacher's Resource Book ISBN 0 7195 7545 1

First published in 1999
by John Murray (Publishers) Ltd
50 Albemarle Street
London W1X 4BD

Reprinted 2000 (twice)

Layouts by Black Dog Design
Artwork by Barking Dog Art, Richard Duszczak and Tony Randell
Cover design by John Townson/Creation

Typeset in 12/14pt Garamond by Wearset, Boldon, Tyne & Wear
Printed and bound in Great Britain by Butler & Tanner, Frome and London

A catalogue entry for this title is available from the British Library

ISBN 0 7195 7544 3
Teacher's Resource Book ISBN 0 7195 7545 1

Contents

Preface

To the pupil

Physics is the scientific study of the interactions between matter and energy. These interactions can produce the colours of the rainbow in a shower, or the roar of the wind in a hurricane. At a greater distance, the interactions of matter and energy in the Sun produce light and heat, while inside our eyes light energy is converted to electrical energy, which passes to our brain and allows us to see.

Every event in the Universe, from your next breath to a star exploding, is an interaction of matter and energy, so physics is really a part of all other scientific subjects, rather than a separate one.

Our knowledge of physics has developed from the observations, investigations and ideas of many people over a long period of time. Today this knowledge is increasing more rapidly as there are more physicists – people who study how matter and energy interact – than ever before.

In the past, few people other than scientists were informed about the latest discoveries. Today, through newspapers and television, everyone can learn about the latest discoveries on a wide range of physics topics, from the exploration of distant galaxies and the nature of tiny particles inside an atom, to the development of scanners that allow doctors to see inside the body and satellites that allow us to communicate with other people around the Earth in seconds.

Physics Now! 11–14 covers the requirements of your examinations in a way that I hope will help you understand how observations, investigations and ideas have led to the scientific facts we use today. The questions are set to help you extract information from what you read and see, and to help you think more deeply about each chapter in this book. Some questions are set so you can discuss your ideas with others and develop a point of view on different scientific issues. This should help you in the future when new scientific issues, which are as yet unknown, affect your life.

The scientific activities of thinking up ideas to test and carrying out investigations are enjoyed so much by many people that they take up a career in science. Perhaps *Physics Now! 11–14* may help you to take up a career in science too.

To the teacher

Physics Now! 11–14 has been written to cover the requirements of the curriculum for the Common Entrance Examination at 13+, the National Curriculum for Science at Key Stage 3 and equivalent junior courses. It aims to help pupils to become more scientifically literate by encouraging them to examine the information in the text and illustrations in order to answer questions about it in a variety of ways. The book presents science as a human activity by considering the development of scientific ideas from the earliest times to the present day, and deals with applications of scientific knowledge and issues that arise from them.

Physics Now! 11–14 and its supporting *Teacher's Resource Book* are designed to provide the physics content of a balanced science course in which biology, chemistry and physics are taught separately. It may also be used as a supplementary text in more integrated courses to demonstrate aspects of science as a human activity and to extend skills in comprehension.

Acknowledgements

I would like to thank Bill Tucker and Peter Knight for reading and advising on the manuscript, Jane Roth for her editorial work and Katie Mackenzie Stuart and Julie Jones for their encouragement, help and support throughout the preparation of this book.

The following are sources from which tables and data have been adapted:

Table 1.7 **p.17** from M Hammond, *School Science Review* June 1993, **74** (269), p.96.
Tables 4.2 & 4.3 **p.89** from RS Holt, *School Science Review* September 1980, **62** (218) with permission.
Table 5.1 **p.103** from MS Byrne, *School Science Review* June 1981, **62** (221), p.749 with permission.

The following have supplied photographs or have given permission for photographs to be reproduced:

Cover Andrew Syred/Science Photo Library; **p.1** China Great Wall Industry Corporation/Science Photo Library; **p.2** ET Archive; **p.4** Science Museum/Science & Society Picture Library; **p.5** *t* © Crown Copyright 1989. Reproduced by permission of the controller of HMSO, photo: National Physical Laboratory, *b* Science Museum/Science & Society Picture Library; **p.6** *t* David Nunuk/Science Photo Library, *b* Northwestern University/Science Photo Library; **p.9** Keith Kent/Science Photo Library; **p.13** Andrew Lambert; **p.19** Ann Ronan at Image Select; **p.21** *tl, tc & br* Sporting Pictures (UK) Ltd, *tr* Robert Harding Picture Library, *bl* Adam Woolfitt/Robert Harding Picture Library; **p.22** Sporting Pictures (UK) Ltd; **p.24** *t* Isobel Cameron/Forest Life Picture Library, © Crown Copyright, *b* Dr Jeremy Burgess/Science Photo Library; **p.25** Sporting Pictures (UK) Ltd; **p.26** Takeshi Takahara/Science Photo Library; **p.27** *t* Action Images, *b* Julian Baum/Science Photo Library; **p.28** *tl* Jeffrey Rotman/Still Pictures, *tr* Richard Herrmann/Oxford Scientific Films, *bl* Martyn F. Chillmaid/Robert Harding Picture Library, *br* Philip Dunn/Rex Features; **p.29** Alex Bartel/Science Photo Library; **p.32** *t* R. Francis/Robert Harding Picture Library, *b* Mary Evans Picture Library; **p.34** Andrew Lambert; **p.38** © Crown Copyright, National Meteorological Office; **p.45** Action Images; **p.46** *t* Bildagentur Schuster/Robert Harding Picture Library, *b* John Townson/Creation; **p.51** Bildagentur Schuster/Herbst/Robert Harding Picture Library; **p.55** Andrew Lambert; **p.56** Sheila Terry/Science Photo Library; **p.57** Adam Woolfitt/Robert Harding Picture Library; **p.60** John Townson/Creation; **p.63** Space Telescope Science Institute/NASA/Science Photo Library; **p.64** Keith Kent/Science Photo Library; **p.67** *tl* John Townson/Creation, *tr* Action Images, *b* Action Images/Bob Martin; **p.69** NASA/Science Photo Library; **p.70** Hartmut Schwarzbach/Still Pictures; **p.71** *t* Mark Edwards/Still Pictures, *b* Jorgen Schytte/Still Pictures; **p.72** Mark Edwards/Still Pictures; **p.73** *tl* Andrew Lambert, *tr* Richard Folwell/Science Photo Library, *b* NASA/Science Photo Library; **p.74** Klaus Andrews/Still Pictures; **p.75** *t* Novosti Press Agency/Science Photo Library, *b* Martin Bond/Science Photo Library; **p.76** Martin Bond/Science Photo Library; **p.77** Mary Evans Picture Library; **p.78** *t* Jean-Loup Charmet/Science Photo Library, *b* Science Photo Library; **p.79** *t* Simon Fraser/Science Photo Library, *b* Robert Francis/Robert Harding Picture Library; **p.80** *l* Mary Evans Picture Library, *r* Science Photo Library; **p.81** ET Archive; **p.84** *tl & tr* Greg Balfour Evans/Greg Evans International, *b* Alsthom; **p.86** Martin Bond/Science Photo Library; **p.88** John Townson/Creation; **p.91** Andrew Lambert; **p.97** © Ove Arup & Partners; **p.100** *t* John Townson/Creation, *b* Robert Harding Picture Library; **p.101** Mark Edwards/Still Pictures; **p.104** John Townson/Creation; **p.106** Last Resort; **p.107** Mary Evans Picture Library; **p.108** Science Museum/Science & Society Picture Library; **p.110** John Walsh/Science Photo Library; **p.111** *t* Robert Francis/Robert Harding Picture Library, *b* Kent Wood/Still Pictures; **p.113** *t & b* Mary Evans Picture Library; **p.115** Peter Menzel/Science Photo Library; **p.118** Mary Evans Picture Library; **p.119** *t* CERN/Science Photo Library, *b* Lawrence Berkeley Laboratory/Science Photo Library; **p.123** John Townson/Creation; **p.129** Andrew Lambert; **p.130** Maplin; **p.131** Andrew Lambert; **p.132** *t* Maplin, *c* Andrew Lambert, *b* AT&T Bell Labs/Science Photo Library; **p.134** John Townson/Creation; **p.135** Andrew Lambert; **p.136** John Townson/Creation; **p.137** Andrew Lambert; **p.138** Andrew Lambert; **p.140** B & C Alexander/Science Photo Library; **p.141** *t* Michael Holford, *b* Science Museum/Science & Society Picture Library; **p.144** *t* Alex Bartel/Science Photo Library, *b* Maplin; **p.145** Maplin; **p.150** Alsthom; **p.151** Nigel Francis/Robert Harding Picture Library; **p.152** *t* Fred Bavendam/Still Pictures, *c* BPL Photo Library, *b* Wostek Laski/Rex Features; **p.153** Gordon Garradd/Science Photo Library; **p.157** Honda Motor Europe Ltd; **p.159** Matthias Breiter/Oxford Scientific Films; **p.160** *t* John Townson/Creation, *b* The Stock Market; **p.166** John Townson/Creation; **p.168** Ann Ronan at Image Select; **p.169** The Times/Rex Features; **p.172** BPL Photo Library; **p.176** *t* Roland Seitre/Still Pictures, *b* Xavier Eichaker/Still Pictures; **p.179** H. Verbiesen/Still Pictures; **p.182** The Stock Market; **p.187** *t* Norbert Wu/Still Pictures, *b* Saturn Stills/Science Photo Library; **p.189** Space Telescope Science Institute/NASA/Science Photo Library; **p.190** Jeff Hester & Paul Scowen, Arizona State University/Science Photo Library; **p.192** Jerry Lodriguss/Science Photo Library; **p.195** *t* Jean-Loup Charmet/Science Photo Library, *b* Science Museum/Science & Society Picture Library; **p.198** George East/Science Photo Library; **p.201** NASA/Science Photo Library; **p.202** NASA/Science Photo Library; **p.203** Science Museum/Science & Society Picture Library; **p.204** *t* Novosti/Science Photo Library, *b* NASA/Science & Society Picture Library; **p.205** NASA/Science Photo Library; **p.206** Dr Fred Espenak/Science Photo Library.

(*b* = bottom, *c* = centre, *l* = left, *r* = right, *t* = top)

The publishers have made every effort to contact copyright holders. If any have been overlooked they will make the necessary arrangements at the earliest opportunity.

1 Measurements

Launching a space rocket

Figure 1.1 A multi-stage rocket leaving the launch pad.

Three, two, one, zero, lift off! Light from the rocket engines can be seen immediately by the distant spectators as the rocket begins to rise from the launch pad. When the roar of the rocket engines reaches the spectators it nearly deafens them. The rocket's speed increases every second as it rises into the sky.

The rocket is divided into parts, called stages. Each stage has fuel tanks and rocket engines. When the fuel is used up in one stage that stage will separate from the rocket and fall back towards Earth. As the stage rushes back through the atmosphere it will become so hot that it will burn up. When the last stage has separated only a small spacecraft will remain in orbit around the Earth and then set off across the Solar System.

Some of the things that are described in the first two paragraphs are called phenomena. Each phenomenon, such as light and sound, can be investigated. The science of investigating phenomena such as light, sound and forces is called physics.

Scientists begin an investigation by asking a question. They think of an explanation to answer the question then test their explanation with an experiment.

A major part of an investigation is the making of observations. We use our senses to make observations – but our senses can be unreliable.

1 Look at the three lines in Figure 1.2a and write down their letters in order of length, starting with the longest. Repeat the exercise with the lines in Figure 1.2b. When you have finished, check your answers by measuring the lines. What does this tell you about your senses and the need to make measurements?

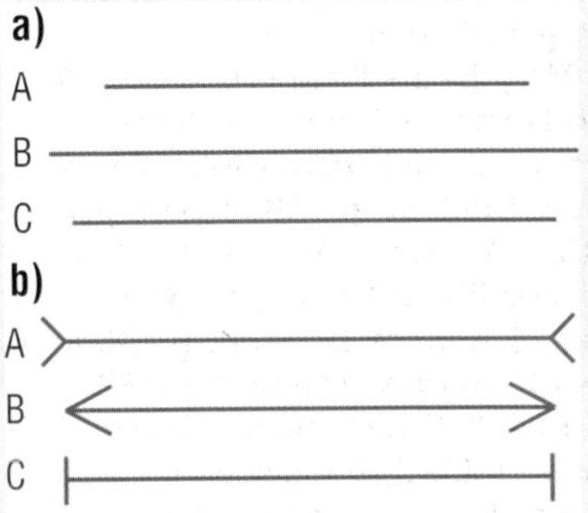

a)
A
B
C

b)
A
B
C

Figure 1.2

2 A girl puts her left hand in a bowl of cold water and her right hand in a bowl of hot water. After a minute she puts both hands in a bowl of warm water. How do you think the left hand and the right hand will feel in the bowl of warm water?

For discussion

After reading about the rocket launch, a person asked, 'Why was light from the rocket seen before the sound of the rocket was heard? Why did the stages fall back to Earth when they separated from the rocket? Why did the stages burn up in the atmosphere?'

What explanations can you give to answer these questions?

Length, mass and time

Rather than relying on senses, more accurate observations of phenomena are made by taking measurements. Three things that are measured in many investigations are length, mass and time. Any measurement is made in units, for example a common unit of length is the centimetre. There is an international system of units that is used by scientists throughout the world. This is known as the Système International d'Unités. The units in this system are known as SI units.

Measuring length

The standard SI unit of length is the metre. Its symbol is m, and, as with all symbols of SI units there is not a full stop placed after it. The metre is divided into smaller units for measuring small lengths or distances, and large

Explaining phenomena

In the period from 600 to 300BC, the Ancient Greek philosophers explained many phenomena but did not test their explanations with experiments. They made observations, formed opinions and argued about what they saw. The opinions of the Ancient Greeks were taught as facts for 2000 years.

Francis Bacon (1561–1626), an English philosopher, disagreed with the way the Ancient Greeks had explained phenomena. He set out the process of investigation that we use today. In this process, he said, the investigator should choose the facts to be investigated, form a hypothesis (an idea that links the facts together and can be tested), perform the test and evaluate the result; investigations should be repeated and from their results general theories and laws could be set up to explain the phenomena that are being studied. This change in how phenomena should be investigated became popular and eventually led to the setting up, in 1660, of the Royal Society in London where scientists could report on their investigations and discuss their work. Later, in 1799, the Royal Institution was set up where scientists demonstrated their experiments to the public.

Figure A Sir James Dewar (see page 95) lecturing on liquid nitrogen at the Royal Institution.

1 Which of the following statements contain
a) facts that can easily be investigated,
b) an opinion that cannot easily be investigated?
i) I am stronger than you.
ii) I am the best person in the world.
iii) You can only see the Moon at night.
iv) Chips are nicer than crisps.
Explain your answer in each case.

numbers of metres are made into bigger units to measure long lengths or distances. Table 1.1 shows some of these other SI units.

Table 1.1 Units of length.

Unit	Symbol	Number of metres
kilometre	km	1000 m
metre	m	1 m
centimetre	cm	0.01 m
millimetre	mm	0.001 m
micrometre	μm	0.000 001 m
nanometre	nm	0.000 000 001 m

Measuring mass

The standard SI unit of mass is the kilogram, whose symbol is kg. The other SI units of mass used in investigations are shown in Table 1.2.

Table 1.2 Units of mass.

Unit	Symbol	Number of kilograms
Megatonne	Mt	1 000 000 000 kg
tonne	t	1000 kg
kilogram	kg	1 kg
gram	g	0.001 kg
milligram	mg	0.000 001 kg

Measuring time

The standard SI unit of time is the second and its symbol is s. Other units of time used in investigations are shown in Table 1.3.

Table 1.3 Units of time.

Unit	Symbol	Number of seconds (minutes or hours)
day	d	86 400 s (1440 minutes, 24 hours)
hour	h	3600 s (60 minutes)
minute	min	60 s
second	s	1 s
millisecond	ms	0.001 s

3 If you saw someone commit a crime, how might you describe to a detective the appearance of the criminal and what happened? Do mass, length and time feature in your answer? If they do, say where they occur.

Finding a standard

If measurements are to be useful to a large number of people, the same units must be used by everyone. At first many people used parts of their own bodies as units of measure. Just as horses are measured in 'hands' today, the Ancient Egyptians around 2000 to 3000BC measured small distances by parts of the hand and arm. One width of the finger was a digit, four digits made a palm, five digits made a hand and 28 digits were a cubit, which was the distance from the finger tip to the elbow. However, as people vary in size the units also varied from one person to the next and led to confusion. In a city in Mesopotamia about 4000 years ago the people removed this confusion by basing their unit of measurement on the foot of a statue of the city's governor.

People measured longer distances, such as those in journeys, in units of time. The journeys were measured in hours, days or even 'moons'.

The first measure of time was the period of daylight and the period of dark. These two periods of time were then each divided up into twelve sections called temporal hours. The first hour of daylight began with the dawn and the first hour of the night began with the sunset. As the time of dawn and sunset varied through the year, the length of the hours of day and night varied too and depended on the time of year. Later the time taken for the Earth to complete one rotation, from midday to the following midday, was divided up into 24 one-hour periods.

The passing of the daylight hours was first measured with a shadow stick, invented in China about 4500 years ago. It was set upright in the ground and the change in position of the shadow was used to tell the time of day. About 1000 years later the Egyptians invented the sundial, which had a tilted bar called a gnomon that cast a shadow across a surface on which the hours were marked. Water clocks, sand clocks and candle clocks were used to measure time during the night.

The invention of mechanical clocks in the 1650s led to a closer synchronising of measured time with the turning of the Earth.

Jean Picard (1620–1682) was a French astronomer. He used his telescope and a set of measuring instruments to measure angles between the Earth and the stars. From his measurements he was able to calculate the circumference of the Earth.

1 a) Are all your digits on one hand the same width?
b) Does this affect your measurement of a short length under four digits? Explain your answer.

2 Is your cubit 28 digits?

3 Why was confusion over measuring removed by using the foot of a statue as a standard length?

4 What time period is a 'moon'?

5 In the first method of time-keeping, how would the length of the twelve temporal hours of **a)** a summer's day compare with those of a winter's day, **b)** a summer's night compare with those of a winter's night?

Figure A Some sand clocks consisted of sets of sand glasses. Each one measured a different period of time.

(continued)

In 1789 the French Revolution began. It brought great change to the way France was run. In 1790 a group of French scientists met to decide on standards that could be used throughout the country. They thought that the standard unit of length should be a fraction of the Earth's circumference. They decided that it should be one ten-millionth of the distance between the north pole and the equator along a north–south line. This unit of length was called the metre. They also decided that the standard unit of mass should be the gram and be based on the mass of a certain volume of water at a certain temperature. The system that they set up is called the metric system.

In time other countries adopted the metric system for all their measurements. In 1875 an International Bureau of Weights and Measures was set up in Paris. The people working there reviewed the standards and decided to replace them. Measurement of the metre based on the Earth's circumference was difficult to check so the standard for the metre became a distance between two marks on a bar of platinum–iridium alloy which was much easier to examine. The standard for mass was also made easier to check. It became a thousand times bigger – the kilogram, and is based on the mass of a platinum–iridium alloy block called the international prototype kilogram.

6 How was the Earth used to provide the standards of time and length?

7 Why is the Earth no longer used to provide these standards?

8 Two of today's standards can be measured by scientists anywhere in the world provided they have the equipment. Which standards are they?

9 How does having standard units of measurement help scientific investigation?

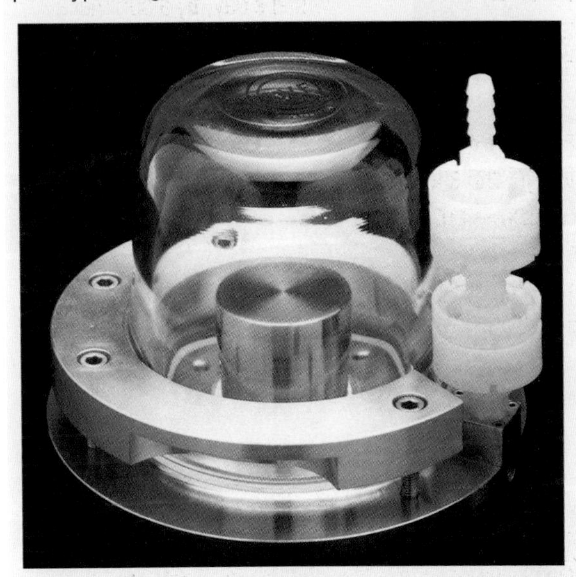

Figure B The international prototype kilogram.

Later the original standards of time and length were found to be unreliable. For example, further studies on the turning of the Earth showed that over the first half of the 20th Century its speed of daily rotation had slowed by two seconds. This led to the search for another standard for measuring time and in 1967 it was decided that a second should be that period of time in which the microwaves produced by hot caesium atoms vibrate 9 192 631 770 times.

Today the standard length of a metre is the distance covered by light in a vacuum in 1/299 792 458th of a second.

Figure C An 'atomic clock' in which the microwaves produced by caesium atoms are measured.

Very large and very small numbers

When very large or very small numbers are written down they are arranged in groups of three from the decimal point, without a comma between the groups.

For example, the Moon is 384 000 000 metres from the Earth and the 'width' of an atom is about 0.000 000 001 metres.

Figure 1.3 The Moon is 384 000 000 metres from the Earth.

Figure 1.4 The arrangement of individual atoms on the surface of a silicon crystal can be seen with an electron microscope.

These numbers can be more quickly written down and understood by using powers of ten. This saves writing down or interpreting large numbers of noughts. The following examples show how powers of ten can be used.

4 It is one thousand four hundred and twenty-seven thousand million kilometres from the Sun to Saturn. Write this down **a)** as an ordinary whole number and **b)** in standard form.

5 A bacterium feeding on a decaying body in the soil has a length of one-millionth of a metre. Write this down **a)** as a decimal fraction and **b)** in standard form.

6 Rewrite the following numbers in standard form:
a) 780×10^3, **b)** 49×10^6,
c) 247×10^{-6},
d) 8032×10^{-3},
e) 0.548×10^4.

- 20 is 2×10 so it can be written as 2×10^1
- 200 is $2 \times 10 \times 10$ so it can be written 2×10^2

The distance between the Earth and the Moon is $384 \times 10 \times 10 \times 10 \times 10 \times 10 \times 10$ metres, which can be written as 384×10^6 metres.

In order to make the system of recording large numbers consistent in science, only one figure is written in front of the decimal point. This way of writing the figure is called the standard form. The standard form of 384×10^6 is 3.84×10^8.

Very small numbers have a number of noughts after the decimal point. They can also be written down using powers of ten. Each time the decimal point is moved one nought or number to the right the power of ten changes by 10^{-1}. For example:

- 0.1 is 1.0×10^{-1}
- 0.01 is 1.0×10^{-2}

The width of an atom is about 0.000 000 001 metre, which is 1.0×10^{-9} metre.

Estimating quantities

At the beginning of an investigation it may be useful to estimate the quantities that are going to be used or the time that is going to be taken for certain observations. At this stage of the investigation accuracy is not essential – that comes later.

Accuracy of measurements

Your accuracy when making a measurement depends on the measuring instrument – how well it has been made, calibrated (compared with the standard) and how well the scale on the instrument has been constructed. A stopclock which only measures time by seconds cannot be used to time events to a tenth of a second. Your accuracy also depends on how well you use the measuring instrument. Care in setting up the device is needed. This includes placing a ruler accurately (both ends are important when measuring length), resetting a stopclock before repeating a timing and making sure that a balance is set at zero before a mass is put on it. If a balance is used with a scale that is read by looking at the position of a pointer, your eye should be placed directly in front of the pointer.

7 Estimate these quantities, then check your answers by measurement:

a) the length of your index finger and the length of your thumb
b) the height of your chair
c) the distance between you and a door
d) the mass of **i)** this book, **ii)** your school bag and its contents
e) the time it takes you to **i)** count the first 50 words on this page, **ii)** say those 50 words, **iii)** write down those 50 words.

8 a) How could you estimate the thickness of a page of this book?
b) Write down your estimate of the thickness of a page of this book and compare it with the estimates made by others. Are all the estimates the same? Explain what you discover.

9 In Figure 1.5, how would looking at the pointer from positions A and B affect the accuracy of the measurement?

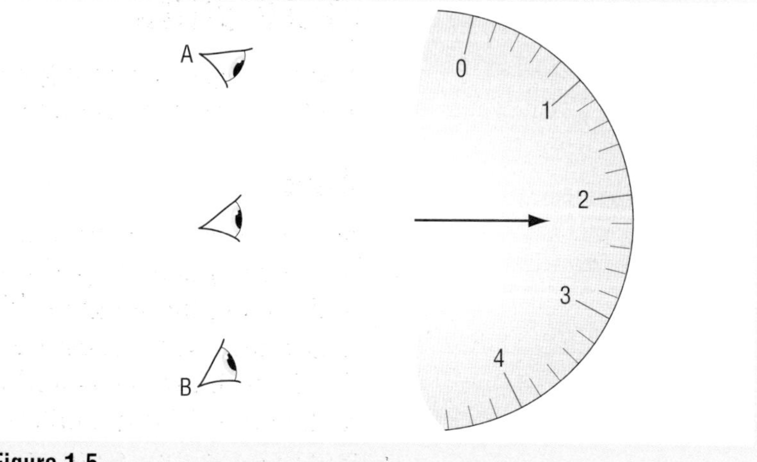

Figure 1.5

The accuracy you claim for a measurement is shown in the way that you write it down, as these examples show:

- A length written down as 10 cm means that the length may be 9.5 cm or 10.5 cm. The difference between the two extremes is 1.0 cm.
- A length written down as 10.0 cm means that the length may be 9.95 cm or 10.05 cm. The difference between the two extremes is 0.1 cm.
- A length written down as 10.00 cm means that the length may be 9.995 cm or 10.005 cm. The difference between the two extremes is 0.01 cm.

10 A length is shown as 10.55 cm.

a) What is the shortest and the longest length it could be?

b) What is the difference between these two possible lengths?

c) How does the accuracy of this reading compare with the 10.5 cm claimed in Figure 1.6?

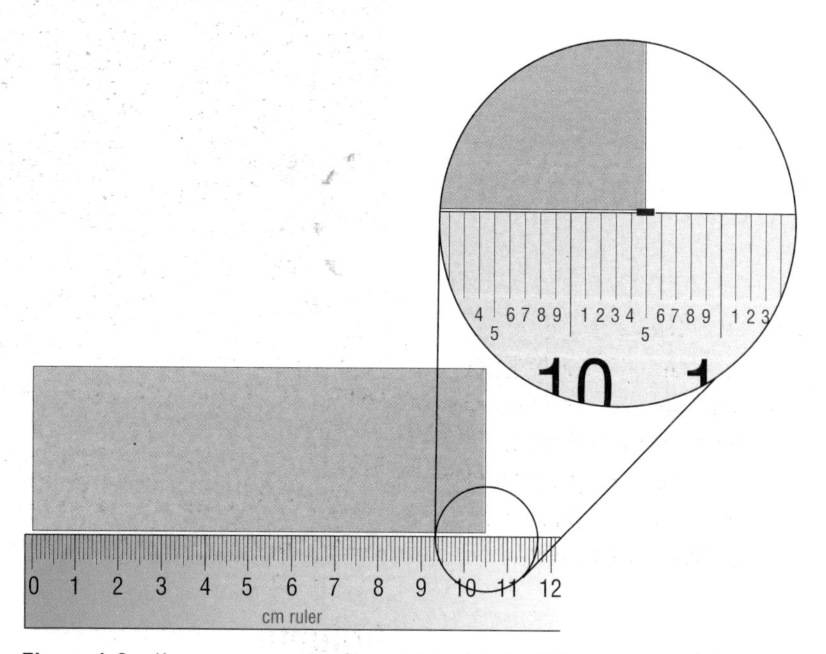

Figure 1.6 If you measure a length and claim it to be 10.5 cm, you are claiming that the ruler and your eyesight are good enough to be sure the edge of the object is in the range 10.45 cm to 10.55 cm.

More units

The units for measuring a wide range of other quantities are built up from the units of length, mass and time.

Area

An area is a measure of a surface. The area of the surface of a rectangular shaped object can be found by multiplying the length of the side by the width. The length and width must be measured in the same units – that is both are measured in metres or centimetres or millimetres. The quantities used to find an area are both length quantities so the area of a surface is a length multiplied by a length, or length squared. The standard SI unit of area is m^2 (square metre) but you may also use cm^2 or mm^2 depending on the length unit which is most convenient. An area of land may be measured in km^2.

Figure 1.7 Measuring an area at an archaeological site.

11 What is your area in contact with the surface of the Earth when you stand up? Estimate the area then find out by measuring the area of the soles of your shoes. Which unit is it easiest to use in doing this?

Many areas are irregularly shaped. They may be measured by drawing the outline of the area on squared paper and counting the number of squares and fractions of squares inside the outline.

Volume

The volume of an object is the amount of space that it occupies.

12 What is the volume of a solid block measuring three metres long by two metres wide and four metres high?

13 What is the volume of your bedroom? Estimate the volume first then make measurements and calculations. How good was your estimate? Which units did you use?

Measuring the volume of a regular shape

The volume of a solid with a regular shape, such as a cube, is found by multiplying together the length, height and width of the cube. All three quantities are lengths so the volume is a length × a length × a length, or length cubed. The volume of a cube with sides of one metre is 1 m^3, or one cubic metre.

This method of multiplying length, width and height can also be used to calculate the volume of rectangular blocks.

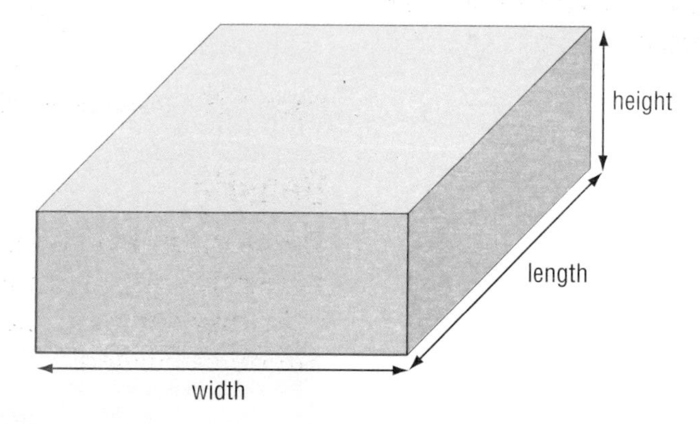

Figure 1.8 The quantities for calculating volume.

14 What is the volume of liquid in cylinders **a)** and **b)** in Figure 1.9?

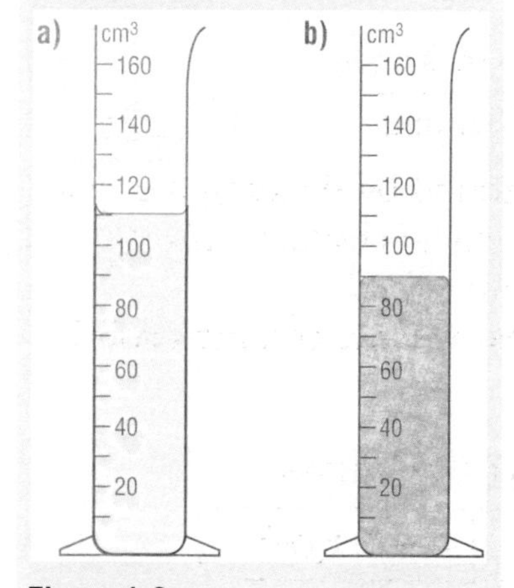

Figure 1.9

Measuring the volume of a liquid

The volume of a liquid can be found by pouring it into a measuring cylinder and reading the volume of the liquid from the scale. (See also *Chemistry Now! 11–14* page 2.) Care must be taken to read the scale level with the horizontal part of the liquid surface and not the curved part (meniscus) which forms where the liquid meets the side of the cylinder. Most liquids curve downwards but mercury curves upwards.

Measuring the volume of an irregularly shaped solid

An irregularly shaped solid, such as a pebble, does not have sides that can be easily measured. Its volume can easily be found by using a liquid. Water is poured into a measuring cylinder until the cylinder is about half full. The volume of the water is measured, then the pebble is lowered gently into it. When the pebble is completely immersed the volume of the water is read again. The volume of the pebble is found by subtracting the first reading from the second.

15 Find the volume of a pebble from these readings:
Original volume of water in cylinder = 50 cm^3
Combined volume of water and pebble = 84 cm^3

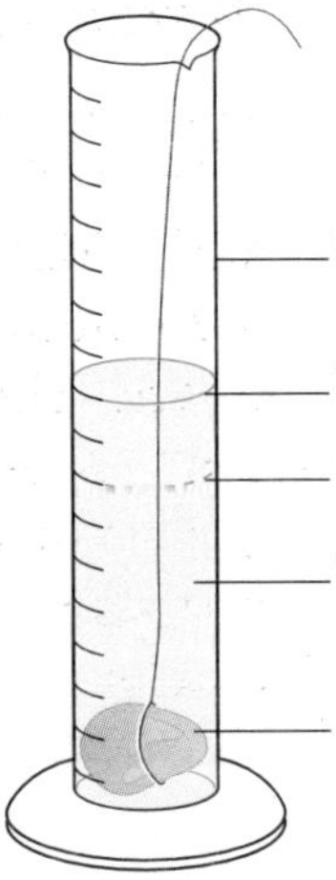

Figure 1.10 Measuring the volume of a pebble.

Density

The density of a substance is a measure of the amount of matter that is present in a certain volume of it. The following equation shows how the density of a substance can be calculated:

$$\text{density} = \frac{\text{mass}}{\text{volume}}$$

The basic SI unit of density is found by dividing the unit of mass by the unit of volume, so it is kg/m^3. This is pronounced kilograms per metre cubed.

Table 1.4 shows the densities of some common solid materials.

Table 1.4 The density of some common solid materials.

Material	**Density kg/m^3**
ice	920
cork	250
wood	650
steel	7900
aluminium	2700
copper	8940
lead	11350
gold	19320
polythene	920
perspex	1200
expanded polystyrene	15

16 Arrange the materials in Table 1.4 in order of density, starting with the least dense material.
17 Which is heavier, a cubic metre of steel or a cubic metre of aluminium?
18 Which is heavier, a kilogram of steel or a kilogram of cork?

19 A block of material is 8 cm long, 2 cm wide and 3 cm high, and has a mass of 46 g. What is its density?

20 a) Convert the density value you found in question 19 to kg/m^3.

b) Compare the density of the material in the block with those in Table 1.4 on page 11. Which materials in the table have densities closest to that of the block?

c) How could you convert the value of a density given in kg/m^3 to g/cm^3?

In the school laboratory when small amounts of materials are used the density of a substance is often calculated using masses measured in grams and volumes in cubic centimetres, giving a density value in g/cm^3. The density value in units of g/cm^3 can be converted to a value in kg/m^3 by multiplying it by 1000.

For example, ice was found to have a density of $0.920\,g/cm^3$. This can also be expressed as $0.920 \times 1000 = 920\,kg/m^3$.

Measuring the density of a rectangular solid block

The mass of the block is found by placing the block on a balance (check the balance reads zero first) and reading the scale. The mass in grams is recorded. The volume is found by multiplying the length, width and height of the block together and recording the value in cubic centimetres. The density of the material in the block is found by dividing the mass by the volume and expressing the quantity in the unit g/cm^3.

Measuring the density of a liquid

The density of a liquid is found in the following way.

A measuring cylinder is put on a balance and its mass found (A).

The liquid is poured into the measuring cylinder and its volume measured (V).

The mass of the measuring cylinder and the liquid it contains is found (B).

The mass of the liquid is found by subtracting A from B (B − A).

The density of the liquid is calculated by dividing the mass of the liquid by its volume:

$$\frac{B - A}{V}$$

Table 1.5 (opposite) shows the densities of some liquids.

Table 1.5 The density of some liquids.

Liquid	Density kg/m^3
mercury	13550
water at 4 °C	1000
corn oil	900
turpentine	860
paraffin oil	800
methylated spirits	790

21 When paraffin oil and water are poured into a container they separate and the paraffin oil forms a layer on top of the water. When water and mercury are mixed the water forms a layer on top of the mercury.
   a) What can you conclude from these two observations?
   b) What do you predict would happen if water and corn oil were mixed together? (Refer to Table 1.5.)

22 What do you think would happen if the following solids were placed in water:
a) expanded polystyrene,
b) polythene, **c)** perspex?
Explain your answers (refer to the values in Table 1.4).

23 What do you think would happen if the following solids were placed in mercury:
a) steel, **b)** gold, **c)** lead?
Explain your answers.

24 Why do you think the temperature of the water is shown when the value of the density is given?

25 Most people can just about float in water (Figure 1.12). What does this tell you about the density of the human body?

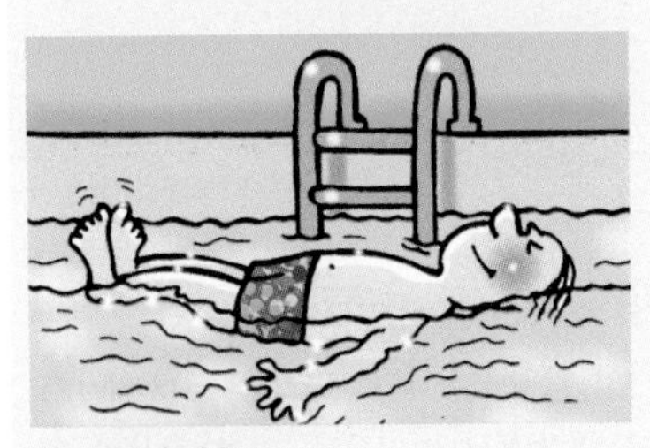

Figure 1.12

Floating and sinking

When a piece of wood is placed in water the wood floats. This is due to the difference in the densities of the wood and the water. From Tables 1.4 and 1.5 you can see that wood is less dense than water. When two substances, such as a solid and a liquid or a liquid and a liquid, are put together the less dense substance floats above denser substance.

When full-fat milk is poured into a container, such as a bottle, the cream, which contains fat and is less dense than the more watery milk, rises to the top.

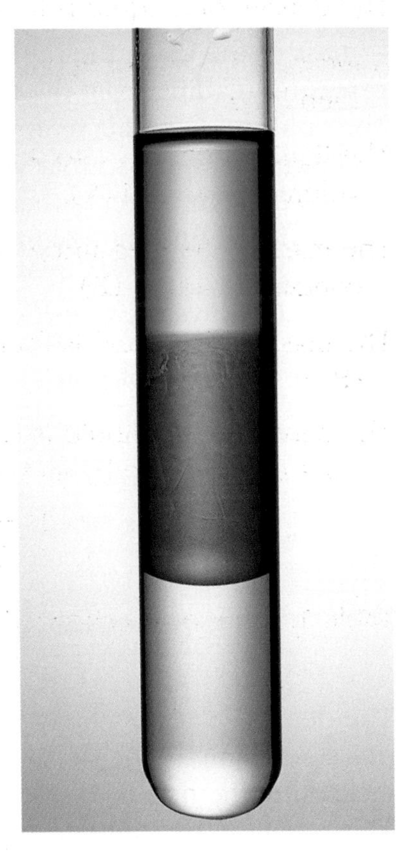

Figure 1.11 Liquids of different densities form layers when they are mixed.

26 When salt is dissolved in water the solution that is produced has a greater density than pure water. An object that floats on pure water is shown in Figure 1.13. When it is placed in salt solution do you predict it will rise higher in the solution than it did in pure water or sink lower?

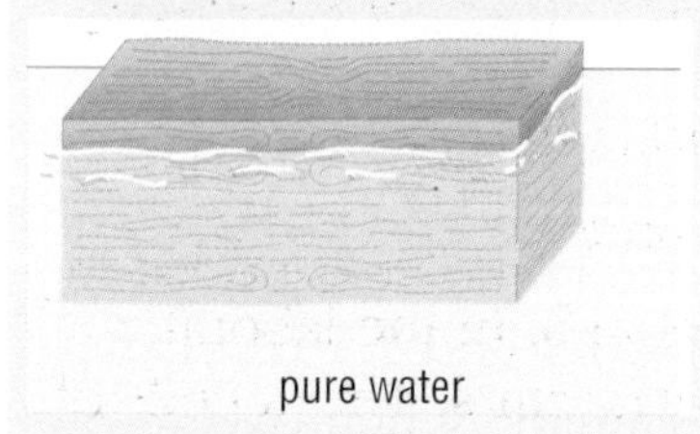

Figure 1.13

Density of gases

Air is a mixture of gases. Its density can be found in the following way.

The mass of a round-bottomed flask with its stopper, pipe and closed clip is found by placing it on a sensitive top-pan balance.

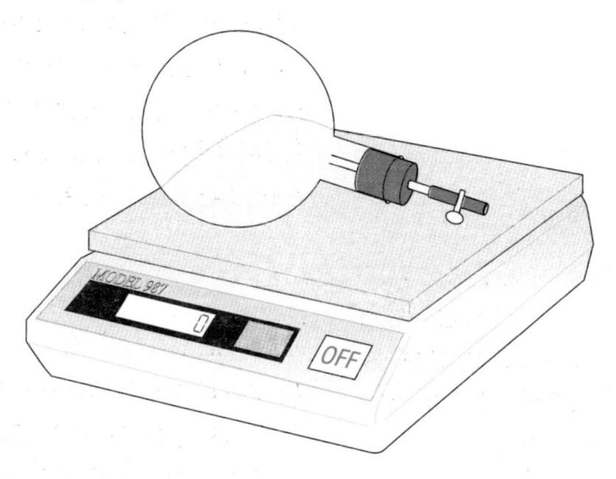

Figure 1.14 Measuring the mass of a flask on a top-pan balance.

The flask is then attached to a vacuum pump and the air is removed from the flask and the clip is closed.

The mass of the evacuated flask, stopper pipe and closed clip is found by placing it back on the balance. The mass of the air in the flask is found by subtracting the second reading from the first.

The volume of the air removed is found by opening the clip under water so that water enters to replace the vacuum. The water is then poured into a measuring cylinder to find the volume.

Table 1.6 shows the densities of some gases.

Table 1.6 The density of gases.

Gas	**Density kg/m^3**
hydrogen	0.089
air	1.29
oxygen	1.43
carbon dioxide	1.98

27 How is the process of finding the mass of a gas different from that of finding the mass of a liquid? Why is the difference necessary?

28 How can gas density be used to explain why hydrogen rises in air and carbon dioxide sinks?

The density of a gas changes as its temperature and pressure change. The densities of gases are compared by measuring them at the same temperature and pressure. This is called the standard temperature and pressure

(STP). The standard temperature is 0 °C. The standard pressure of a gas is that pressure that will support 760 mm of mercury in a vertical tube.

When two gases meet the less dense gas rises above the denser gas.

Speed

The speed at which something moves is a measure of how fast or slow it is. Scientifically, the speed is the distance travelled in a certain interval of time. The following equation shows how the speed of something can be calculated:

$$\text{speed} = \frac{\text{distance}}{\text{time}}$$

29 Two toy cars move round a 2 m track. Car A takes 4 seconds to complete a lap and car B takes 6 seconds. What is the speed of each car in m/s?

The standard SI unit for speed is m/s. In the laboratory speeds may be measured in m/s or cm/s. The speeds of vehicles may be measured in km/h, although miles per hour (mph) is still commonly used in Britain.

Distance/time graph

The distance travelled by an object over a period of time can be plotted on a graph called a distance/time graph. The distance covered by the object is recorded on the Y axis and the time taken for the object to cover the distance is recorded on the X axis. When a distance/time graph is complete it can be used to study the speed of an object over different time periods of its journey.

Figure 1.15 shows the distance/time graph for an object which moved at a steady speed (line A) then stopped and remained stationary (line B). If the object had been travelling at a higher speed, line A would be steeper. If the object had been travelling at a lower speed, line A would be less steep.

The speed of an object, that is how far the object moved in a certain time, can be calculated from the distance/time graph. For example, the object in Figure 1.15 moved at 10 cm/s.

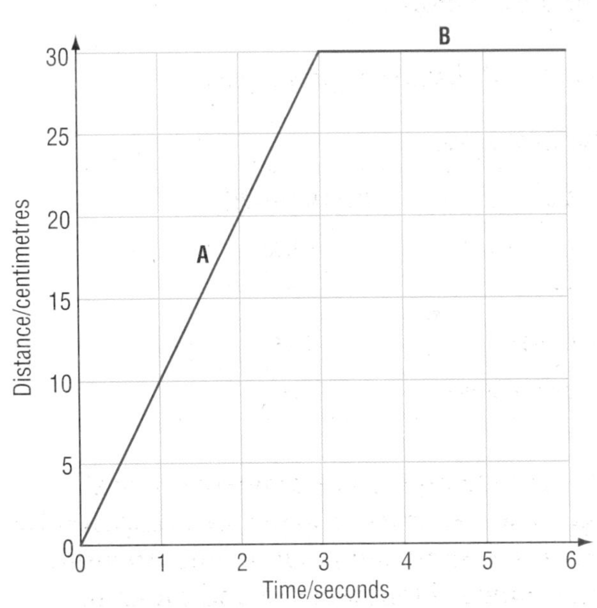

Figure 1.15 Distance/time graph.

Velocity

When something moves it goes in a particular direction. An aeroplane, for example, may move at 900 km/h in a direction due north. The speed and the direction of movement when given together are called the velocity.

30 Figure 1.16 shows the distance/time graph for two trucks, A and B, on an expedition across the Mongolian desert.

a) How far did truck A move in the first hour of its journey? What was its speed?

b) How did the speed of truck A change in the second hour of its journey?

c) Was truck B moving faster or slower than truck A in the first hour of its journey?

d) What do you think might have happened to truck A in the third hour of the journey?

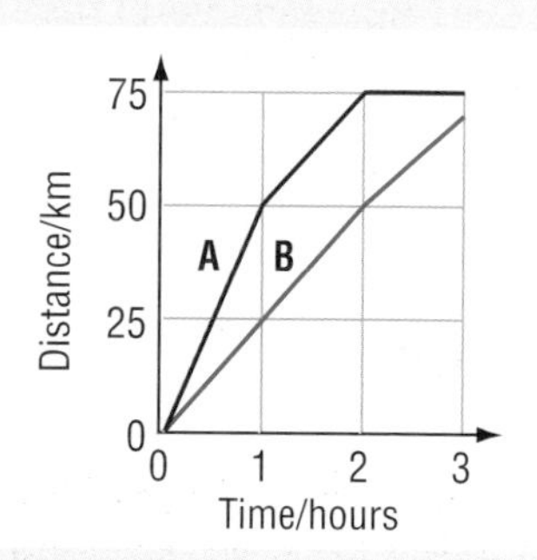

Figure 1.16

Acceleration

The acceleration of a moving object is a measure of how its velocity changes in a certain interval of time. The following equation shows how the acceleration of an object can be calculated:

$$\text{acceleration} = \frac{\text{change in velocity}}{\text{time}}$$

The SI unit for acceleration is m/s/s or m/s^2. This is pronounced metres per second per second or metres per second squared.

♦ SUMMARY ♦

- Better observations are made by taking measurements and an international system of units has been developed (*see page 2*).
- Powers of ten are used for dealing with very large and very small numbers (*see page 6*).
- It is useful to estimate quantities at the beginning of an investigation (*see page 7*).
- There are techniques for accurate measuring (*see page 7*).
- The units for measuring a wide range of other quantities, such as area, volume, density and speed, are built up from units of length, mass and time (*see pages 9–15*).
- The densities of solids, liquids and gases are measured in different ways (*see pages 12 and 14*).
- Speed, velocity and acceleration are all measurements of movement (*see pages 15–16*).

End of chapter questions

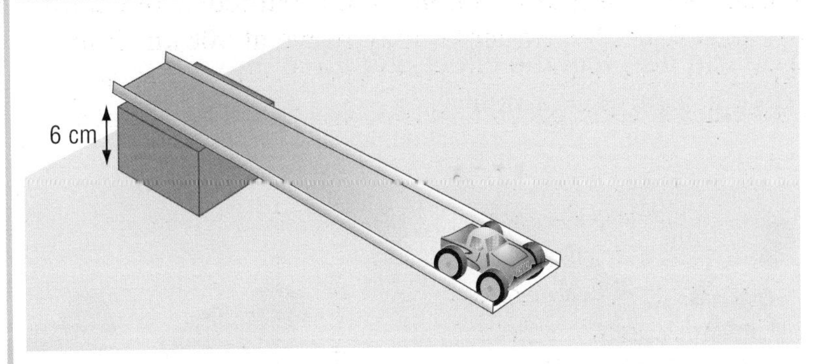

Figure 1.17

A group of pupils investigated the movement of a model car. They set up a ramp at 6 cm height and let the car roll down it and across the floor (Figure 1.17). They measured the distance travelled by the car after it left the ramp and moved across the floor. The experiment was repeated three more times with the ramp set at 6 cm then the height was reset and more of the car's movements were recorded. Table 1.7 shows the results of the investigation.

Table 1.7

Height/cm	Distance/cm			
6	20	21	20	19
7	24	25	22	21
8	32	32	33	33
9	40	40	39.5	38
10	45	42	45	44
11	55	53	55	55
12	60	60	58	59
13	67	62	63	64

1 How many times was the height of the ramp changed?
2 How is an average calculated?
3 Calculate the average distance travelled for each height of the ramp.
4 Plot a graph to show the relationship between the height of the ramp and the distance travelled from the ramp by the car.
5 What conclusions can you draw from your analysis of the results of this investigation?

2 *Forces*

You cannot see a force but you can see what it does. You can also feel the effect of a force on your body. A force is a push or a pull.

1 Describe the pushing and pulling forces shown in Figure 2.1.

Figure 2.1 Forces act in many ways.

Early ideas on forces

The Ancient Greeks' ideas on forces and movement were thought to be correct for nearly 2000 years. The Greeks thought that movements of objects in a curved path, like the movement of the planets and the apparent movement of the Sun across the sky, were celestial movements and only occurred in the heavens. They believed that each of the planets, the Sun and the Moon were held in a crystal sphere which surrounded the Earth, and that each was moved at a different speed by some unknown 'prime mover'.

Figure A The arrangement of the Sun and planets around the Earth according to the Ancient Greeks.

The Greeks also believed that everything was formed from four elements – earth, air, water and fire. These elements tended to form layers, the lowest layer being earth and the highest fire. The elements present in objects and substances tried to move towards their layer. For example, a metal object would fall because it contained a great deal of the earth element and it tried to reach the lowest layer. Flames leapt upwards to reach the highest layer. To the Greeks these upward and downward movements of objects and substances differed from celestial movements.

1 Write down the order you would expect for the four layers of the elements starting with the lowest, earth.

Figure B The Ancient Greeks believed that things rose or fell according to the elements they possessed.

(continued)

Horizontal movements were considered to be 'forced' or even violent movements. They thought that an object moving horizontally was pushed along throughout its journey. For example, when an arrow was released from a bow the pushing force of the bow string was taken up by the air. The Greeks believed that the air eventually tired of pushing the arrow and when that happened the arrow stopped moving horizontally and fell vertically to the ground.

Figure C The Ancient Greeks thought that the air pushed an arrow throughout its flight.

The Greeks also believed that the speed of a moving object was related to the resistance that it experienced as it moved through the air or water around it. They reasoned that if the resistance was high the movement would be slow but if there was no air to offer resistance, an object would move at an infinitely fast speed, changing its position instantaneously. As this did not happen the Greeks concluded that there could not be such a thing as a place without air. Such a place we now know is possible, and is called a vacuum.

Nicolaus Copernicus (1473–1543) [see also page 194] studied the movement of the planets and suggested that they did not move around the Earth in crystal spheres but moved around the Sun instead. He suggested that the Earth also moved around the Sun. This idea helped other scientists to think that perhaps movement in a curved path could also occur on Earth.

Niccolo Tartaglia (about 1500–1557) was a mathematician who studied the way cannons fired cannon balls. This study was important to armies and allowed the soldiers to set up their cannons to fire more accurately. Tartaglia published a book of his observations which showed that cannon balls did not move in a straight line and then drop as the Greeks had believed, but fell in a curved path.

Figure D Contrary to what the Ancient Greeks believed, curved motion is possible on Earth.

2 What were the three types of movements according to the Greeks?

3 Which types of movement needed a 'mover'?

4 Why did the Greeks believe a vacuum could not exist?

5 According to the Greeks, why did an arrow fall to the ground?

6 Why did Tartaglia's description of the movement of a cannon ball not fit in with the Greeks' ideas?

What forces do

- A force can make an object move. For example, if you throw a netball your muscles exert a pushing force on the ball and it moves through the air when you let it go.
- A force can make a moving object stop. For example, a goalkeeper moves into the path of a moving ball to exert a pushing force on the ball to stop it.
- A force can change the speed of a moving object. For example, a hockey player uses a hockey stick to push a slow moving ball to send it shooting past a defender.
- A force can change the direction of a moving object. For example, a batsman can change the direction of a cricket ball moving towards the wicket by deflecting it so that it moves away from the wicket towards the boundary.
- A force can change the shape of an object. For example, when a racket strikes a tennis ball, part of the ball is flattened before the ball leaves the racket.

Figure 2.2 A force makes the ball move.

Figure 2.3 A force makes the ball stop.

Figure 2.4 A force increases the speed of the ball.

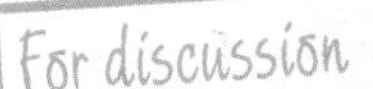

Watch a short video recording of part of a football or tennis match and identify the different effects of forces acting in the game.

Figure 2.5 A force changes the direction of the ball.

Figure 2.6 A force changes the shape of the ball.

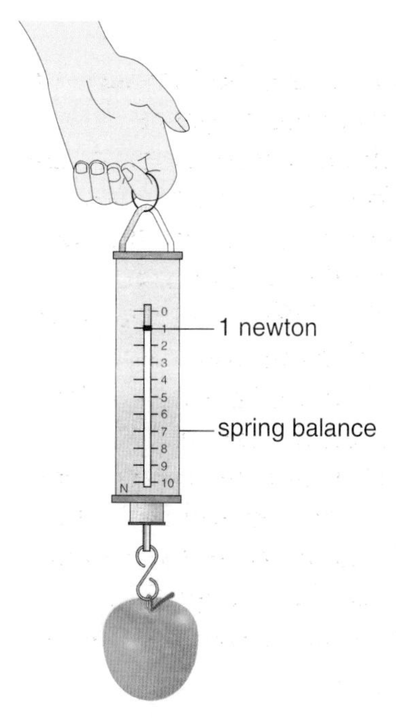

Figure 2.7 The apple pulls on the spring balance with a force equal to its weight.

How to measure a force

A force can be measured with a Newton spring balance (see page 34). The SI unit for measuring force is the newton (symbol N). This force is quite small and is equal to the gravitational force on (the weight of) an average-sized apple, or the pulling force needed to peel a banana!

Different types of forces

There are two main types of forces: contact forces and non-contact forces. A contact force occurs when the object or material exerting the force touches the object or material on which the force acts. A non-contact force occurs when the objects or materials do not touch each other (see page 29).

Contact forces

All the situations described so far are examples of contact forces in action. Some more examples follow.

Impact force

When a moving object collides with a stationary object an impact force is exerted by one object on the other. The size of the force may be large such as when a hammer hits a nail or it may be very tiny such as when a moving molecule of gas in the air strikes the skin.

Figure 2.8 The car behind exerts an impact force on the car in front.

2 a) i) What do you feel if you hook the two ends of an elastic band over your index fingers and slowly move your hands apart?
ii) What happens to the elastic band when you bring your hands together again?
iii) What happens if one end of a stretched elastic band is released?
b) Describe how the strain force changes in each part of question **a)**.

Strain force

When some materials are squashed, stretched, twisted or bent they exert a force which acts in the opposite direction to the force acting on them. These materials are called elastic materials and the force they exert when they are deformed is called a strain force. When the force applied to the material is removed the strain force exerted by the material restores the deformed material to its original shape. For example, the strain force in the squashed tennis ball in Figure 2.6 returns the ball to its original shape when the ball has left the racket.

Tension is a strain force that is exerted by a stretched spring, rope or string. At each end the tension force acts in the opposite direction to the pulling force. (See *How to measure a force* page 22, *Balanced forces* page 37.)

A force is shown in a diagram as an arrow pointing in the direction of the push or the pull.

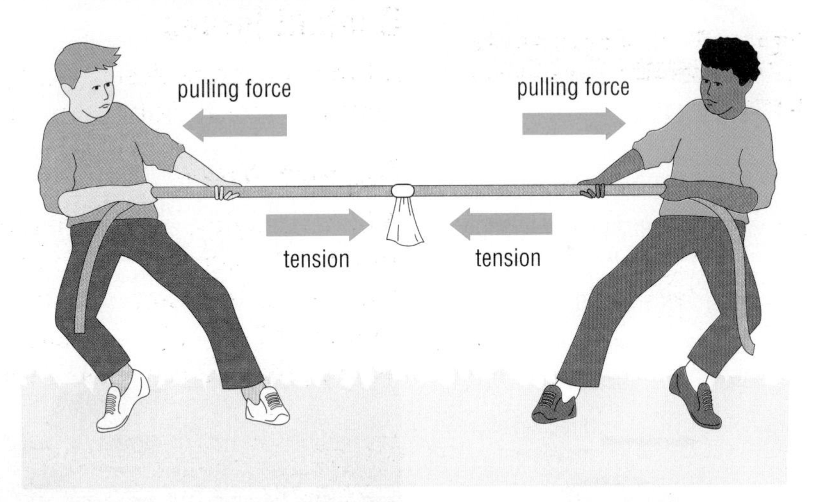

Figure 2.9 Tension is a strain force which acts against the force applied.

Friction

This contact force occurs between two objects when there is a push or a pull on one of the objects which could make it move over the surface of the other object. Friction acts to oppose that movement.

As the push or pull on the object increases, the force of friction between the surfaces of the objects also increases. This force matches the strength of the push or the pull up to a certain value and so, below this value, the object does not move. The friction which exists between the two objects when there is no movement is called static friction.

3 Imagine you are asked to push a heavy box across the floor. At first you need to push very hard but once the box has started to move you can push less strongly yet still keep it moving. Why is this?

4 When you take a step forwards you push backwards on the ground with your foot as Figure 2.11 shows.

Figure 2.11

Make a sketch of this diagram and draw in an arrow to show the frictional force that stops your foot slipping.

5 Figure 2.12 shows a wheel turning.

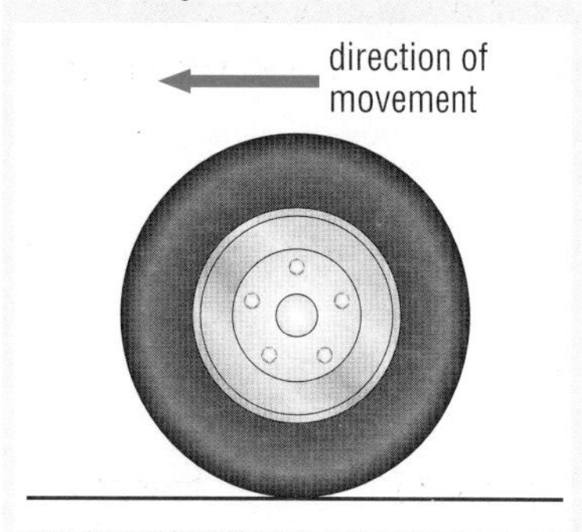

Figure 2.12

Make a sketch of the wheel and draw in **a)** the force exerted by the wheel pushing backwards on the road and **b)** the force of friction preventing the wheel slipping. Label the forces.

If the strength of the push or pull on the object is increased beyond this value the object will start to slide. There is still a frictional force between the two surfaces, acting on each surface in the opposite direction to the direction of its movement. This frictional force is called sliding friction. The strength of this force is less than the maximum value of the static frictional force.

Figure 2.10 Friction between the log and the ground opposes the pulling force of the horse.

A closer look at friction

The surfaces of objects in contact are not completely smooth. Under a microscope it can be seen that they have tiny projections with hollows between them (Figure 2.13).

Figure 2.13 A metal surface that appears smooth to the naked eye has projections which can be seen when it is magnified 180 times.

Where the projections from the surface of one object meet the projections from the surface of the other, the materials in the projections stick. These connections between the surfaces produce the force of friction between the objects.

Reducing friction

If a liquid is placed between the two surfaces the projections are forced apart a little and the number of connections is reduced, which in turn reduces the force of friction. This can cause problems or it can be helpful. For example, water running between the surface of a tyre and the road reduces the friction between them and increases the chance of skidding. However, oil between the moving metal parts of an engine and the parts in the bearings reduces friction and also reduces wear on the metal parts.

6 Why does oiling the axles of a bicycle make the bicycle move more easily?

Increasing friction

The friction between two surfaces can be increased by pressing the surfaces together more strongly. This makes the projections press against each other more strongly and increases the size and number of connections between them.

When brakes are applied on a bicycle or car the brake pads press against a moving part of the wheel and the force of friction increases. This opposes the rotation of the wheel and slows down the bicycle or car until it stops.

The tread on a car tyre is designed to move water out of the way as the tyre rolls over a wet road, reducing the risk of skidding. Racing cars have smooth tyres that are ideal for a dry track. If it rains they slide and skid all over the place and the tyres need to be replaced.

Figure 2.14 Tyres with treads are designed so that water squirts out from between the treads.

Friction and road safety

When a driver in a moving car sees a hazard ahead the car travels a certain distance before the driver reacts and applies the brakes. The distance travelled by the car in this time is called the thinking distance. This is followed by the braking distance, which is the distance covered by

7 a) What happens at the beginning of the time during which a car covers the thinking distance?

b) What happens at the end of the time during which the car covers the thinking distance?

8 What may affect the thinking time of the driver? How would the thinking distance of the car be affected? Explain your answer.

9 What, other than speed, may affect the braking distance of the car? Explain your answer.

10 A car is travelling along a road at 80 km/h when a tree falls across the road 54 metres away. What would probably happen and why?

For discussion

How safe is a) driving close to the car in front, b) driving fast on winding country roads with high hedges? Explain your answers to each part of the question.

'It's the driver that's dangerous not the car.'

Assess the usefulness of this slogan for a road safety campaign.

the car after the brakes are applied and before the car stops. Table 2.1 shows the thinking and braking distances that will bring a car with good brakes to a halt on a dry road.

Table 2.1

Speed	Thinking distance/m	Braking distance/m	Total stopping distance/m
48 km/h (30 mph)	9	14	23
80 km/h (50 mph)	15	38	53
112 km/h (70 mph)	21	75	96

Resistance

In air

Air is a mixture of gases. When an object moves through the air it pushes the air out of the way and the air moves over the object's sides and pushes back on the object. This push on the object is called air resistance or drag. The Ancient Greeks (see page 20) were right that it slows down moving objects.

The value of the air resistance depends on the size and shape of the object. Many cars are designed so that the air resistance is low when the car moves forwards. The car's body is designed like a wedge to cut its way through the air and the surfaces are curved to allow the air to flow over the sides with the minimum drag. Shapes that are designed to reduce air resistance are called streamlined shapes.

Figure 2.15 Testing a streamlined sports car in a wind tunnel.

A dragster is a vehicle which accelerates very quickly. In a dragster race two vehicles accelerate along a straight track. At the end of the race the dragsters are slowed down by brakes and a parachute. The parachute offers a large surface area against which the air pushes. The high air resistance of the parachute slows down the dragster and helps it stop in a short distance.

Figure 2.16 These parachutes are used to slow down a dragster after a race.

11 How would the size of parachute required on a space probe to allow it to land safely differ on **a)** a planet such as Venus which has a thick atmosphere and **b)** a planet such as Mars which has a thin atmosphere? Explain your answer.

The air resistance produced by a parachute is also used to bring sky divers safely to the ground (see *Balanced forces* page 37). The resistance of the gases in the atmospheres of other planets in the Solar System is used to slow down space probes so they can land safely and the devices on board are able to carry out their investigations.

Figure 2.17 A safe landing for the Mars Pathfinder equipment.

In water

When an object moves through water it pushes the water out of the way and the water moves over the object's sides and pushes back on the object. This push on the object is called water resistance or drag. Objects that can move through the water quickly have a streamlined shape (see page 26). A fish such as a barracuda which moves quickly through the water has a much more streamlined shape than a slow-moving sunfish.

Barracuda

A sunfish

Figure 2.18

Water resistance affects the movement of ships and boats on the water surface. Boats designed for high speeds have a hull shaped to reduce water resistance as much as possible. Some boats are equipped with a device called a hydrofoil which reduces the area of contact between the boat and the water so that water resistance is kept to a minimum. The boat (itself called a hydrofoil) can then move quickly over the water surface.

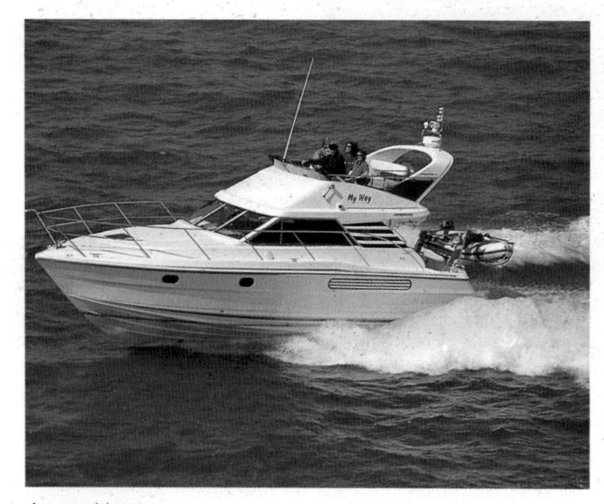

A speed boat

A hydrofoil

Figure 2.19

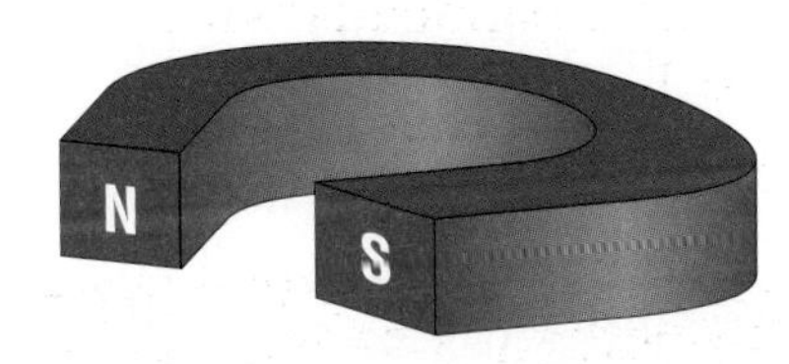

N = north pole
S = south pole

Figure 2.20 Bar, horseshoe and ring magnets.

Non-contact forces

These include magnetic forces, electrostatic forces and gravitational forces. They all exert their force without having to touch the object.

Magnetic force

A magnet has a north-seeking pole and a south-seeking pole. These are usually known as the north pole and the south pole (see page 135). If you pick up two magnets and bring either their north poles or their south poles together you will feel a force pushing your hands apart as the two similar poles repel each other. You will feel your hands being pushed away even though the magnets are not touching. The strength of the push increases as you bring the two similar poles closer together.

If you bring the north pole of one magnet towards the south pole of another magnet you will feel your hands being pulled together as the different poles attract each other. The strength of this pull increases as the poles get closer together.

A magnet can also exert a non-contact force on objects made of iron, steel, cobalt or nickel. Either pole of the magnet exerts a pulling force on these magnetic materials. The strength of the force increases as the magnet and the magnetic material are brought closer together.

12 If you had a magnet with its north and south poles marked on it and a magnet without its poles marked, how could you identify the poles of the unmarked magnet? Explain your answer.

Figure 2.21 This 'Maglev' train is supported above its track by strong magnetic forces. It travels quietly on a 'cushion' of air which eliminates friction between the train and the tracks.

Electrostatic force

If certain electrical insulator materials are rubbed an electrostatic charge develops on them (see page 105). There are two kinds of charge: positive charge and negative charge. The forces between the charges can be investigated by suspending a plastic rod so that it can swing freely (Figure 2.22), giving the rod an electrostatic charge then bringing rods with different charges close to it. If the suspended rod has a positive charge it will move away from a plastic rod which also has a positive charge, as the similar charges repel each other. If a rod with a negative charge is brought near the positively charged suspended rod, the rod swings towards it as the opposite charges attract each other. The strength of the force between electrostatic charges increases as the rods are brought closer together.

13 Compare magnetic and electrostatic forces. In what ways are they **a)** similar, **b)** different?

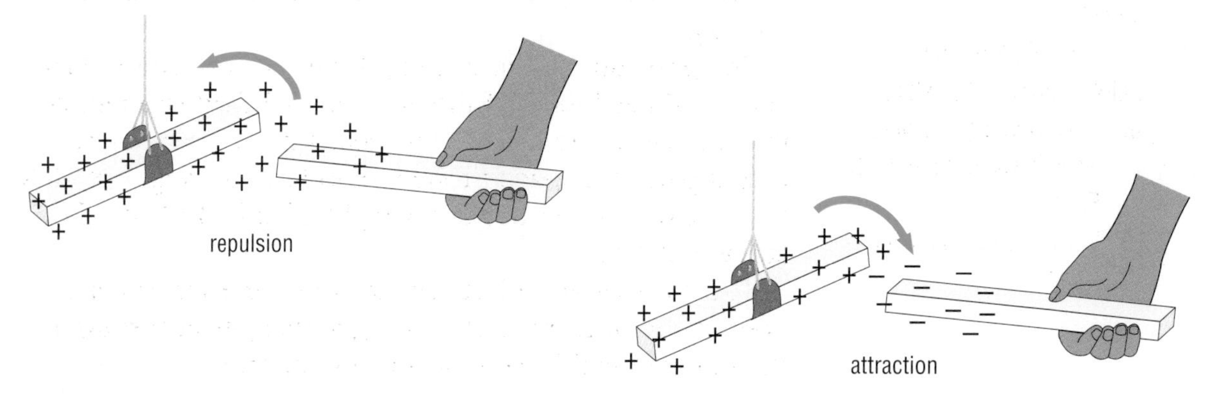

Figure 2.22 Investigating charges with a suspended plastic rod.

Gravitational force

There is a force between any two masses in the universe. The masses may be small such as those of an ant and a pebble or they may be very large such as those of the Sun and the Earth. The force that exists between any two masses because of their mass is called the gravitational force. The force acting between small masses is too weak to have any noticeable effect on them but the gravitational force between two large masses such as the Sun and the Earth is large enough to be very important. It is the gravitational force between the Sun and all the planets in the Solar System that holds the planets in their orbits (see page 197). The gravitational force between an object on the Earth and the Earth itself pulls the object down towards the centre of the Earth and is called weight of the object.

14 What is the weight of the following masses on Earth: **a)** 2 kg, **b)** 3.5 kg, **c)** 5.25 kg?

15 What is the weight of a 6 kg object on the surface of Mars?

16 It is planned to bring samples of Mars rock back to the Earth. If 50 kg samples were collected by a space probe robot, what would be the weight of the rocks on
a) Mars, **b)** Earth?

17 The Moon's gravitational field strength is one-sixth that of the Earth. What would be the weight of a 1 kg object on the Moon?

18 A sample of Moon rock weighed 30 N on the Moon.
- **a)** What would be its weight when it was brought to the Earth?
- **b)** What is the mass of the sample?

Mass and weight

The mass of an object is a measure of the amount of matter in it. The weight of an object is the pull of the Earth's gravity on the object. For example, an object may have a mass of 1 kg. The pull of the Earth's gravity on 1 kg is a force of almost 10 newtons (actually 9.8 N but it is often rounded up to make the calculations easier). The weight of the 1 kg mass is therefore 10 N.

The region in which a force acts is called a field. There is a gravitational field around the Earth. The gravitational field strength is calculated by the equation:

$$\text{gravitational field strength} = \frac{\text{weight}}{\text{mass}}$$

At the Earth's surface we have seen that the pull on a mass of 1 kg is 10 N so the gravitational field strength is 10 N/kg.

The gravitational field strength on the surface of Mars is three times less than the gravitational field strength on the surface of the Earth. This means that a 1 kg object that is part of a space probe would have a weight of 10 N when it was on Earth but a weight of only 3.3 N on the surface of Mars.

The mass of an object remains the same wherever it goes in the universe but its weight changes according to the gravitational force that is acting upon it.

Weightlessness

The gravitational field strength around a planet, moon or star gets weaker and weaker as you move further away.

A space station in orbit above the Earth is still in the Earth's gravitational field. The force of gravity pulls on the space station but because the space station is moving with a velocity parallel to the surface of the planet the force pulls the space station so that its path is curved. The force is just enough to keep the space station at exactly the same height. It does not move closer to Earth but 'falls' in a circular path around it. Inside the spacecraft every object that is not held down floats about. These objects, including the astronauts, are also 'falling' around the planet in the same way as the space station. The floating state is called apparent weightlessness because it feels like having no weight but the objects are, in fact, still being pulled by the Earth's gravity.

You may feel something similar to this weightlessness for a moment when you begin moving downwards in a lift or travel on a ride at a fair where you fall directly downwards. Both you and the ride are falling so you briefly feel lighter than usual. You may feel heavier just as the ride stops.

True weightlessness could only occur far out in deep space where there are no large objects with gravitational fields. This is beyond the distance travelled by any space exploration undertaken so far.

Figure 2.23 These people are enjoying a fairground ride where motion affects their apparent weight.

The study of falling objects

Aristotle was a Greek philosopher who believed that objects fell to the ground because they had the element earth in them which was trying to find its way back to the lowest of the layers of elements. He also believed that heavier objects fell to the ground faster than lighter objects because they contained more of the element earth.

Giovanni Benedetti (1530–1590) was an Italian mathematician who also studied how things fell. He challenged Aristotle's idea that heavier objects fell faster than lighter objects. He observed how two objects fell then joined them together with a thread and observed them fall again. If Aristotle was correct the objects should fall faster than before but Benedetti found that they did not.

Galileo Galilei (1564–1642) was a professor of mathematics at the University of Padua in Italy. He is usually known simply as Galileo. He studied the work of Tycho Brahe (see pages 194–5) about the movements of the planets and made investigations about how objects fell on the Earth. He believed that the movements on Earth and in the heavens could be linked together. His ideas were used later by Newton (see page 196).

Figure A Galileo explains his ideas to one of his students.

1 Why should two objects fastened together have fallen faster than they did when they were separated, if Aristotle was correct?

2 **a)** How did Galileo slow down a falling ball?
b) Why did he have to find a way of slowing it down?

3 If Galileo's ramp was divided into three sections, how would you expect the speed of the ball over the first (highest) section be different from the speed of the ball in the third (lowest) section?

4 If Galileo had released the two cannon balls from the top of the Leaning Tower of Pisa, what do you think would have been the result of the experiment?

(continued)

As objects fall very quickly when they are dropped and Galileo only had a water clock to time the fall, he devised a way of making the objects fall more slowly. He used a long piece of wood with a groove in it. He set the piece of wood like a ramp or inclined plane and let a polished brass ball roll down the groove. The ball rolled slowly enough down the ramp to allow Galileo to use his water clock to time its progress. He weighed the amount of water that had flowed out of the clock during the ball's journey to give him a measure of time.

With this equipment he showed that balls of the same size but different mass rolled down the slope in the same time. He also showed that the ball rolled faster and faster as it went down the ramp – the ball accelerated. He measured how the ball accelerated over different portions of the slope. There is a story that Galileo dropped two different-sized cannon balls from the Leaning Tower of Pisa to test his ideas further but it is probable he never did this.

For discussion

What would happen if you dropped a feather and a ball bearing from a height of two metres? Explain your answer.

In what way might the experiment give different results if you did the same thing on the surface of the Moon where there is no air?

How springs stretch

Robert Hooke (1635–1703) investigated the way in which springs stretched when masses were attached to them. He first hung up a spring and measured its length without any mass attached to it. He then hung a mass on the bottom and measured the new length of the spring. He calculated the extension of the spring by subtracting the original length of the spring from the new length of the spring with the mass attached. Hooke repeated the experiment with different sizes of masses. Each time he found the total extension by subtracting the original length from the new length. He found that as the size of the mass increased the size of the extension increased in proportion: the extension of the spring was proportional to the mass attached to it.

Each time Hooke removed the mass the spring returned to its original length. However, he eventually placed a mass on the spring that stretched the spring so much that it remained slightly stretched when the mass was removed. The spring had gone beyond a point called the elastic limit and was permanently deformed. When a larger mass was then added to the spring it no longer extended in proportion to the mass. The spring beyond its elastic limit was in a state known as plastic deformation (see Figure 2.24).

19 A spring is 6 cm long when it is unstretched but is stretched to 9 cm when a mass is hung from it. What is the extension of the spring?

20 An unstretched spring is 6 cm long but becomes 7 cm long when a 100 g mass is hung from it. The spring becomes 8 cm long when a 200 g mass is hung from it.

a) What is the extension for each mass?

b) What extension do you predict when a mass of **i)** 300 g and **ii)** 350 g are hung from it in turn? Can you be sure that the extension values you predict will in fact occur? (Hint: think about the elastic limit.)

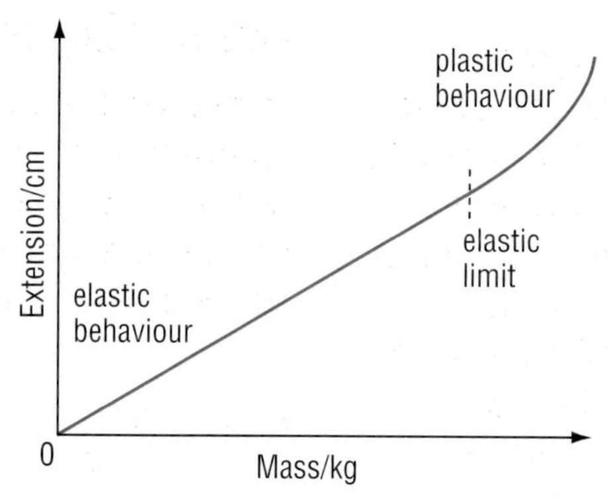

Figure 2.24 How the extension of a spring varies with the mass attached to it.

The Newton spring balance

The discovery made by Robert Hooke has led to the development of a force measurer using a spring which is not stretched beyond its elastic limit. This instrument is called a spring balance. The extension of the spring, and hence the reading on a scale, is proportional to the weight of the mass hung from it, or the force with which it is pulled. The scale of the balance is calibrated in newtons so it is sometimes called a Newton spring balance or a newtonmeter.

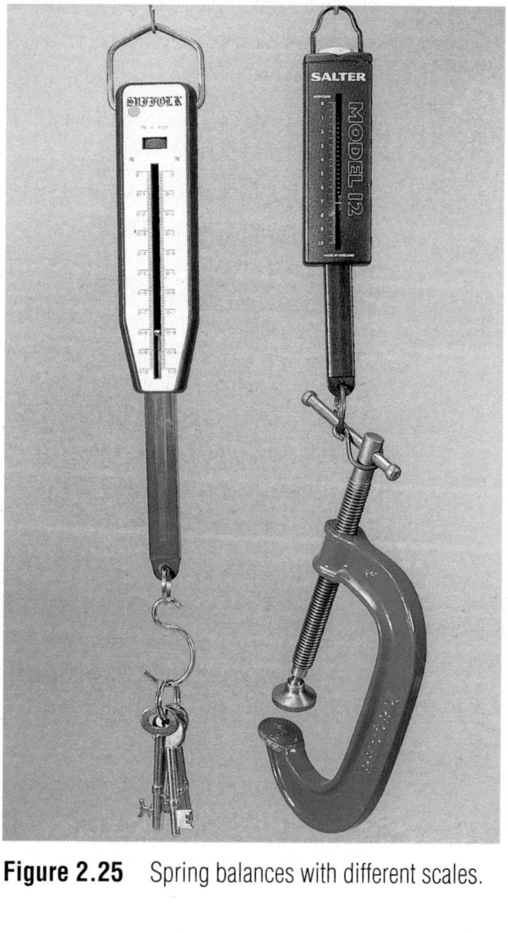

There is a range of spring balances which measure forces of different sizes. For example, a spring balance may measure forces with values in the range 0–10 N, 0–100 N or 0–200 N.

There is a device called a stop on most spring balances. It prevents the spring from stretching beyond its elastic limit.

Figure 2.25 Spring balances with different scales.

21 How do you think the spring in a spring balance with a scale of 0–10 N compares with a spring in a spring balance that measures forces up to 500 N?

22 A spring balance without a stop would not give correct readings for the weights of the masses hung from it if large masses were used. Explain the reason for this.

23 Two identical springs each extended 2 cm when a mass was added to them separately. They were then connected in series and the same mass hung on the bottom spring.

a) How far did each spring extend when it was arranged in this way?

b) What was the total extension of the two springs together?

24 Two springs each extended 1 cm when a mass was added to them separately.

a) How far did each spring extend when the same mass was added to them when they were connected in parallel?

b) How far did the mass sink as the springs stretched?

25 Three similar springs, A, B and C, extended 4 cm when a mass was added to each of them separately. The springs were then arranged as shown in Figure 2.27 and the same mass was attached at point P.

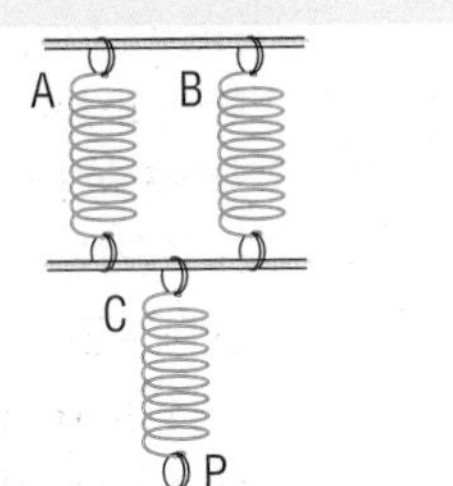

Figure 2.27

a) What was the extension of each of the springs A, B and C?

b) How far altogether did the mass sink when it was attached to point P?

c) How far did the connecting bar move?

Combining identical springs

Springs can be combined in two ways. They can be combined in series or in parallel (see Figure 2.26). These terms are taken from the way we describe how components can be combined in electrical circuits (see pages 123 and 124).

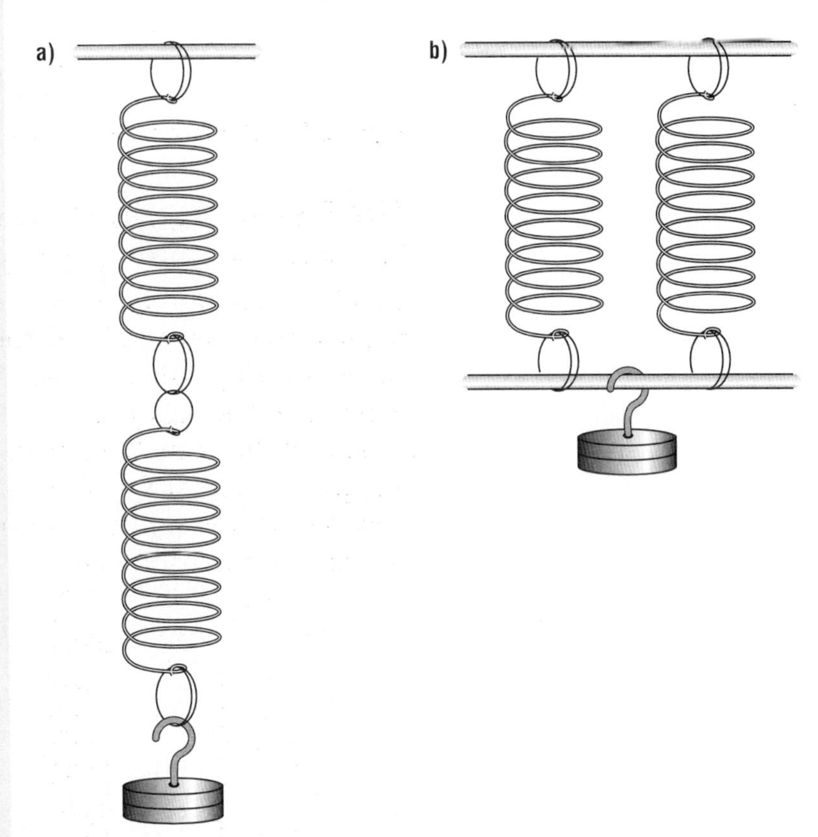

Figure 2.26 Identical springs in **a)** series and **b)** parallel.

Springs in series

The extension of each spring when a mass is added to the lower one is the same as if each spring were supporting the mass separately. The total extension is therefore double what it would be with just one spring.

Springs in parallel

Each spring, in effect, carries half the mass so it stretches less far. In fact, the extension of each spring when the mass is added to the middle of a light bar connecting them is half the extension it would have if it were supporting the full mass on its own.

Pairs of forces

Action and reaction

A force exerted by one object on another is always accompanied by a force equal to it acting in the opposite direction. For example, if you lean against a wall you exert a contact force that pushes on the wall and the wall exerts a contact force that pushes on you. The forces are equal. The force that you exert on the wall and the force the wall exerts on you are called an action–reaction pair. The action and reaction forces that form the pair act simultaneously: one does not cause the other.

Figure 2.28 An action–reaction pair.

Two model railway trucks each with a spring can be used to demonstrate an action–reaction pair. When the two trucks are pushed together the springs exert a force on each other due to the strain forces (see page 23) which develop in them. The force spring A exerts on spring B is always the same size but opposite in direction to the force exerted by spring B on spring A (Figure 2.29). The action force of A on B pushes B while the reaction force of B on A pushes A the other way. When the two trucks are suddenly released the action–reaction pair between the springs pushes the trucks in opposite directions.

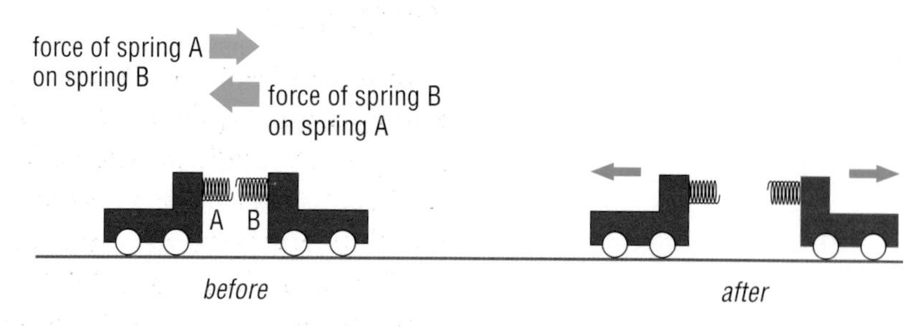

Figure 2.29 Action and reaction forces act in opposite directions.

Balanced forces

A pair of balanced forces is different from the action–reaction pair in the previous section because balanced forces act on one object only. When you stand still you do not rise above the ground or sink into it, because of the two balanced forces acting on you. Your weight acts downwards into the ground because of gravity and the ground exerts a contact force upwards on the soles of your shoes. This contact force is equal to your weight.

A person sitting in a stationary go-kart does not move up or down because the weight of the person and the kart is balanced by the contact force of the ground on the tyres. When the kart is moving in a straight line at a constant speed there is another pair of balanced forces acting on the kart. These forces are the driving force pushing the kart forwards and air resistance pushing backwards on the kart.

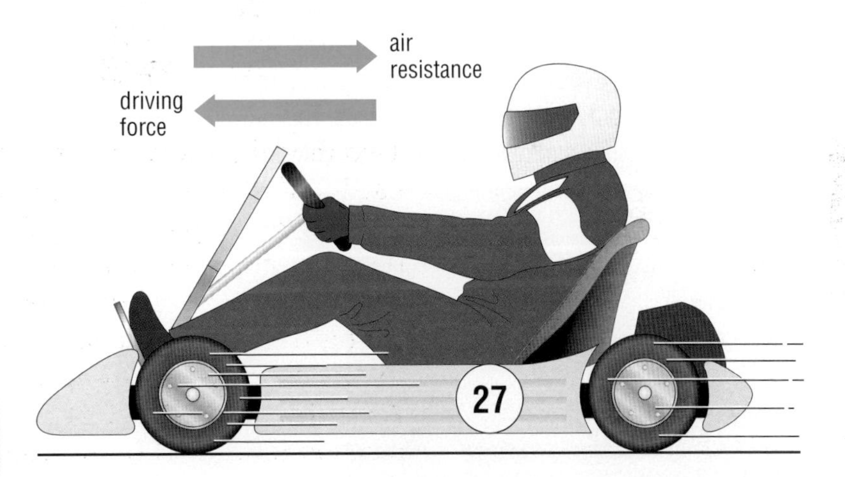

Figure 2.30 Balanced forces act on the go-kart when it is moving at a steady speed.

26 Describe the forces between you and a chair when you sit on it.

Upthrust

When an object is placed in any liquid or gas it pushes some of the liquid or gas out of the way. The liquid or gas pushes back on the object with a force called the upthrust. This force is equal to the weight of the liquid or gas that has been pushed out of the way.

The buoy in Figure 2.31 is carrying a weather station. It floats on the sea surface due to the upthrust acting on it from the sea water.

27 What are the forces acting on a duck when it floats in water?

Figure 2.31 This floating buoy carries an automatic weather station. Its weight is balanced by the upthrust from the sea water.

Plimsoll lines

In the 19th Century trade between countries increased and many kinds of goods were transported by sea. Some ships were loaded with so much cargo that they could barely float and when they encountered stormy conditions they sank. To reduce the number of shipping disasters and to save the lives of the sailors the politician Samuel Plimsoll brought in a law in 1876 requiring each ship to be marked with lines showing the maximum level to which the water should rise up its sides in dock. This prevented any ship from being overloaded and reduced the chance of it sinking in a storm. The lines became known as Plimsoll lines.

1. What effect does the temperature of the water have on the upthrust of the water on a ship?
2. How does the presence of salt in water affect the upthrust of the water on a ship?
3. What might happen to a ship that was loaded to the line in cold sea water and then sailed into warm fresh water? Explain your answer.

Figure A Plimsoll lines.

The symbol on the right of Figure A shows the loading limit in different situations. It shows how the level of the water will change as the ship moves into different kinds of water. These changes in level are due to the different densities of the different kinds of water, which leads to differences in upthrust. For example, the upthrust on a fully loaded ship in cold, dense sea water in the North Atlantic Ocean in winter is so strong that the ship only sinks to the level marked by WNA. If the fully loaded ship sailed into a warm, tropical, freshwater river it would sink to the level marked by TF.

Unbalanced forces

When the forces on a stationary object are unbalanced the object starts to move. For example, when the driver of a go-kart presses the accelerator pedal on the stationary kart the wheels connected to the engine turn and the frictional force between the ground and the tyres pushes the kart forwards. As the kart moves forwards the air pushes on it (and the driver) with a force called drag or air resistance. To begin with this force is smaller than the frictional force and the kart continues to accelerate forwards (Figure 2.32).

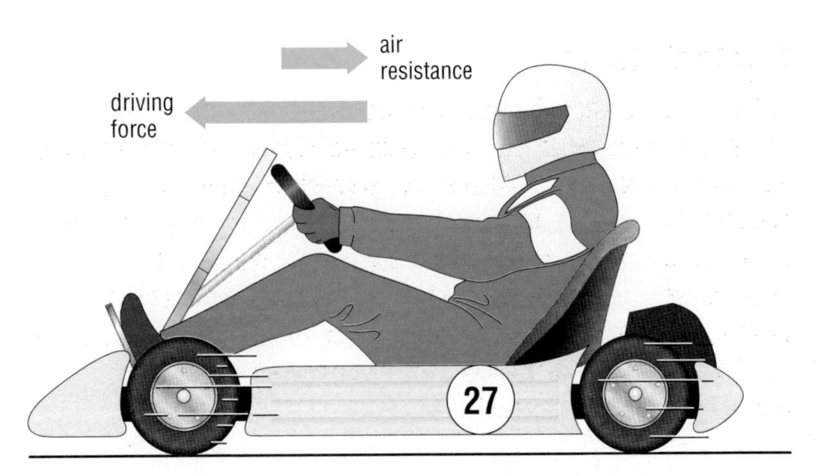

Figure 2.32 The forward force is greater than the backward force so the kart speeds up.

Note that the size of a force on a diagram is indicated by the size of the arrow. A large force is shown by a longer arrow than a small force.

As the kart increases speed the air resistance also increases. Eventually the kart moves at a constant speed in a straight line, as shown in Figure 2.30, with the two horizontal forces balanced.

When the driver takes his or her foot off the accelerator pedal the frictional driving force is reduced. The air resistance is now stronger than the driving force and kart slows down.

The driver can slow down the kart faster by applying the brakes. The brake pads exert a frictional force on the wheels which make it harder for the wheels to turn. This produces an additional resistance backwards which slows the kart down.

28 How does friction help you ride your bike?

29 Draw a submarine sinking in water. Draw and label the forces acting on it and indicate the strength for each one by the size of its arrow.

30 Figure 2.34 shows a speed/time graph of a sky diver's jump.

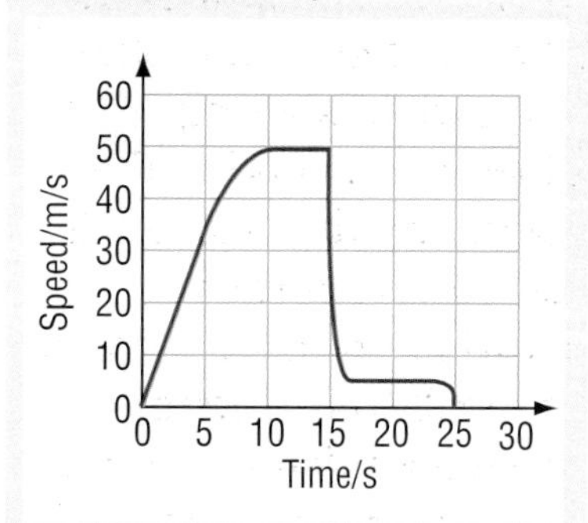

Figure 2.34

a) At what time is the acceleration greatest?
b) When did the diver begin to fall at the terminal velocity?
c) For how long did the sky diver fall at the terminal velocity?
d) When was the parachute opened?
e) At what speed did the sky diver hit the ground?

For discussion

During free fall, how does a sky diver alter the terminal velocity by altering his or her shape?

Why are tangled parachutes dangerous?

Falling through the air

When a sky diver leaps from an aeroplane the diver's weight pulls him or her down. The air resistance is small compared to the weight as he or she starts to fall and so the diver accelerates (Figure 2.33a). Eventually the force of the air resistance balances the force pulling the diver towards the ground and he or she falls steadily at what is called the terminal velocity (Figure 2.33b). Eventually the sky diver opens the parachute and the air resistance greatly increases (Figure 2.33c). This slows down the sky diver to a new, slower terminal velocity so he or she can make a safe landing.

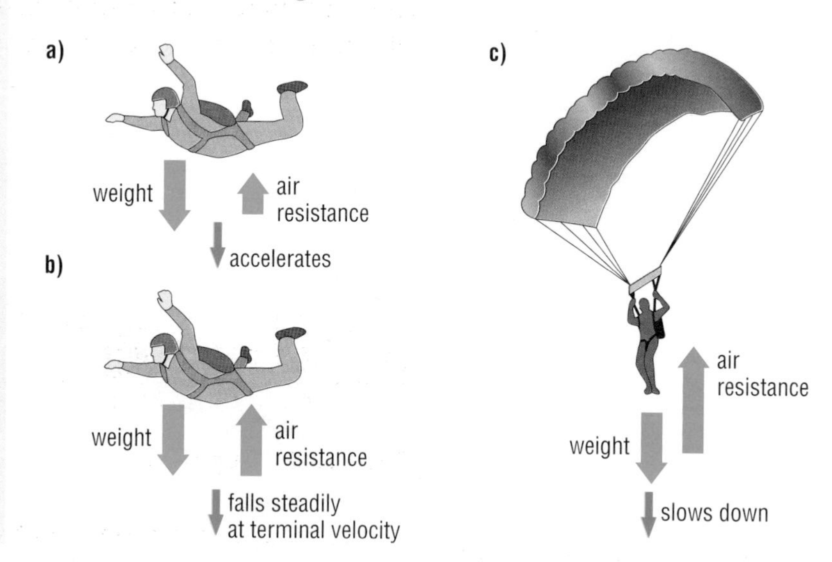

Figure 2.33 The motion of a sky diver.

The turning effect of forces

A force can be used to turn an object in a circular path. For example, when you push down on a bicycle pedal the cog wheel attached to the crankshaft turns round.

A nut holding the hub of a bicycle wheel to the frame is turned by attaching a spanner to it and exerting a force on the other end of the spanner in the direction shown in Figure 2.35.

Figure 2.35 Tightening a nut.

A device that changes the direction in which a force acts is called a lever. It is composed of two arms and a fulcrum or pivot. The lever also acts as a force multiplier. This means that a small force applied to one arm of the lever can cause a large force to be exerted by the other arm of the lever. For example, a crowbar is a simple lever. It is used to raise heavy objects. One end of the crowbar is put under a heavy object and the crowbar is rested on the fulcrum. When a downward force is applied to the long arm of the crowbar an upward force is exerted on the heavy object. A small force acting downwards at a large distance from the fulcrum on one side produces a large force acting upwards a short distance from the fulcrum on the other arm.

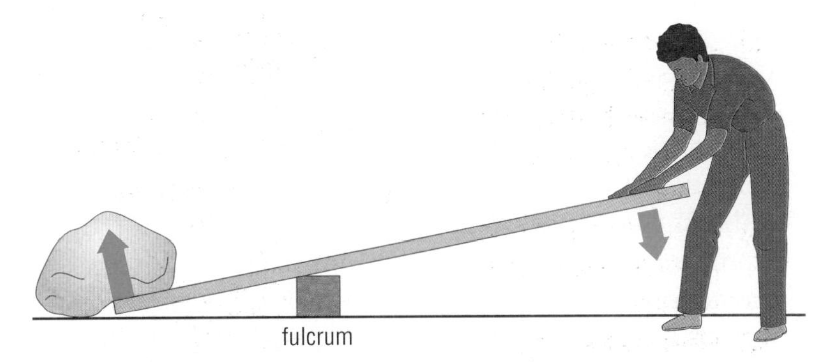

Figure 2.36 Using a lever.

The turning effect produced by a force around a fulcrum is called the moment of the force. The direction of the moment is usually specified as clockwise or anticlockwise about the fulcrum. The size of the moment is found by multiplying the size of the force by the distance between the point at which the force acts and the fulcrum. The moment of a force can be shown as an equation:

moment of force = force × distance from the pivot

The moment is measured in newton-metres (N m). The moment of the force applied to one arm of a lever is equal to the moment of the force exerted by the other arm. For example, a 100 N force applied downwards 2 m from the fulcrum on one arm produces a 200 N force upwards 1 m from the fulcrum on the other arm.

In the case of a see-saw, which is another simple type of lever, the moment of the weight on one arm must equal the moment of the weight on the other arm for the see-saw to balance.

31 What is the moment of a 100 N force acting on a crow bar
a) 2 m from the fulcrum,
b) 3 m from the fulcrum,
c) 0.5 m from the fulcrum?

32 A 100 N force acting on a lever 2 m from the fulcrum balances an object mass 0.5 m from the fulcrum on the other arm. What is the weight of the object (in newtons)? What is its mass (in kg)?

33 Is it possible to balance a mass of weight 5 N with a mass of weight 15 N on a model see-saw with 10 cm arms? Explain your answer. Suggest where you might place each mass to get an exact balance.

34 Where will the strongest force be exerted by scissor blades to cut through a piece of material? Explain your answer.

35 Why can a lever be described as a force multiplier?

A pair of pliers is made from two levers. When they are used to grip something a small force applied to the long handles produces a large force at the short jaws.

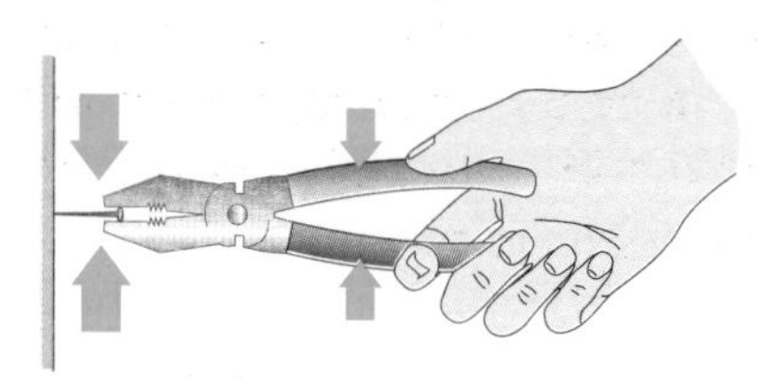

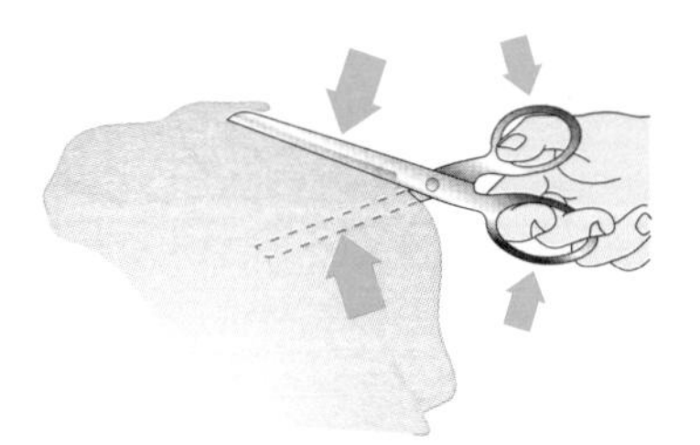

Figure 2.37 Using pliers and scissors.

♦ SUMMARY ♦

- A force is a push or a pull (*see page 18*).
- A force can make an object move, stop, change speed or change direction, or can change the object's shape (*see page 21*).
- Examples of contact forces are impact forces, strain forces, friction, air resistance and upthrust (*see pages 22–28 and 37*).
- Examples of non-contact forces are magnetic forces, electrostatic forces and gravitational forces (*see pages 29–30*).
- Springs stretch when forces are applied to them (*see page 33*).
- Forces act in pairs (*see page 36*).
- Forces on an object may be balanced (*see page 37*).
- Forces on an object may be unbalanced (*see page 39*).
- A force can produce a turning effect (*see page 40*).

End of chapter question

1 Identify the forces acting in this scene.

3 Pressure

In the previous chapter we examined forces acting at a point on an object. In this chapter we consider the effect of a force acting over an area.

When a force is exerted over an area we describe the effect in terms of pressure. Pressure can be described by the equation:

$$\text{pressure} = \frac{\text{force}}{\text{area}}$$

The SI unit for pressure is N/m^2 but it can also be measured in N/cm^2.

Pressure on a surface

Weight is a force produced by gravity acting on a solid, liquid or a gas, pulling the material downwards towards the centre of the Earth. The weight acts on the mass of that material. For example, the weight of a solid cube acts on that cube (Figure 3.1).

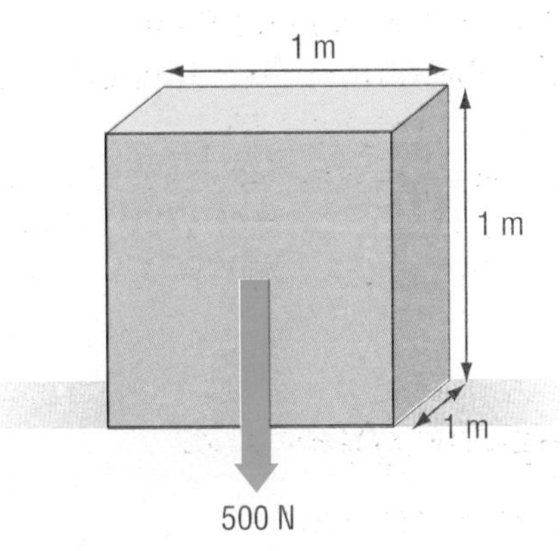

Figure 3.1 The weight acting on a cube.

The cube pushes down on the ground (or other surface that it rests on) with a force equal to its weight. The pressure that the cube exerts on the ground is found by using the equation above. For example, if the cube has a weight of 500 N and the area of its side is $1\,m^2$, the pressure it exerts on the ground is:

$$\text{pressure} = 500/1 = 500\,N/m^2$$

If the cube had a weight of 500 N and the area of its side was $2\,m^2$, the pressure it would exert on the ground is:

$$\text{pressure} = 500/2 = 250\,N/m^2$$

1 What is the pressure exerted on the ground by a cube which has a weight of 600 N and a side area of **a)** 1 m^2, **b)** 3 m^2?

2 What is the pressure exerted on the ground by an object which has a weight of 50 N and a surface area in contact with the ground of **a)** 1 cm^2, **b)** 10 cm^2, **c)** 25 cm^2?

3 **a)** What pressure does a block of weight 600 N and dimensions 1 m × 1 m × 3 m exert when it is **i)** laid on its side, **ii)** stood on one end?

b) Why does it exert different pressures in different positions?

An object exerts a pressure on the ground according to the area of its surface that is in contact with the ground.

For example, a block with dimensions 1 m × 1 m × 2 m and a weight of 200 N will exert a pressure of 200/1 = 200 N/m^2 when it is stood on one end (Figure 3.2a) but a pressure of only 200/2 = 100 N/m^2 when laid on its side (Figure 3.2b).

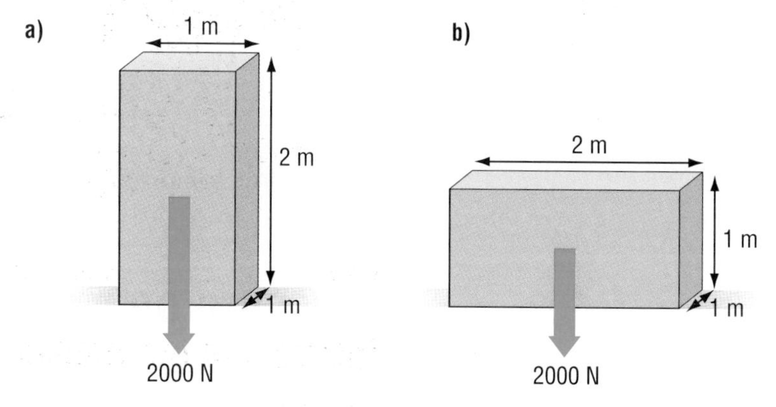

Figure 3.2 The weight acting on a block in two positions.

Your weight acting downwards causes you to exert a force on the ground through the soles of your shoes. If you lie down this force acts over all the areas of your body in contact with the ground. These areas together are larger than the areas of the soles of your shoes and you therefore push on the ground with less pressure when lying down than when you are standing up.

Figure 3.3 The force you exert downwards acts over a larger area when you lie down.

Reducing the pressure

When people wear skis the force due to their weight acts over a much larger area than the soles of a pair of shoes. This reduces the pressure on the soft surface of the snow and allows the skier to slide over it without sinking.

4 Drivers in Iceland, when going out on the snow, let their tyres down until they are very soft. The tyres spread out over the surface of the snow as they drive along. Why do you think the drivers do this?

Figure 3.4 Skis stop you sinking into the snow.

Increasing the pressure

Studs

Figure 3.5 The studs on this soccer boot help the player to grip the turf.

Sports boots for soccer and hockey have studs on their soles. They reduce the area in contact between your feet and the ground. When you wear a pair of these boots your downward force acts over a smaller area than the soles of your feet and you press on the ground with increased pressure. Your feet sink into the turf on the pitch and grip the surface more firmly. This makes it easier to run about without slipping while you play the game.

5 A girl wearing trainers does not sink into the lawn as she walks across it but later when she is wearing high-heeled shoes she sinks into the turf. Why does this happen?

Pins and spikes

When you push a drawing pin into a board the force of your thumb is spread out over the head of the pin so the low pressure does not hurt you. The same force, however, acts at the tiny area of the pin point. The high pressure at the pin point forces the pin into the board.

Sprinters use sports shoes which have spikes in their soles. The spike tips have a very small area in contact with the ground. The weight of the sprinter produces a downward force through this small area and the high pressure pushes the spikes into the hard track, so the sprinter's feet do not slip when running fast.

Figure 3.6 The spikes stop the sprinter from slipping on the track.

Knives

As we have seen, high pressure is made by having a large force act over a small area. The edge of a sharp knife blade has a very small area but the edge of a blunt knife blade is larger. If the same force is applied to each knife the sharp blade will exert greater pressure on the material it is cutting than the blunt knife blade and will cut more easily than the blunt blade.

Figure 3.7 Knives cut well when they are sharp because of the high pressure under the blade.

Particles and pressure

Matter is made from particles. In solids the particles are held in position. In liquids the particles are free to slide over each other and in gases the particles are free to move away from each other. A full description of particles in matter is given in Chapter 2 of *Chemistry Now! 11–14*.

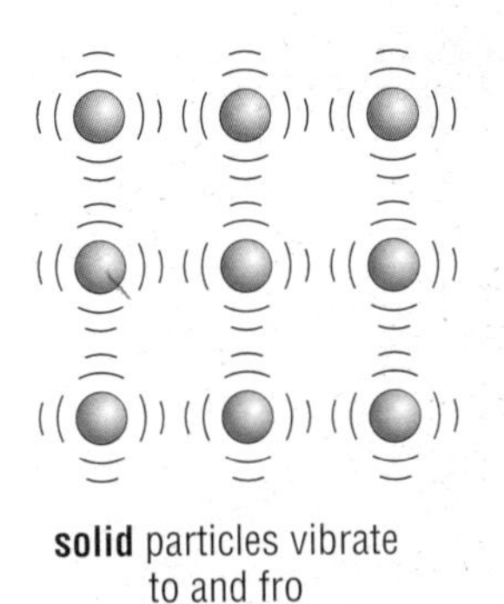

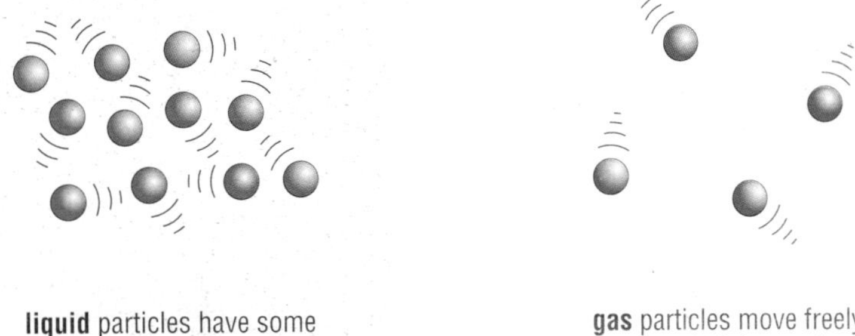

Figure 3.8 Arrangement of particles in a solid, a liquid and a gas.

Pressure in a liquid

In a solid object the pressure of the particles acts through the area in contact with the ground. In a liquid the pressure of the particles acts not only on the bottom of the container but on the sides too (Figure 3.9).

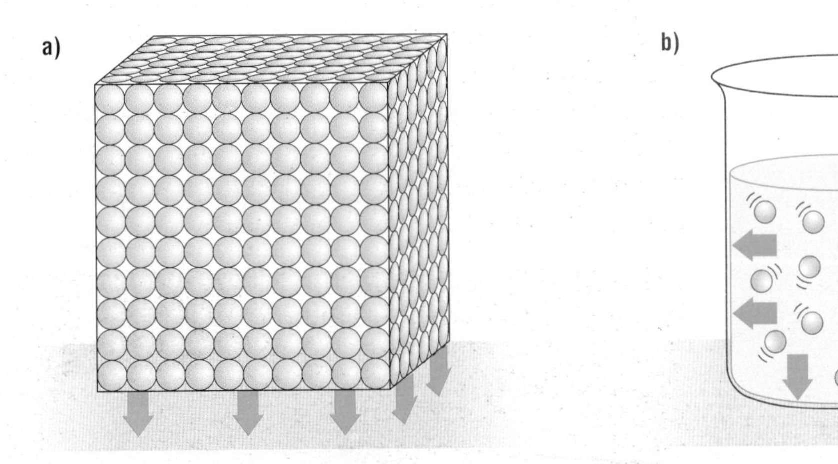

Figure 3.9 Pressure exerted by **a)** particles in a solid block and **b)** particles in a liquid.

Pressure and depth of a liquid

The change in pressure with depth in a liquid can be demonstrated by setting up a can as shown in Figure 3.10. When the clips are removed from the three rubber

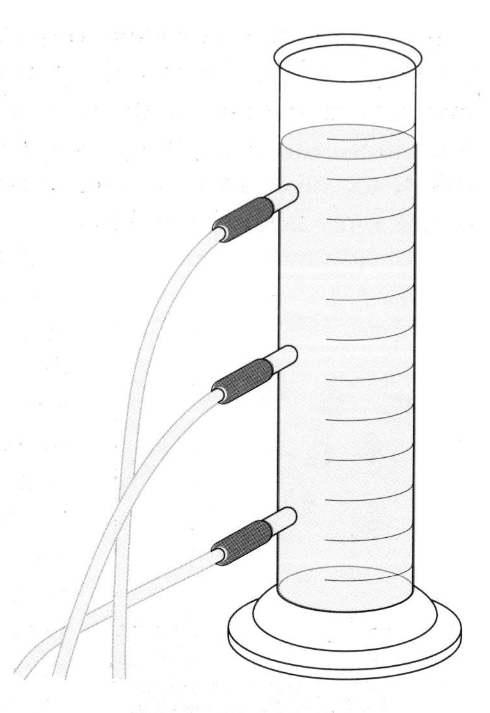

tubes, water flows out as shown. All three jets of water leave the can horizontally but the force of gravity pulls them down. The water under the greatest pressure travels the furthest horizontally before it is pulled down. The water under the least pressure travels the shortest distance horizontally before it is pulled down.

Figure 3.10 Jets of water leaving a can at different depths.

6 How does the path of the jet of water at the bottom of the can in Figure 3.10 change as the water level in the can falls? Why does it change?

A closer look at pressure and depth

The mass of a cubic centimetre of water is 1 g or 0.001 kg. The force of gravity (10 N/kg) means that this mass exerts a force downwards. The size of the force (equal to its weight) is calculated by:

$$0.001 \times 10 = 0.01\,\text{N}$$

This force acts on an area of $1\,\text{cm}^2$ (Figure 3.11a) so the pressure it exerts is:

$$\frac{0.01}{1} = 0.01\,\text{N/cm}^2$$

If a second cube of water is placed over the first, the pressure beneath the lower cube is increased to $0.02\,\text{N/cm}^2$ since the weight of water has doubled but the area it rests on has not (Figure 3.11b).

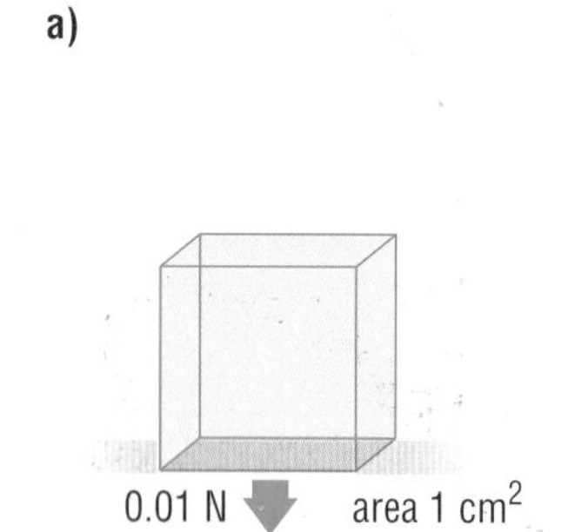

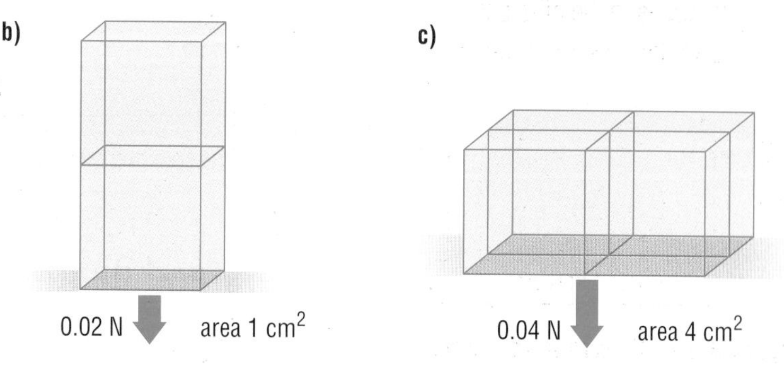

Figure 3.11 The pressure doubles when the depth of water doubles, but the pressure does not depend on the area of the column of water.

In fact, the pressure exerted by a liquid depends on the height of the column of liquid above its base, no matter what the area of the base of the column. Consider four cubes of water placed as in Figure 3.11c. A force of 0.04 N acts over an area of $4\,cm^2$ so the pressure is $0.01\,N/cm^2$, as in Figure 3.11a.

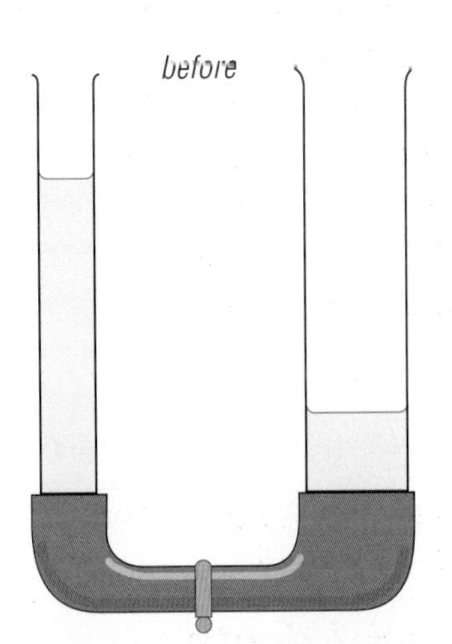

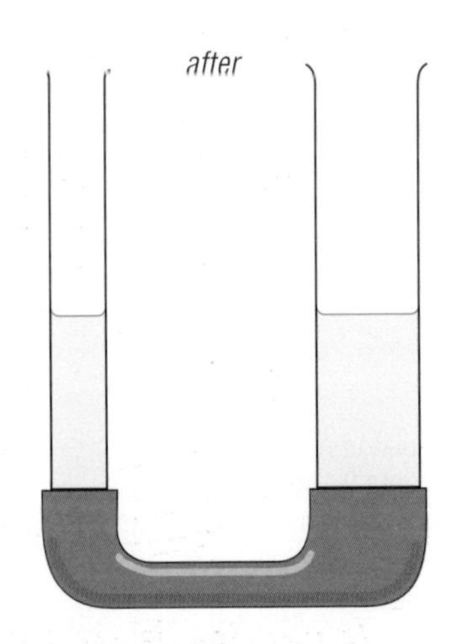

Figure 3.12 Water flows until the pressure in each column is the same.

If water is placed in the two arms of a vessel as shown in Figure 3.12 and the partition between the arms is removed, the water moves down the left arm and up the right arm until the water in both arms is at the same level. When this happens both columns of water are exerting the same pressure on the bottom of the vessel.

You can see that although the arms are of different widths the water in them settles to the same level in each. The wider arm has more of the liquid in it but it also has a larger area. The water level indicator on some jug kettles uses this fact to allow you to see where the water level is inside.

7 Why does a dam need a wall shaped like that in Figure 3.14?

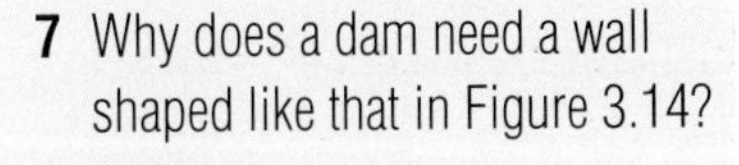

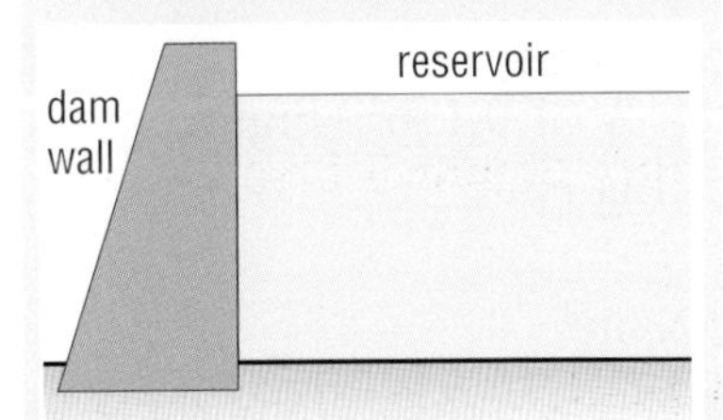

Figure 3.14 Cross-section of a dam wall.

8 Make a copy of Figure 3.15 and mark in the positions of the water levels in the different parts of the vessel B, C and D.

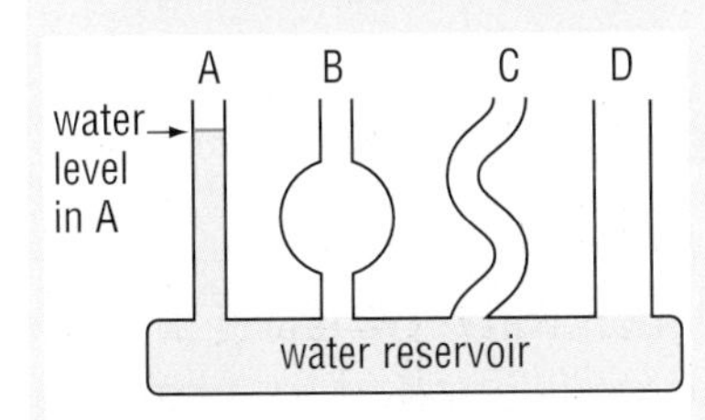

Figure 3.15 Pascal's vases (named after Blaise Pascal, see page 54).

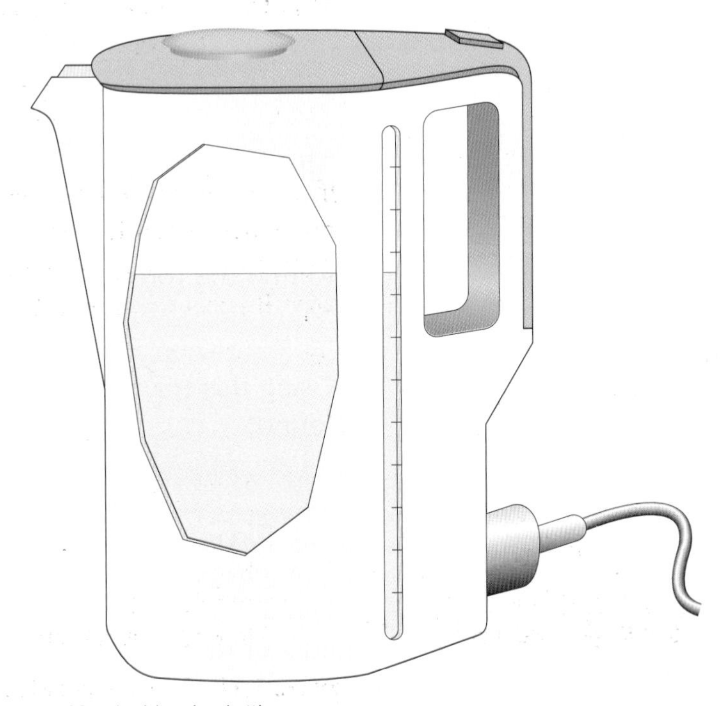

Figure 3.13 Inside a jug kettle.

Hydraulic equipment

If pressure is applied to the surface of a liquid in a container, the liquid is not squashed. It transmits the pressure so that pressure pushes on all parts of the container with equal strength.

In hydraulic equipment a liquid is used to transmit pressure from one place to another. The pressure is applied in one place and released in another. If the area where the pressure is applied is smaller than the area where the pressure is released, the strength of the force is increased as the following example shows.

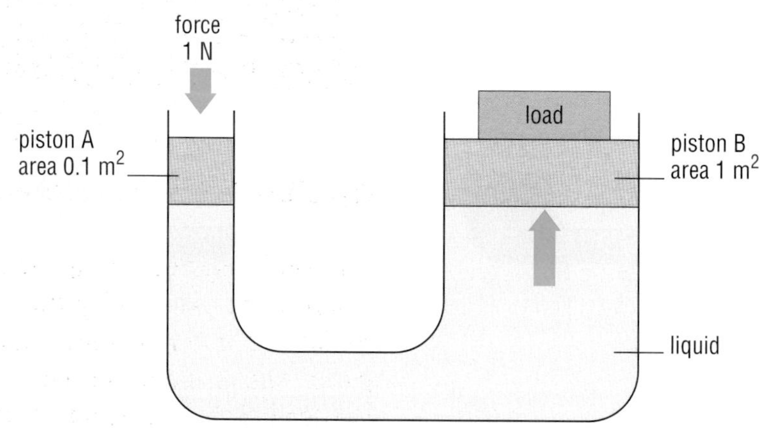

Figure 3.16 A simple hydraulic system.

A force of 1 N is exerted on area A of $0.1\,m^2$ (Figure 3.16). The pressure exerted on this is:

$$\frac{1}{0.1} = 10\,N/m^2$$

This same pressure is transmitted throughout the liquid and acts over area B. Area B is $1\,m^2$.

The equation pressure = force/area can be rearranged to find the force:

$$\text{force} = \text{pressure} \times \text{area}$$

Using this rearranged equation the force at B can be found:

$$\text{force} = 10\,N/m^2 \times 1\,m^2 = 10\,N$$

The force has been increased from 1 N to 10 N.

A car may be raised with a small force by using a hydraulic jack. When a small force is applied to a small area of the liquid in the jack, a larger force is released across a larger area and acts to raise the car.

9 Why are hydraulic systems known as 'force multipliers'?

Figure 3.17 This car has been raised into the air for repairs by a hydraulic jack.

The brake system on a car is a hydraulic mechanism. The small force exerted by the driver's foot on the brake pedal is converted into a large force acting at the brake pads. This results in a large frictional force that makes it harder for the wheels to turn and so stops the car.

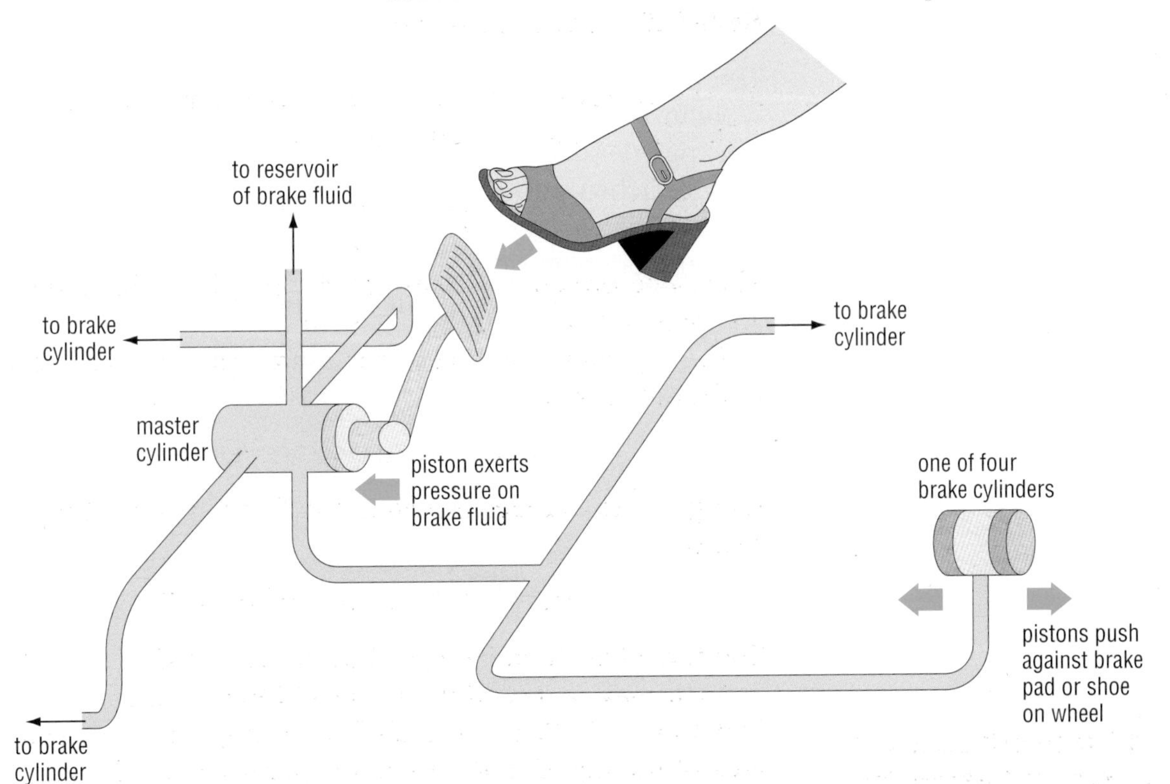

Figure 3.18 Hydraulic car brakes.

Pressure of the atmosphere

The atmosphere is a mixture of gases. The molecules from which the gases are made move around but are pulled down by the force of gravity exerted on them by the Earth. The atmosphere forms a layer of gases over the surface of the Earth which is about 1000 km high. This creates a pressure of about 100 000 N/m^2 – equivalent to a mass of 10 tonnes on 1 m^2 – although this gets less as you go up through the atmosphere.

You do not feel the weight of this layer of air above you pushing down because the pressure it exerts acts in all directions, as it does in a liquid. Thus, the air around you is pushing in all directions on all parts of your body. You are not squashed because the pressure of the blood flowing through your circulatory system (see *Biology Now! 11–14* page 49) is strong enough to balance atmospheric pressure.

The atmosphere does not crush ordinary objects around us. For example, the pressure of the air pushing down on a table top is balanced by the pressure of the air underneath the table pushing upwards on the table top.

Ear popping

The middle part of the ear (Figure 3.19) is normally filled with air at the same pressure as the air outside the body. The air pressure can adjust because when you swallow, the Eustachian tubes in your throat open and air freely enters or leaves the middle ear. For example, if the air pressure is greater outside the body and in the mouth, when you swallow more air will enter the middle ear to raise the air pressure there.

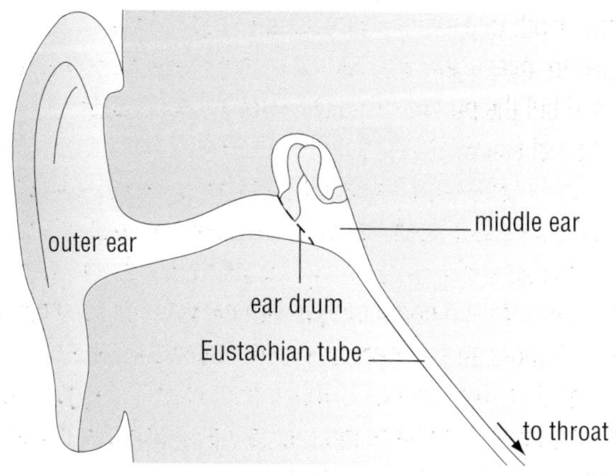

Figure 3.19 The ear and throat.

10 What happens if the air pressure in the throat and outside the body is less than the air pressure in your middle ear when you swallow?

11 If you ride quickly down a hill on a bicycle your eardrums are pushed in before they pop back. Why is this?

If you travel in a car which quickly climbs a steep hill, your ears sometimes 'pop'. This is because you are rising rapidly into the atmosphere where the pressure is lower. The popping sensation is caused by the air pressure being lower in the throat and outside the body than in the middle ear. The difference in pressure causes the eardrum to push outwards. When you swallow the air pressure in your middle ear reaches the same pressure as the air in your throat and outside, and the eardrum moves quickly back – or 'pops' – into place.

Discovering air pressure

A major hazard of underground mining is the water that drains through the rocks and fills the mine shafts which have been dug for the miners to work in. In the 17th Century a lift pump was invented to remove the water but it would only raise the water about 10 metres in a pipe.

1 Why was Galileo asked to investigate how a lift pump worked?

2 Why was Galileo's investigation with his pump not successful?

3 What information from Galileo's experiments did Torricelli use in explaining his observations?

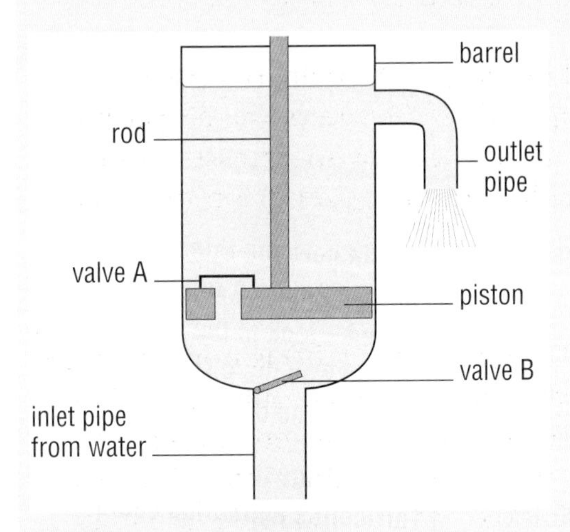

Figure A Inside a lift pump.

At the time, it was still believed, from the teaching of Aristotle, that a vacuum or a place without air could not possibly exist. If this were true the water should rise from any depth to prevent a vacuum forming in the pump.

Galileo was asked to investigate. He made a pump to test the idea of a vacuum being created but the pump leaked and was made of opaque materials so he could not see what was going on inside.

Evangelisto Torricelli (1608–1647) worked with Galileo in the last few months of Galileo's life and continued testing the idea of a vacuum after Galileo's death. Galileo had shown that air has weight by weighing a glass vessel at normal air pressure and comparing it with the weight of a second glass vessel into which more air had been pumped. The second vessel weighed more than the first. Torricelli used this information to suggest that the water moved up the pipe of the lift pump due to the pressure of the air outside rather than because of the suction inside.

(continued)

He decided that using water and a pipe over 10 metres long would be difficult so he scaled down the experiment. He could do this because a liquid that is denser than water forms a shorter column than water when the air pressure holds it up. Torricelli chose mercury which is a liquid about 13 times as dense as water. He set up the apparatus shown in Figure B by filling a tube of mercury then inverting it in a bowl of mercury in such a way that no air could get in. When he did this the column of mercury in the tube fell until the top of the column was at a height of 76 cm above the level of the bowl. This was the height that he had predicted. The space in the tube above the mercury was a vacuum.

4 a) How do you think the height of the mercury column changed in Torricelli's apparatus when it was moved from the bottom of a mountain to the top?

b) Why was there a change in the height of the column of mercury?

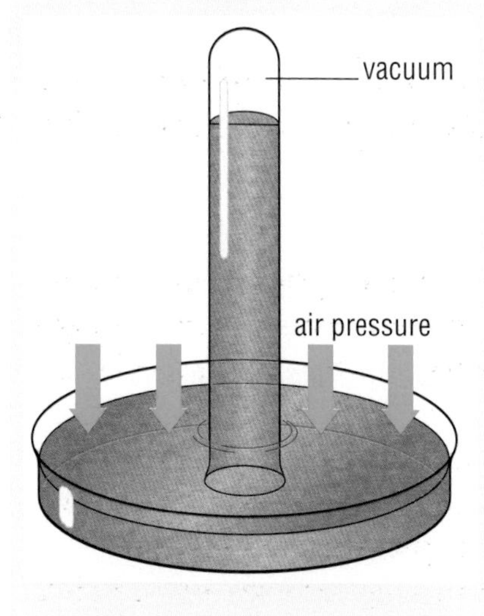

Figure B Torricelli's column of mercury.

Torricelli noticed that the size of the vacuum space varied from day to day. He reasoned that it was not the vacuum itself that changed but the strength of the air pressure supporting the mercury column. Unfortunately he died before he could test his idea.

Blaise Pascal (1623–1662) continued Torricelli's work. He had an idea that the air over the Earth behaved like a huge pile of wool. The bottom part of the wool pile would be compressed by the weight of the wool above it and would be under greater pressure than wool higher in the pile. When the air pressure at the bottom and the top of a mountain were tested with Torricelli's apparatus, Pascal was shown to have predicted correctly.

For discussion

Explain how you think the lift pump in Figure A might have worked – look at the valves and the way the piston could move up and down.

It was suggested that Torricelli's apparatus could be used to measure the height of a mountain. How realistic is this suggestion? Explain your answer.

How a sucker sticks

When an arrow with a sucker on the end hits a target the arrow stays in place due to air pressure. As the elastic sucker hits the flat surface it deforms and pushes out some of the air from beneath the cup. The pressure of the remaining air in the cup is less than that of the air pressure outside the cup. The higher pressure of the air outside the cup holds the sucker in place (Figure 3.20).

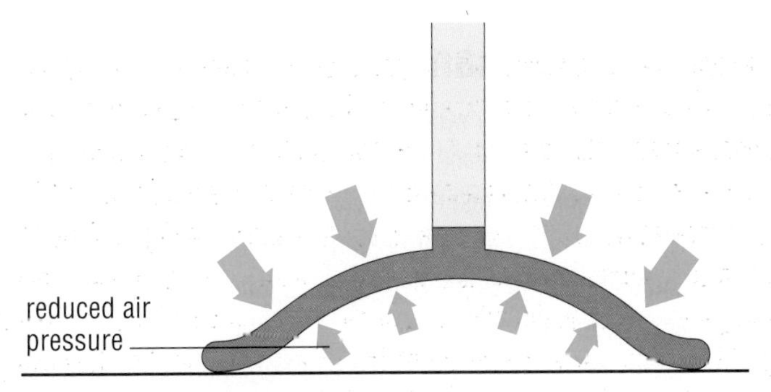

Figure 3.20 Side view through a sucker.

Crushing a can

The strength of the air pressure in the atmosphere can be demonstrated by taking the air out of a can. This can be done in two ways.

Using steam

The can has a small quantity of water poured into it and is heated from below. As the water turns to steam it rises and pushes the air out of the top of the can. If the heat source is removed and the top of the can immediately closed, the remaining steam and water vapour in the can will condense leaving only a small quantity of air in the can. This air has a much lower pressure than the air pressure outside the can and the higher pressure crushes the can.

Using a vacuum pump

A vacuum pump can reduce the pressure in containers. If one is used to remove air from a can, the can collapses due to the greater pressure of the air on the outside (Figure 3.21).

Figure 3.21 Removing air from this oil can has made it collapse.

A scientific showman

Otto von Guericke (1602–1686) was the mayor of Magdeburg in Germany for 35 years. He was also interested in discovering if a vacuum could really exist. He made an air pump to test his ideas. He used his pump to draw air out of a variety of vessels. When he tried barrels he found they collapsed. He eventually found that hollow copper hemispheres joined together to make a globe were much stronger.

Aristotle had believed that if a vacuum could exist then sound would not be able to pass through it. When von Guericke put a bell in one of his vessels and removed the air he discovered that a ringing bell could not be heard (see page 177).

Von Guericke greatly enjoyed demonstrating his discoveries to large numbers of people and in one demonstration had two teams of eight horses pull on the evacuated hemispheres without separating them. This spectacular demonstration helped people to realise the strength of the air pressure pushing on the hemispheres.

1 Why did von Guericke believe he had made a vacuum?
2 Why did the Magdeburg hemispheres not come apart when the teams of horses pulled on them?
3 How did von Guericke help people to become interested in science?

For discussion

How could an investigation you have done in your physics course be made into an informative and entertaining demonstration?

How successful are television producers and presenters at making science programmes entertaining and informative?

Figure A Otto von Guericke's demonstration with 'Magdeburg' hemispheres.

Aerosols

An aerosol spray can contains a gas which is at a higher pressure than air pressure. It is held in the can by a valve in the nozzle (Figure 3.22). When the nozzle is pressed down a spring is squashed and the nozzle opening enters the inside of the can, effectively opening the valve. The higher pressure of the gas in the can pushes on the liquid in the can and it rushes up the tube and through the jet where it forms a fine spray. When the nozzle is released the spring is no longer squashed and

12 How many uses of aerosol cans in the home can you think of?

pushes the nozzle upwards. This removes the nozzle opening from inside the can, effectively closing the valve, and stops the flow of spray.

Aerosols used to contain a gas made from chlorofluorocarbons (CFCs). These chemicals are now known to damage the ozone layer. In many countries they have now been replaced with gases such as refinery gases which do not damage the ozone layer.

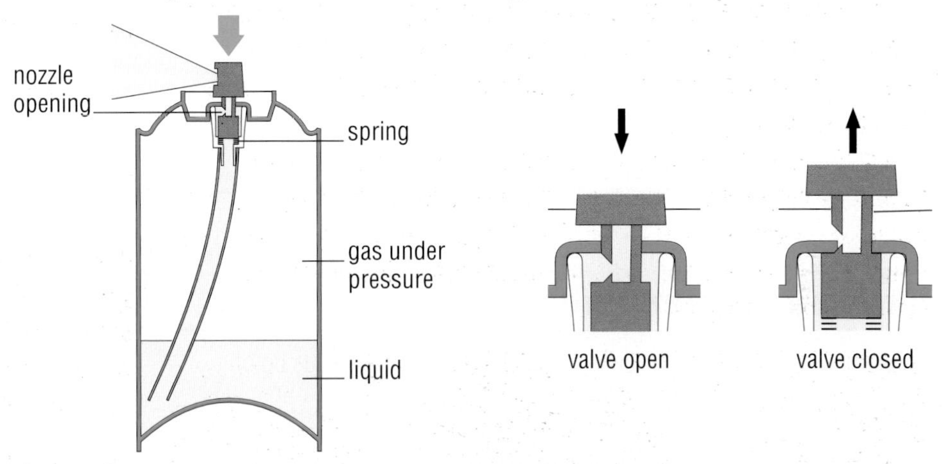

Figure 3.22 Inside an aerosol can.

Hovercraft

A hovercraft uses the pressure of air to raise it from the ground. It does this by drawing air from above with powerful fans. There is a skirt around the edge of the hovercraft which prevents the air from escaping quickly and the air pressure beneath the hovercraft increases. The upward pressure of the air trapped beneath the hovercraft lifts the hovercraft off the ground. The fans continue to spin to replace air that is lost from the edges of the skirt. The cushion of air beneath the hovercraft reduces friction between it and the ground. The cushion of air is also maintained when the hovercraft moves over water. The forward or backward thrust on the hovercraft is provided by propellers in the air above the hovercraft.

13 What are the advantages of using a hovercraft as a means of transport?

Figure 3.23 A hovercraft.

♦ SUMMARY ♦

- Pressure acts when a force acts over an area of surface (*see page 43*).
- When a solid object exerts a pressure on the surface below it, the smaller the area of contact, the greater the pressure (*see page 44*).
- Pressure in a liquid acts in all directions and increases with the depth of the liquid (*see page 47*).
- In hydraulic systems pressure is transmitted through a liquid (*see page 50*).
- The atmosphere exerts a pressure (*see page 52*).
- Air pressure is made use of in various devices such as pumps, suckers, aerosols and hovercraft (*see pages 53–57*).

End of chapter questions

How could you explain the following using the model of air made up of particles which move freely?

1 How air pushes on a surface.
2 Why the pressure in an inflated tyre is higher than the air pressure outside.
3 Why a sucker stays in place on a flat surface.

The section on pressure on pages 26–27 of *Chemistry Now! 11–14* may help you answer this question.

4 *Energy*

Figure 4.1 Does this seem familiar?

These are two sayings that are familiar to most people at some time in their lives and they show how we link the words work and energy. One way of thinking about energy is to say that energy is the property of something that makes it able to do work.

In science the word work is only used to mean one thing and is linked to forces and movement in the following way.

Work occurs when a force moves an object through a distance.

The amount of work done is given by the equation:

$$\text{work} = \text{force} \times \text{distance}$$

Force is measured in newtons (see page 22) and distance moved is measured in metres so the amount of work done is measured in the units N m.

When something or someone does work, the amount of work done is equal to the amount of energy used in doing the work. Work and energy are so closely related that they have the same unit, the joule.

$$\text{joule} = \text{N} \times \text{m}$$

For discussion

How many different kinds of work can you think of? Make a list.

1 How are the words energy and work linked together in science?
2 How does the amount of energy used by a person differ when he or she lifts a heavy object **a)** 10 cm off the ground and **b)** 1 metre above the ground? Explain why the amount of energy differs in **a)** and **b)**.
3 Why do you use less energy when you are lying in bed than when you are walking about your home?

Types of energy

Energy exists in many forms. In the following pages the main forms of energy are described.

Chemical energy

Energy can be stored in the chemicals from which a material is made. The chemicals are made from atoms that are linked together to make molecules. The chemical energy is stored in the links between the atoms. Food, fuel and the chemicals in an electrical cell (or battery) are examples of stored chemical energy.

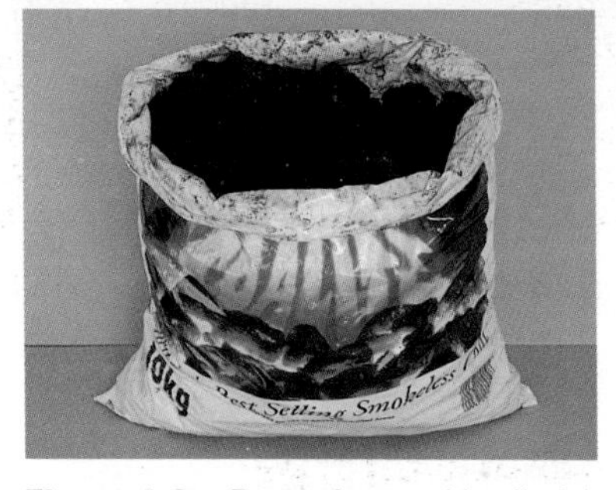

Figure 4.2 Energy is stored in all of these objects.

The energy is released when the links between some of the atoms are broken and the molecule in which the energy was stored is broken down into smaller molecules. For example, carbohydrates are a store of chemical energy in food. During respiration carbohydrate is broken down into carbon dioxide and water. The energy that is released in this process is used by your body to keep you alive (see *Biology Now! 11–14* page 42). The energy released by a fuel is used to heat homes, to heat water to produce steam in power stations for generating electricity (see page 85) and for the production of new materials (see *Chemistry Now! 11–14* pages 151 and 165).

For discussion

What is a fuel? Give some examples.

Gravitational potential energy

The force of gravity between an object and the Earth pulls the object down towards the centre of the planet. If an object is in a position above the surface of the Earth, it possesses stored energy called gravitational potential energy. Examples of objects with this stored energy are plates on a table, books on a shelf, a child at the top of a slide and an apple growing on a branch. Each of these objects is supported by something but if the support is removed they will move downwards to the Earth's surface and their gravitational potential energy is released.

4 If you are holding this book or it is resting on a table or desk why does it possess gravitational potential energy?

5 If you held a stone over the mouth of a well then let it go what would happen to the stone? Explain your answer.

Figure 4.3 When the objects fall their stored gravitational potential energy is released.

Strain energy

Some materials can be easily squashed, stretched or bent, but spring back into shape once the force acting on them is removed. They are called elastic materials. When their shape is changed by squashing, stretching or bending they store energy, called strain energy or spring energy, which will allow them to return to their original shape. This form of stored energy is also called elastic potential energy.

A spring stores energy when it is stretched or squashed. Gases store strain energy in them when they are squashed. For example, when the gas used in an aerosol (see Figure 3.22) is squashed into a can it stores strain energy. Some of this is used up when the nozzle is pressed down and some of the gas is released in the spray.

6 Look at Figure 4.4 on the next page. When is elastic potential energy stored and when is it released in **a)** a toy glider launcher, **b)** the elastic cords or springs beneath a sun lounger, and **c)** a diving board?

Figure 4.4 Places where strain energy can be stored and released.

Nuclear energy

Every substance is made from atoms and at the centre of each atom is a nucleus. It is made from particles called protons and neutrons (see page 104). In the atoms of most elements these particles are bound strongly together. These atoms are said to be stable atoms. In some large atoms the nuclear particles are not bound strongly together and the unstable nuclei may split up to form different, smaller nuclei which are more stable. As the unstable atoms form more stable atoms they release energy. This process of releasing nuclear energy is called nuclear fission.

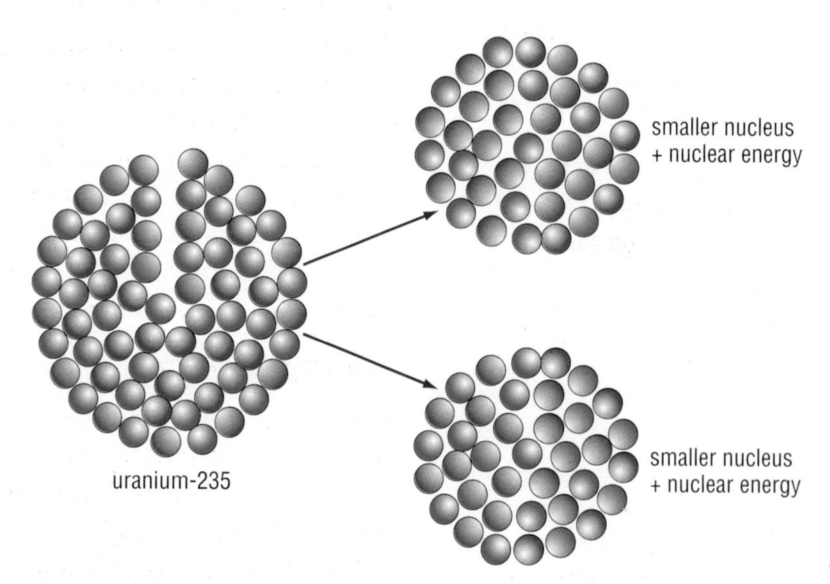

Figure 4.5 The nucleus of the heavy metal uranium is unstable and may split to form two smaller nuclei, releasing stored nuclear energy.

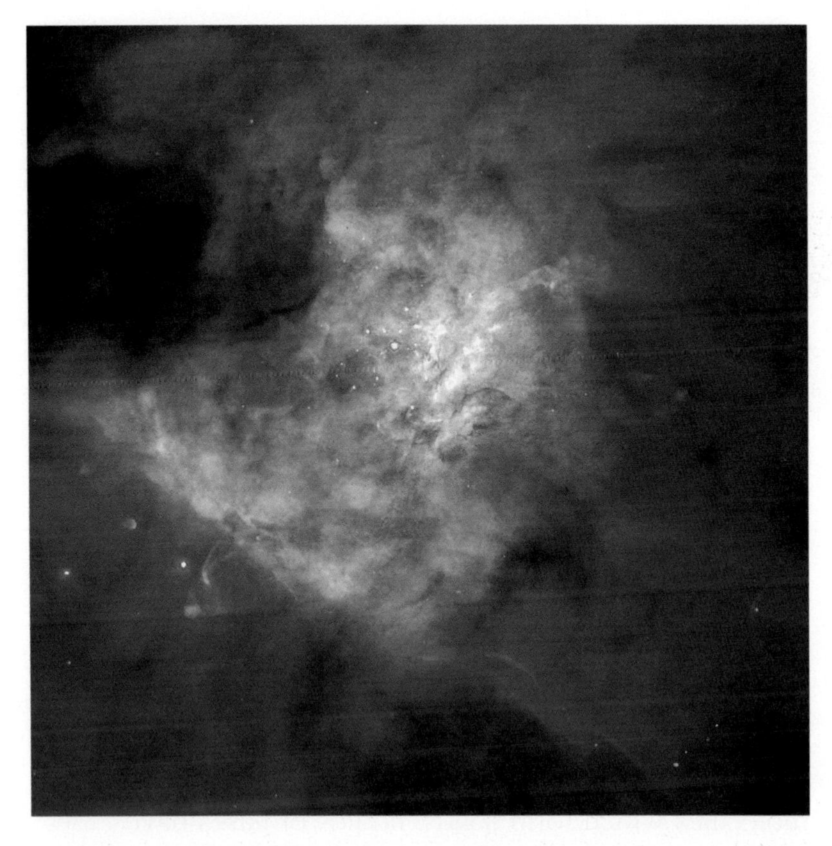

In the Sun and other stars nuclear energy is released instead by nuclear fusion. The gravitational forces are very strong at the centre of the star and the hydrogen nuclei collide at such high speeds that they actually join together (fuse) to form helium nuclei. During this process large amounts of energy are released. Most of this energy escapes from the star as heat and light.

Figure 4.6 These young stars shine because of nuclear fusion.

7 What is the difference between nuclear fission and nuclear fusion?

For discussion

A nail held close to a magnet has magnetic potential energy. Why is this so?

What happens to the magnetic potential energy of the nail when it is let go close to the magnet?

Other forms of stored energy

Two other forms of stored energy are magnetic potential energy – the energy of a magnetic field, and electrostatic potential energy – the energy of an electric field.

Work and stored energy

Energy may be stored as a result of work being done. For example, the child at the top of the slide in Figure 4.3 has gravitational potential energy because of the work she has done in climbing to the top. She had to do work against the force of gravity.

Similarly, a stretched elastic band has stored strain energy because of the work done on it in stretching it against the strain forces.

Kinetic energy

Kinetic energy is also known as movement energy. When an object with kinetic energy touches another object it exerts a contact force (see page 22) which may set the second object moving too.

Any moving object has kinetic energy. The object may be as large as a planet or as small as an atom or an electron.

8 Look out of a window and make a list of everything you can see that has kinetic energy.

Figure 4.7 Breaking the land speed record.

The powerful rocket engines in the car in the photograph converted the chemical energy in the fuel to kinetic energy so quickly that the car reached an average speed of 1227 km/h.

Internal energy

In fact, you could have listed everything you can see when answering question 8 since all the atoms and molecules which form solids, liquids or gases have kinetic energy and move at random (see Figure 3.8). The atoms in a solid move the least. Each has a position in the solid structure about which it vibrates to and fro. The atoms in a liquid move around and past each other and the atoms in a gas can move freely in all directions. This movement of the atoms inside a solid, liquid or gas is due to the internal energy of the substance. The internal energy is increased by heating a substance. This increases the movement and separation of the atoms.

9 How can the internal energy of an object be reduced?
10 How does reducing the internal energy affect the atoms inside the object?

Thermal energy

The energy supplied to a substance which increases its internal kinetic energy, or the energy lost from a substance which decreases its internal kinetic energy, is commonly called heat, or heat energy. The correct scientific term is thermal energy.

The process by which thermal energy moves is called thermal energy transfer or thermal transfer (see page 92).

Sound energy

Sound energy is produced by the vibration of an object such as the twang of a guitar string. The energy passes though the air by the movement of the atoms and molecules. They move backwards and forwards in an orderly way. This makes a wave that spreads out in all directions from the point of the vibration. Sound energy can also pass through solids, liquids and other gases. The atoms move in a similar way to the turns on a slinky spring when a 'push-pull' wave moves along it.

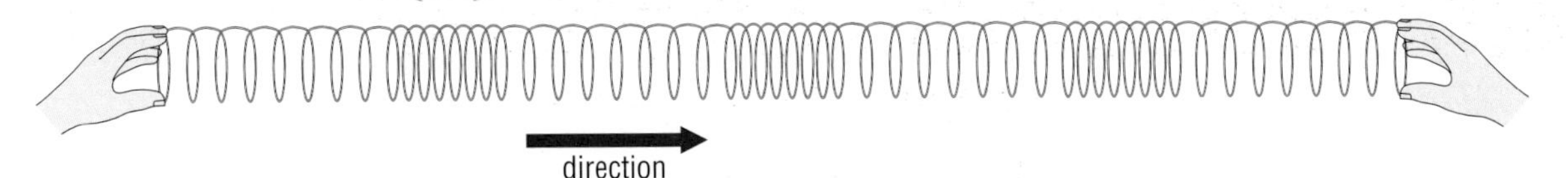

Figure 4.8 A slinky shows how sound waves move.

11 In what ways is electrical energy put to work in your home?

Electrical energy

Electrical energy is due to the movement of electrons though an electrical conductor such as copper or graphite when it is part of a circuit with a power supply (such as a battery) and the switch is closed (see page 121).

Radiation energy

This kind of energy travels in waves that have some properties of electricity and some properties of magnetism. They are called electromagnetic waves. There is a huge range of possible wave sizes, or wavelengths. Electromagnetic waves are split into seven groups according to wavelength, as Figure 4.10 on the next page shows. The different groups have different properties and different uses. The two most familiar groups are light and radio waves.

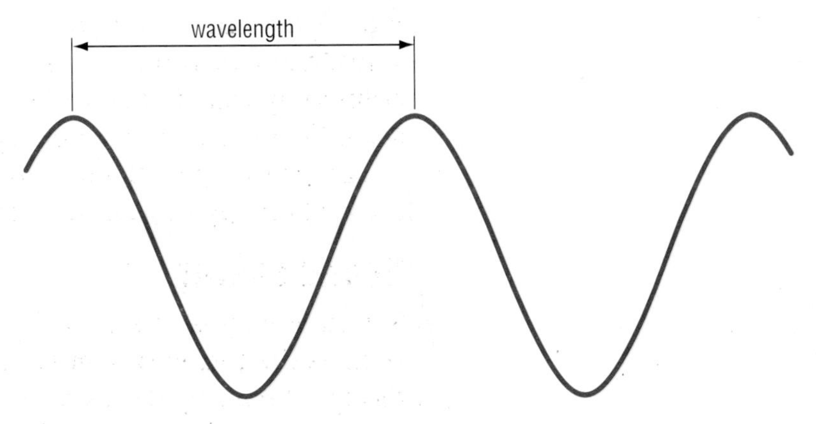

Figure 4.9 A wave showing wavelength.

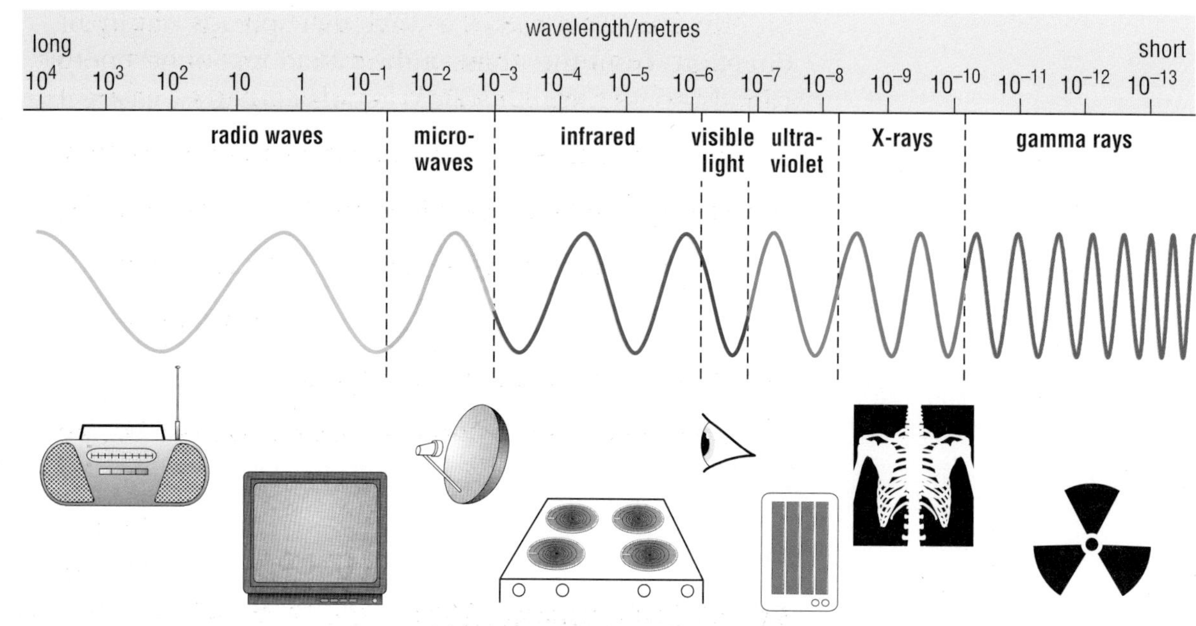

Figure 4.10 The electromagnetic spectrum.

12 Which radiation energy has
a) the longest waves and
b) the shortest waves?

13 Which radiation energy can our eyes detect?

Light energy

The light energy escaping from the Sun can be spread out by a prism or a shower of raindrops into light of different wavelengths. This forms the colours of the rainbow (see page 170) because our eyes see different wavelengths of light as different colours.

Infrared radiation

Infrared radiation carries heat (thermal) energy in the form of electromagnetic waves which we detect as warmth on our skin.

Ultraviolet light

Ultraviolet or UV light causes chemical changes in our skin that gives the skin a tan. The excessive amounts of ultraviolet light reaching the Earth because of the destruction of parts of the ozone layer (see *Chemistry Now! 11–14* page 153) may also stimulate the growth of skin cancers.

For discussion

Is radiation energy harmful? Explain your answer.

Energy changes

Energy can be transferred from one form to another. When an amount of energy is transferred none is lost. There is the same amount of energy afterwards as there was before. This constancy of energy is known as the Law of the Conservation of Energy.

The object or material in which the energy changes form is called the energy converter or energy transducer. The transfer of energy can be written using this format:

energy input → *energy converter* → energy output

For example, when a candle burns the energy transfer is:

chemical energy → *candle* → light energy
→ heat energy

When you run the energy transfer is:

chemical energy in food → *human body* → kinetic energy
→ heat energy

14 What are the energy transfers when **a)** a dog barks and **b)** a television set is switched on?

Figure 4.11 A candle is an energy converter.

Figure 4.12 People are energy converters.

The flow of energy through one or more energy converters is called an energy chain. For example, the energy chain produced when a motor on an electric golf buggy is switched on and moves the vehicle is:

chemical energy → *electrical cell* → electrical energy → *motor* → kinetic energy

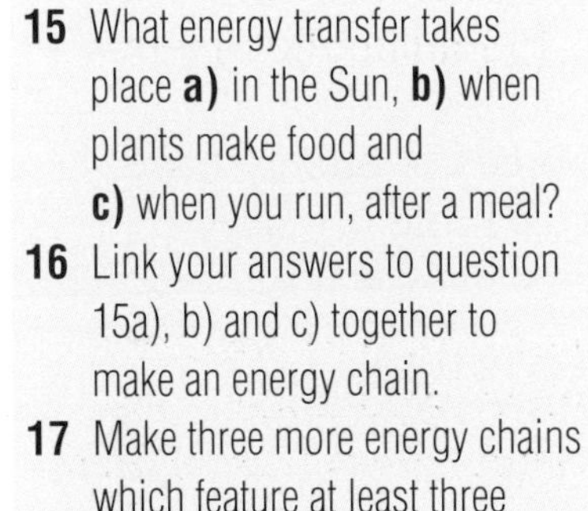

15 What energy transfer takes place **a)** in the Sun, **b)** when plants make food and **c)** when you run, after a meal?

16 Link your answers to question 15a), b) and c) together to make an energy chain.

17 Make three more energy chains which feature at least three energy converters.

Figure 4.13 There are several energy transfers going on in a device like an electric golf buggy.

A closer look at energy changes

The energy chains above have shown the main transfers in energy but if we considered them in more detail we would find that other transfers also take place. Here are the ones that take place when a ripe apple falls off a tree.

An apple on a tree has gravitational potential energy. When its stalk weakens and breaks, the apple's weight pulls it down and its stored energy becomes kinetic energy. As the apple falls through the air it collides with atoms in the air and causes them to move faster – the air is warmed a little. This means that some of the apple's energy is transferred to heat energy. When the apple strikes the ground a thud is heard. This means that some of the energy is transferred to sound energy. The apple and the ground are warmed slightly by the collision, so more of the apple's kinetic energy is transferred to heat energy, which increases the internal energy of the apple and the ground.

The energy transfers that occurred when the apple fell to the ground can be written as:

gravitational potential energy → kinetic energy
→ heat energy to air
→ heat energy to ground and apple
→ sound energy

In fact, whenever energy changes some of it is always lost as heat (thermal) energy.

18 Look back at the energy chains you made in answer to questions 16 and 17. See if you can add more detail to the energy changes.

For discussion

What energy changes occur when you jump up and down?

Sources of energy

We use many different sources of energy to provide everything we use in our everyday lives. The sources of energy may be as close as the wind in your face or as distant as the inside of the Sun, 150 million kilometres away.

In the following pages the sources of energy have been divided into three groups as Table 4.1 shows.

Table 4.1 Sources of energy.

Nuclear fusion in the Sun	Nuclear reactions on Earth	Gravitational forces between Earth, Moon and Sun
produces **a)** light energy which is changed into: • biomass • fossil fuels • electrical energy by solar cells	produce internal (heat) energy from **a)** controlled fission reactions of minerals from the Earth's crust, e.g. uranium	produce tidal energy
b) infrared (heat) energy which is changed into: • movement energy in the atmosphere used to drive the water cycle • movement energy in water waves • internal energy of water in solar panels	**b)** naturally occurring nuclear reactions in radioactive rocks below the Earth's crust; this internal energy is called geothermal energy	

19 Why does the Sun release energy?

Nuclear fusion in the Sun

The Sun is a star, a huge fireball of hydrogen and helium gases which is 1 392 000 kilometres in diameter. Over one million planets the size of the Earth could fit inside the Sun. At the centre of the star it is so hot that hydrogen nuclei move fast enough to hit each other and fuse together to produce helium. As this happens energy is released which is radiated from the Sun's surface as electromagnetic waves, mostly light and infrared radiation. It is believed that the Sun will continue to release energy in this way for another 5000 million years. The Sun is our main source of energy.

Figure 4.14 A close-up of the Sun's surface.

Energy from the Sun's light

Biomass

Biomass is the amount of matter in a living thing. Plant biomass is produced by plants from the raw materials of carbon dioxide, water and minerals.

Green plants possess a pigment called chlorophyll which traps some of the energy in sunlight. The plants use this energy to join chemicals together to make food which is then used to build up the plant's body or to take part in processes in the plant which keep it alive.

Food

The food stored in plants may be eaten by herbivores, such as sheep, and omnivores such as ourselves. We have bred certain plants for cultivation as crops which provide us with food rich in energy (see *Biology Now! 11–14* page 108). Food provides animals with chemical potential energy. They use this energy to keep alive and build up their own bodies. We also take in stored chemical energy from animals when we eat their meat.

20 Why does food from **a)** plants and **b)** animals contain energy?

Fuel wood

The energy stored in plants can be released by drying them and setting fire to them. In many parts of the world, particularly in developing countries where there is no coal, wood is used as a fuel for cooking and heating.

Figure 4.15 In Nepal, ovens are fuelled by wood.

Ethanol

Some countries, such as Brazil, have few natural supplies of oil from which to make petrol. A shortage of fuel for vehicles is prevented by fermenting plants such as sugar cane and grain to make ethanol, a type of alcohol. This is mixed with petrol and reduces the demand for oil.

Figure 4.16 This pump delivers alcohol petrol.

Energy from food wastes

Biogas

The wastes produced when food has been eaten can be used as a source of energy. Vegetable waste and the wastes from humans and animals can be stored in biogas digesters, where microorganisms feed. As they feed, methane gas is produced. This gas can be used for cooking or lighting and as a fuel to generate electricity.

Figure 4.17 Biogas digester in Egypt.

In sewage works the solid wastes are stored in digesters where they form the food for microorganisms. The methane gas produced can be used as a source of heat energy to help in the sewage treatment.

Dung

In countries without coal and where fuel wood is scarce the dung of domestic animals, such as cattle, is collected, dried, made into fuel cakes for burning.

Figure 4.18 Making fuel cakes from animal dung.

Fossil fuels

Coal is formed from large plants which grew in swamps about 275 million years ago. These plants used energy from sunlight in the same way that plants do today. When they died they fell into the swamps. There was a lack of oxygen in the swamp water which prevented bacteria growing and decomposing the dead plants (see *Biology Now! 11–14* page 189). Eventually the plants formed peat. Later the peat became buried and was squashed by the rocks that formed above it. The increase in pressure squeezed the water out of the peat and warmed it. These processes slowly changed the peat into coal.

Tiny plants and animals live in the upper waters of the oceans and form the plankton. When they die they sink to the ocean floor. Over 200 million years ago the dead plankton which collected on the ocean floor did not decompose because there was not enough oxygen there to allow bacterial decomposers to grow. The remains formed a layer which eventually became covered by rock. The weight of the rock squeezed the layer and heated it. This slowly converted the layer of dead plankton into oil and methane gas. This is the gas that is supplied to homes as natural gas. Several fuels are obtained from oil (see *Chemistry Now! 11–14* page 146).

21 What conditions helped fossil fuels to form?

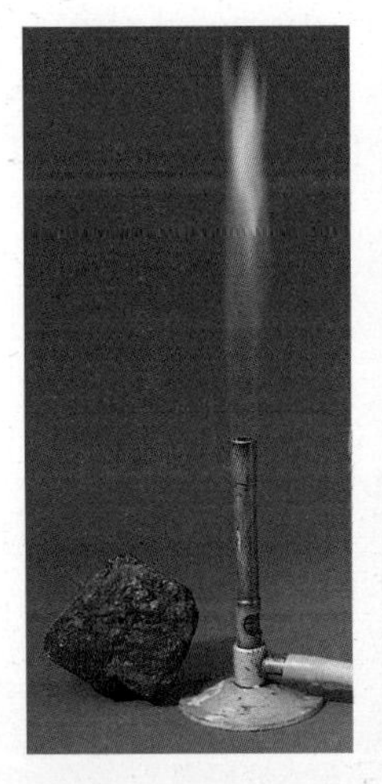

Figure 4.19 The three fossil fuels.

Figure 4.20 Arrays of solar cells project from a space station to collect some of the Sun's energy.

Solar cells

A solar cell is made from a material which converts some of the energy in sunlight into electrical energy. Solar cells are used on satellites, space probes and space stations to provide power to work the machines on board.

Energy from the Sun's heat

Most of the energy from the Sun is in the form of infrared radiation (see page 66). This warms the Earth and its atmosphere.

Movement of the atmosphere

The air nearest the Earth's surface warms the fastest and then rises. It is replaced by cooler air. The cycle repeats itself and a convection current is set up (see page 93). Various circulations of this type occur in the Earth's atmosphere. Regions of high and low pressure develop in the atmosphere which in turn lead to the production of winds.

The kinetic energy in wind can be used to turn the blades of a wind turbine and produce electricity (see page 86).

Figure 4.21 Wind turbines on a wind farm.

Movement of water

Flowing water

The Sun's heating effect causes the evaporation of water from the surfaces of the oceans and lakes. The water vapour that is produced rises in the warm air then condenses to form clouds as the air cools. Winds blow the clouds around the globe and further falls in temperature over land or sea make the clouds produce rain. The water falling on land forms rivers which flow back to the oceans and complete the water cycle (see *Chemistry Now! 11–14* page 23).

The energy in river water can be used in the following way. If a dam is built across the river the water collecting behind it has stored gravitational energy. When the water is released from the lower part of the dam the high pressure there makes it flow very fast.

It therefore has a large amount of kinetic energy and this can be used to spin a turbine and generate electricity (see page 86).

Figure 4.22 Array of turbines in a hydroelectric power station in Russia.

Waves

The winds blow on the surfaces of the oceans and produce waves. The kinetic energy in the wind is converted into kinetic energy of the water. Machines are being developed to use the energy in waves to generate electricity.

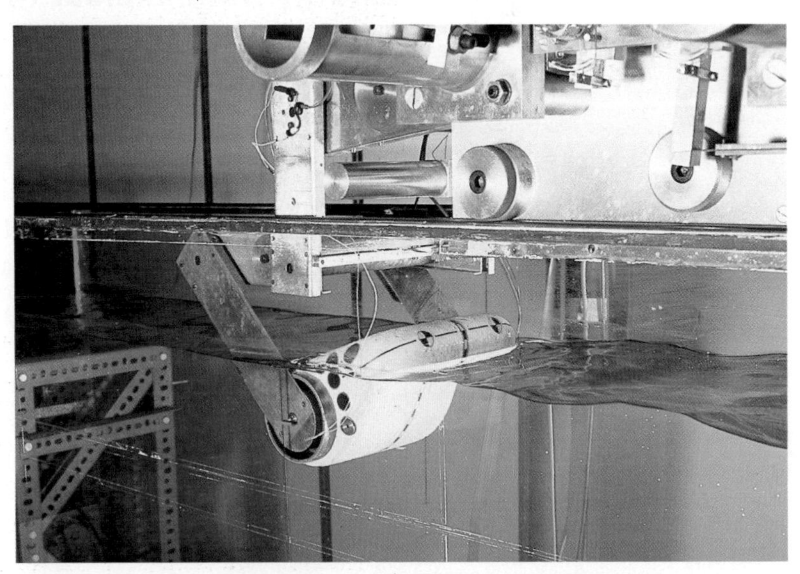

Figure 4.23 This machine converts the energy in the up and down motion of passing waves into a turning motion required to make an electric generator work.

Solar panels

A solar panel is designed to heat water in a house in sunny weather. In the panel are pipes which carry water. They are connected to a coiled pipe in the domestic hot water tank. The pipes in the panel run over a black surface which absorbs infrared radiation from the sun. The panel is double glazed to reduce the loss of heat (thermal) energy from around the pipes. The hot water produced in a solar panel on a sunny day is circulated through the coil in the hot water tank to warm the water there.

Figure 4.24 These roofs in Sweden are fitted with solar panels.

22 Make a chart showing the relationship between the Sun and the different energy sources described so far.

Energy from nuclear reactions on Earth

Almost all the elements which form the matter from which the Earth is made have been made by nuclear fusion in stars in the distant past. Some elements are unstable and 'decay' in nuclear reactions to form more stable elements. These unstable elements are called radioactive elements. When they undergo radioactive decay they release particles and energy.

We use energy from radioactive materials which are found in and below the Earth's crust. The structure of the Earth is shown in Figure 4.25.

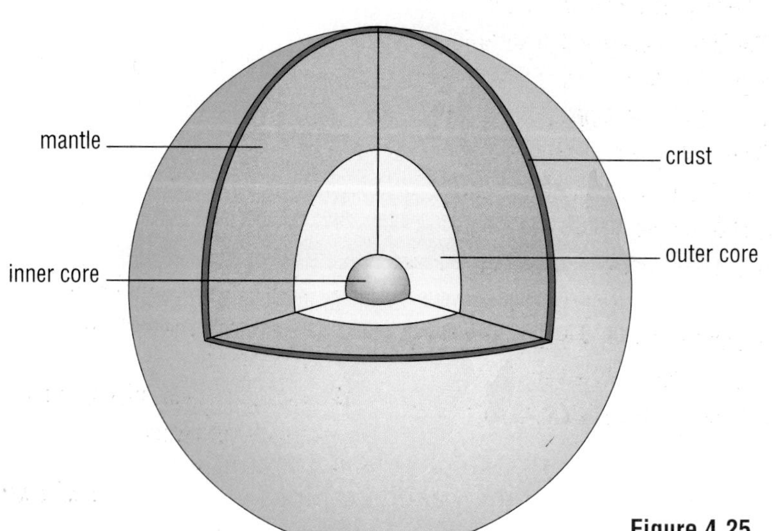

Figure 4.25 The structure of the Earth.

Fission

The atoms of some heavy elements such as uranium are very unstable and can split up into two smaller, more stable atoms (see page 62). The process, called nuclear fission, releases large amounts of energy.

Pitchblende or uraninite is a mineral in the Earth's crust which contains uranium. This element is used as fission fuel in nuclear power stations. Energy from the fission reactions is used to heat water to make high pressure steam to turn the turbine (see page 86).

The discovery of radioactive materials

William Roentgen (1845–1923), a German physicist, was working on passing electricity through a vacuum tube when he saw a sheet of paper which was coated in a chemical start to glow. The sheet was some distance from the vacuum tube. When Roentgen switched off the current of electricity the paper stopped glowing. He discovered that the paper glowed even if sheets of plain paper or even thin metal were put in front of it. Roentgen decided that the glow of the paper was made by invisible but penetrating rays coming from the vacuum tube. He had no idea what the rays could be so he called them X-rays.

Figure A Roentgen at work in his laboratory.

Antoine Becquerel (1852–1908), a French physicist, studied fluorescent materials (see page 152). When he read about Roentgen's work he wondered if fluorescent materials produced X-rays. By then it was known that X-rays made a photographic plate become foggy so Becquerel used photographic plates in his experiments. He exposed the fluorescent material to sunlight, placed it close to a photographic plate and discovered that the plate became fogged.

One day he was prevented from experimenting by cloudy weather and the fluorescent material and the photographic plates he was to use were left together in a drawer. The fluorescent material had been used in a previous experiment so Becquerel decided to examine the plates to see if any X-rays were still being produced by the material. When he developed the plate he found that it was very foggy. Becquerel then performed a series of experiments on the material and discovered that it produced rays in all directions all the time. Later experiments showed that the rays were like X-rays and that they were produced by uranium which was in the fluorescent material.

Today we distinguish between the two types of rays in the following ways. The term X-rays is used to describe the rays produced by an electrical device, and the term gamma rays is used to describe the rays produced from the nuclei of a radioactive material.

1 How are X-rays and visible light rays **a)** similar and **b)** different?
2 How did chance play a part in Becquerel's work?

(continued)

Figure B Antoine Becquerel.

3 What do you think Becquerel expected when he investigated the fluorescent material and the photographic plate that had been left in the drawer?
4 What contribution did Marie Curie make to the study of radioactive materials?
5 Why do you think polonium was given that name by Marie Curie?

Marie Curie (1867–1934), a scientist born in Poland, invented the word radioactivity to describe the rays released by uranium. She used her husband's discoveries with electricity and crystals to make a device to accurately locate radioactive substances and with it she discovered that the element thorium was also radioactive. Her work led to the discovery of two more radioactive elements which she named radium and polonium.

Figure C Marie Curie with her daughter, Irene.

Radioactivity beneath the Earth's crust

There are radioactive materials beneath the Earth's crust which release energy that heats the core and mantle. The hot rock from the mantle which pushes its way into the crust may produce volcanoes or cause heating of water in the rocks which make geysers as shown in Figure 4.26.

Figure 4.26 The energy to heat a geyser is provided by hot rocks below ground.

The heat in the rocks of the crust is used as a source of energy in some countries, for example New Zealand and the USA. Cold water is pumped down to the hot rocks where it is turned to steam. This returns through pipes to the surface where it is used to generate electricity in a power station.

Figure 4.27 A geothermal power station.

Using nuclear fission

Albert Einstein (1879–1955), a German-born self-taught physicist, began by studying the work of other scientists. Among other enlightened theories, he produced an equation which linked mass and energy. The equation is:

$$E = mc^2$$

where E is energy, m is mass and c is the velocity of light.

This equation showed that mass is a store of energy which can be released when matter is destroyed. This idea successfully explained the phenomenon of radioactive materials by showing that they produced energy in the form of radiation because part of their mass was destroyed.

Otto Hahn (1879–1968), a German chemist, and Lise Meitner (1878–1968), an Austrian physicist, studied how radioactive materials decayed and in 1939 Meitner described how uranium atoms broke in half.

Figure A Albert Einstein.

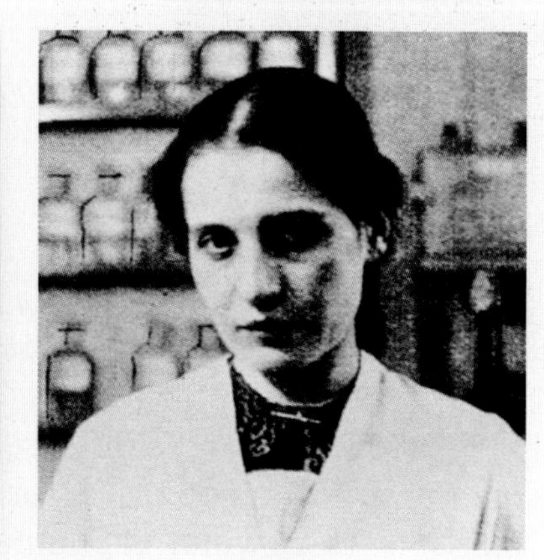

Figure B Lise Meitner.

Leo Szilard (1898–1964), a Hungarian-born physicist who studied atomic nuclei, had an idea of how the break-up of one atom may cause the break-up of surrounding atoms and lead to a chain reaction. When Szilard heard of Hahn's and Meitner's work he realised that uranium could be investigated to see if a chain reaction would be set up. If such a reaction could take place then a large amount of energy could be released quickly.

Szilard was drawing up his plans and predictions in the United States during the Second World War. He realised that the chain reaction could be used to release energy for a bomb. He and other scientists, including Einstein, informed the United States president of the explosive power of uranium. This led to the development of nuclear bombs. Szilard and many scientists believed the bombs were too devastating to be used like other bombs and should only be demonstrated in an uninhabited part of the world, to show the enemy the power that was now set against them. However, politicians in charge of the armed forces and some scientists believed it right to use the nuclear bombs like other bombs, and two were dropped on Japan with catastrophic results.

1 Why do radioactive materials release energy?
2 What was Szilard's idea and how was the work of Hahn and Meitner useful to him?
3 Why did you think the scientists first considered making nuclear bombs instead of reactors for power stations?

(continued)

Figure C Devastation caused by a nuclear explosion in Hiroshima, Japan.

After the War scientists began investigating ways of using nuclear energy for peaceful purposes. This meant that the energy released in the chain reaction had to be released more slowly than in a bomb.

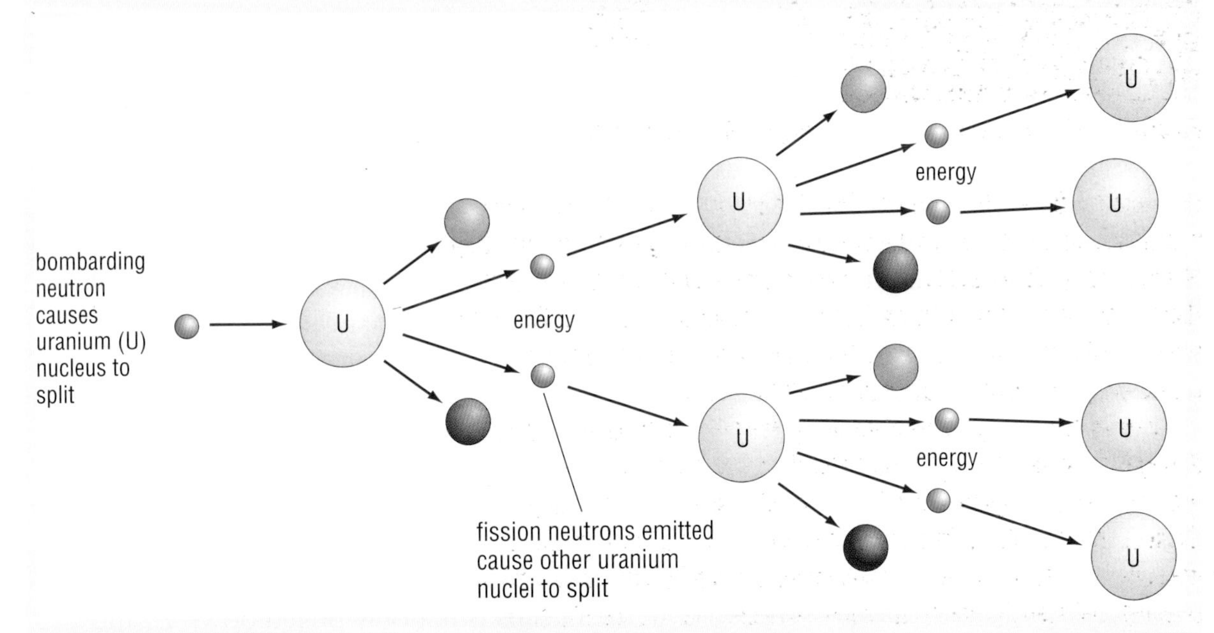

Figure D A chain reaction.

The nuclear reactor was developed to release energy in sufficient amounts to heat water to steam. This could then be used to spin a turbine in a generator to produce electricity. Today there are about 400 nuclear reactors operating in more than 30 countries.

(continued)

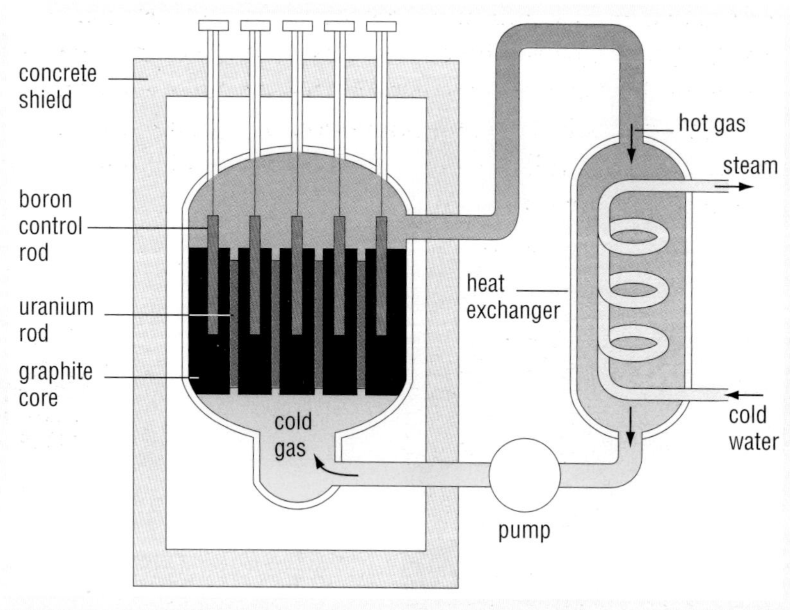

Figure E The inside of a nuclear reactor.

4 How does inserting the control rods in the graphite affect fission in the reactor? Explain your answer.
5 A reactor has all its control rods inserted in the graphite. What must be done so that it produces more heat? Explain your answer.
6 What do you think is the purpose of the thick concrete walls?
7 What could be the consequences of an explosion at a nuclear reactor?
8 What are the advantages and disadvantages of using nuclear fuel for generating electricity?

Figure E shows the structure of a nuclear reactor. The uranium fuel is packed into rods and surrounded by graphite. Neutrons from the chain reaction travel at a high speed but collisions with uranium atoms are more likely when the neutrons move more slowly. The graphite slows down the neutrons so that nuclear fission is increased.

Boron absorbs neutrons and is used to make the rods which control the rate at which fission takes place. The control rods can be raised or lowered into the graphite around the tubes of uranium.

The heat produced by nuclear fission is transferred to carbon dioxide gas which circulates between the reactor and the heat exchanger, where the heat is transferred to the water to make steam.

Nuclear reactors are built and operated to very strict safety rules to prevent them overheating and exploding. They do not produce sulphur dioxide and carbon dioxide like the power stations using fossil fuels, but the nuclear wastes that they produce have to be stored for thousands of years while they decay to harmless materials.

For discussion

Discuss this statement: 'The study of radioactive materials has been a great benefit to humankind'.

Energy from gravitational forces

The Moon, the Sun and the tides

The water in the oceans is not only pulled down by the Earth's gravity but is also affected by the gravitational pull of the Moon, and to a smaller extent by the gravitational pull of the Sun. Differences in the force of attraction of the Moon on different parts of the Earth causes the water beneath the Moon and on the opposite side of the Earth to rise up slightly, causing a high tide. The level of water in other parts of the ocean falls, and produces a low tide at those places. As the Earth rotates different regions of the seas and oceans move under the Moon and experience the full force of its gravitational pull. This brings a period of high tide to that region which is followed by a period of low tide as the Earth continues its rotation.

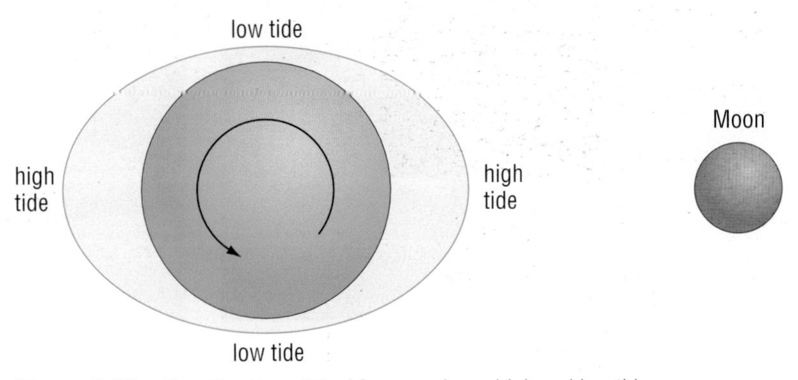

Figure 4.28 The attraction of the Moon produces high and low tides.

Twice a month the Sun and the Moon are in line as the Moon orbits the Earth (Figure 4.29). At these times the difference in the sea level at high and low tide is greatest as the small gravitational pull of the Sun reinforces the effect of the stronger pull of the Moon. The tides at these times are called spring tides.

When the Moon is furthest out of line with the Sun and the Earth, the difference in the high and low tides is least since the gravitational pull of the Sun counteracts that of the Moon. The tides at these times are called neap tides.

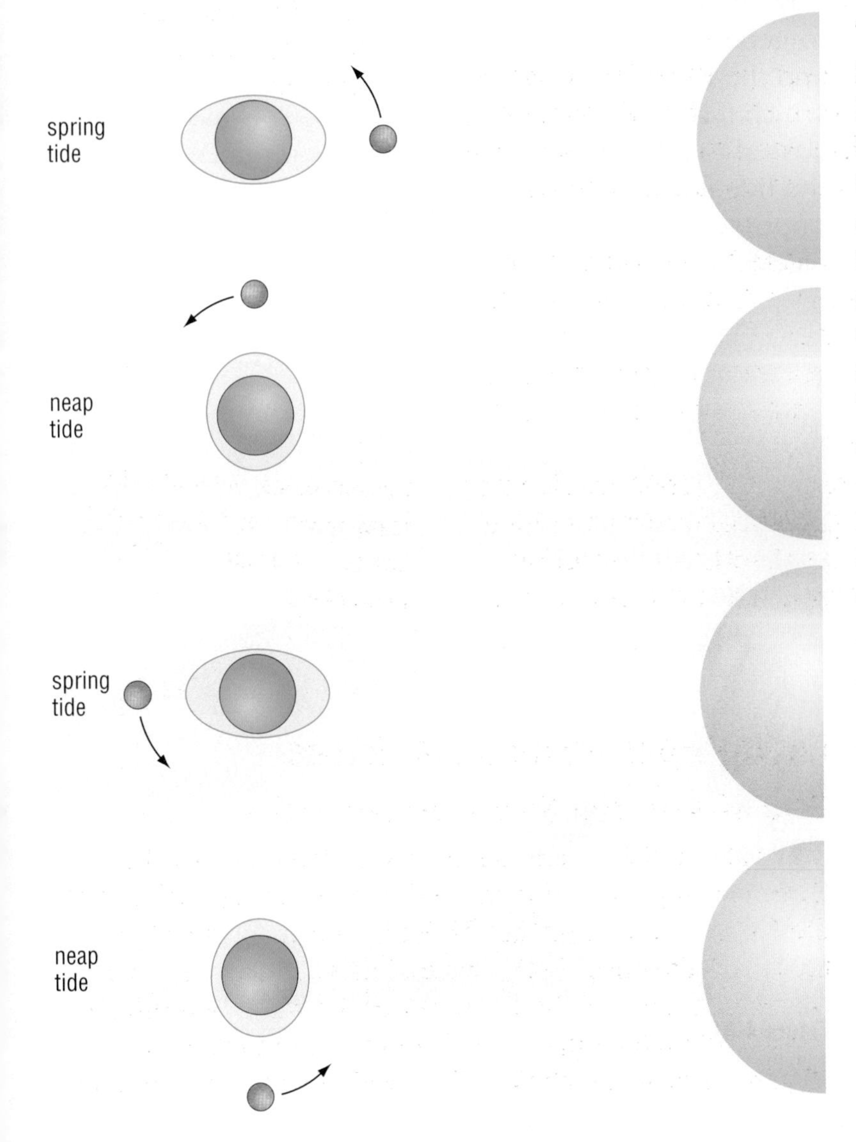

Figure 4.29 How the positions of the Sun and the Moon cause a change in the tides.

High tide

Low tide

Figure 4.30

23 The Sun is much larger than the Moon yet its gravitational pull on the oceans is less than that of the Moon. Why is this?

The energy stored in the water at high tide can be used to generate electricity. A dam is built across an estuary and the rising water of the tide passes through pipes in which turbines can turn (see page 75). This movement is passed to a generator and electricity is produced. When the tide falls the water passes through the pipes in the opposite direction and turns the turbines again, so more electricity can be generated.

Figure 4.31 The La Grande I hydroelectric project in Canada generates electricity from the tides.

Non-renewable and renewable energy sources

The sources of energy can be divided into two groups according to whether they will eventually be used up or whether they can be constantly replaced.

Non-renewable energy sources

These sources cannot be replaced once they have been used up. These energy sources are the fossil fuels and radioactive materials.

Renewable energy sources

These sources can be replaced. They are light and heat from the Sun, biomass, geothermal energy and kinetic energy of the wind, water, waves and the tides.

The power station

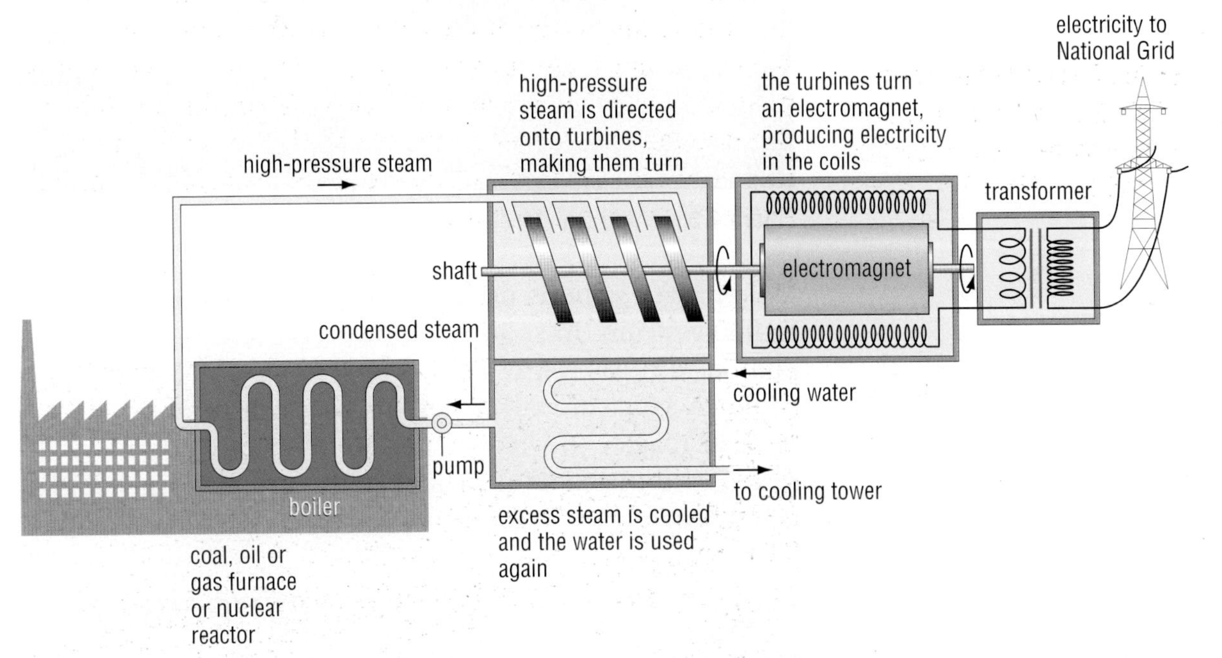

Figure 4.32 The parts of a power station.

In about two-thirds of the world's power stations water is heated to make steam. This takes place in a boiler. The energy that the water molecules receive increases their kinetic energy so much that they move apart from each other to form a gas – steam. The steam expands rapidly and exerts a force which drives it from the boiler to the turbine blades. Here as much as possible of the kinetic energy of the steam is passed to the turbine blades as the steam pushes past them, making the blades spin on a central shaft. An electromagnet is connected to the end of the shaft. It is one part of the electrical generator. The other part consists of coils of wire that surround it. As the electromagnet spins using kinetic energy from the turbine blades it generates a current of electricity in the coils of wires. The electricity flows away from the power station to towns and cities in overhead power lines or underground cables.

Figure 4.33 A gas turbine power station.

24 Construct an energy chain to show the path of energy through a power station which uses coal as its fuel.

Most power stations use fossil fuels to produce the heat to make steam. In some gas-powered stations the combustion gases are used as well as steam to turn turbines. Nuclear power stations use heat produced in a nuclear reactor to make steam. In other power stations steam is not used at all. The turbines are made to spin by water (see Figure 4.22) or wind (see Figure 4.21).

Using energy and the environmental impact

Most power stations today use the fossil fuels coal and oil. When these fuels are burnt they produce sulphur dioxide gas and carbon dioxide gas. The sulphur dioxide dissolves in water droplets in clouds and makes acid rain which damages forests, streams and lakes. The increase in the amount of carbon dioxide in the atmosphere is believed by many scientists to cause global warming. (For more details of environmental damage see *Chemistry Now ! 11–14* Chapter 12.)

For discussion

As non-renewable sources of energy are used up how could renewable sources be developed in the area shown in Figure 4.34?

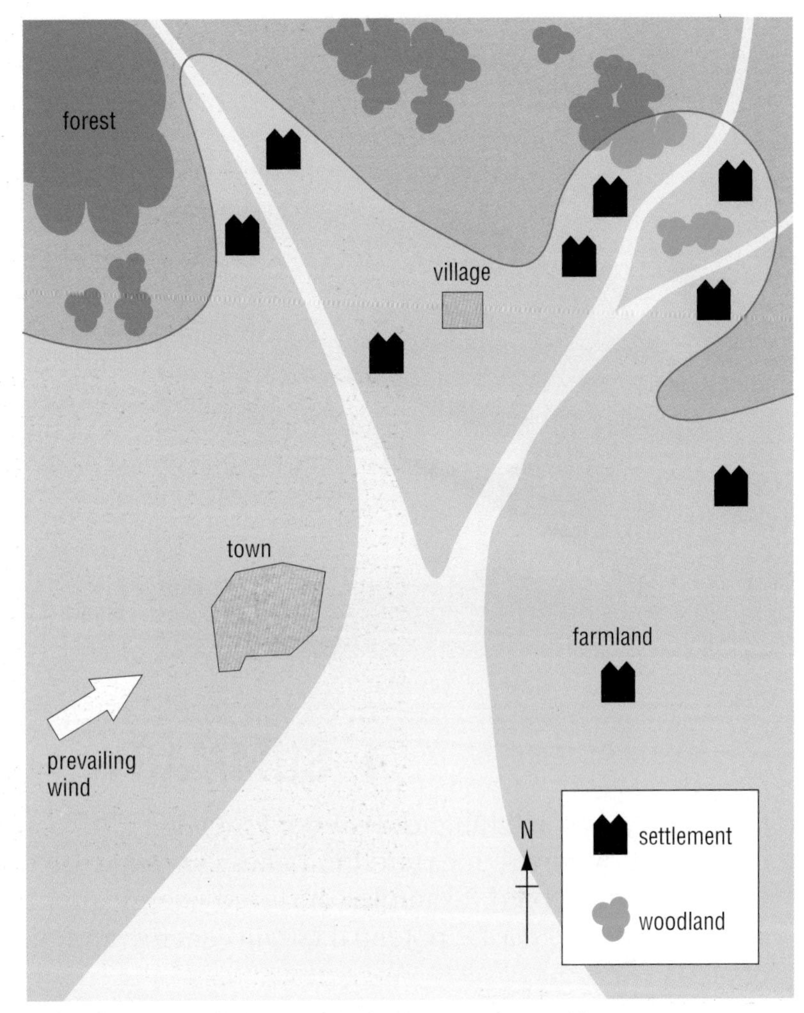

Figure 4.34 An area proposed for development of renewable energy sources.

The use of renewable resources may also affect the environment. For example, reservoirs for hydroelectric power stations are made by flooding valleys. This means that the habitats of plants and animals are lost, some people may have to leave their homes and farmers may have to give up their land. Wind farms are considered unsightly by some people and the turning of the blades may produce noise.

Cells and batteries

We use cells and batteries as sources of electrical energy but they are manufactured sources of energy and more energy is used to make them than they release. They are really energy stores which are particularly useful because they are small and can be used in portable equipment.

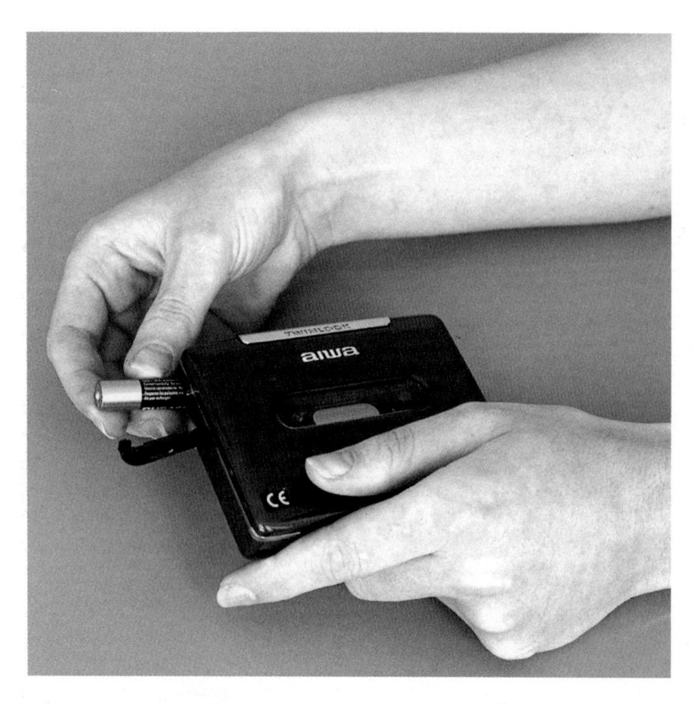

A cell or a battery contains chemicals. When the cell or battery is placed in a conducting circuit and the switch is closed the chemicals react and produce a flow of electrons round the circuit. The chemicals for use in cells and batteries have been extracted from raw materials such as metal ores and minerals. Energy has been used in the extraction of these raw materials. This energy has come from other energy sources such as fuels and hydroelectric power.

Figure 4.35 This cell is being inserted into a portable cassette player.

♦ SUMMARY ♦

- Energy allows something to do work (*see page 59*).
- Energy and work are measured in joules (*see page 59*).
- Energy can be stored. Examples of stored energy are chemical energy, gravitational potential energy, elastic potential (strain) energy and nuclear energy (*see pages 60–63*).
- Movement energy is known as kinetic energy (*see page 63*).
- Internal energy in a substance is due to the movement of its atoms and molecules (*see page 64*).
- Thermal energy is the correct scientific term for heat energy. When thermal energy is transferred the internal kinetic energy of a substance increases (*see page 64*).
- Sound energy is transferred by waves in which atoms move backwards and forwards (*see page 64*).
- Electrical energy is produced by the movement of electrons (*see page 65*).
- Radiation energy is transferred by electromagnetic waves (*see page 65*).
- Energy can change from one form into another (*see page 66*).
- The Sun is the major source of energy for our planet (*see page 69*).
- Radioactive materials release energy (*see page 76*).
- Heat energy is released from inside the Earth (*see page 79*).
- The gravitational forces of the Moon and the Sun cause the tides (*see page 82*).
- Electricity is generated in power stations (*see page 85*).
- Chemicals can be used to provide compact energy sources for electricity (*see page 87*).

End of chapter questions

A group of pupils was investigating the gravitational potential energy in a 15 cm long nail. They suspended it above a block of clay, measured the distance to its tip then let it go. The pupils measured the depth to which the nail sank in the clay. Table 4.2 shows their results for four experiments.

Table 4.2

Height of nail above clay/cm	Depth of indent/cm
25	0.9
50	1.6
75	2.3
100	3.0

1 How do you think they measured the depth of the indent in the clay?
2 Plot a graph of their results.
3 How could you use the graph to predict the indent made by the nail from a height greater than 1 metre? Give an example.

A second group of pupils investigated the gravitational potential energy of a brass sphere which was dropped from different heights into soft clay. They measured the diameter of the indent made by the sphere. Table 4.3 shows the results for four experiments.

Table 4.3

Height of sphere above clay/cm	Diameter of indent/cm
5	1.0
20	1.7
50	2.2
70	2.5

4 How do you think the pupils measured the diameter of the indent?
5 Plot a graph of their results.
6 How do these results compare with the results of the first experiment?
7 Suggest a reason for any differences you describe.
8 Can the graph be used to predict indentations produced by falls from any height greater than 70 cm? Explain your answer.

5 A closer look at heat

A great deal of the energy we use in the home is used to provide heat for cooking, for heating water for washing ourselves and our clothes, and for keeping us warm. Heat (thermal energy) is also produced in significant quantities whenever energy is converted from one form to another (see page 68).

1 How much hotter is **a)** 45 °C than 30 °C and **b)** 20 °C than −15 °C?

2 Why are two fixed points needed for a temperature scale and not just one?

Heat and temperature

The hotness or coldness of a substance is measured by taking its temperature. The temperature of a substance is measured on a scale which has two fixed points. The most widely used temperature scale is the Celsius scale. Its two fixed points are 0 °C (the melting point of ice or freezing point of water) and 100 °C (the boiling point of water). In between the two fixed points the scale is divided into one hundred units or degrees. The scale may be extended below 0 °C and above 100 °C; laboratory thermometers usually have a scale reading from −10 °C to 110 °C.

The thermometer compares the temperature of the substance in which the bulb is immersed with the freezing point and boiling point of water. It compares the hotness or coldness of a substance. It does not measure the total internal energy (see page 64) of the substance.

The lowest possible temperature, known as absolute zero, is −273 °C. Temperatures can go as high as millions of degrees Celsius.

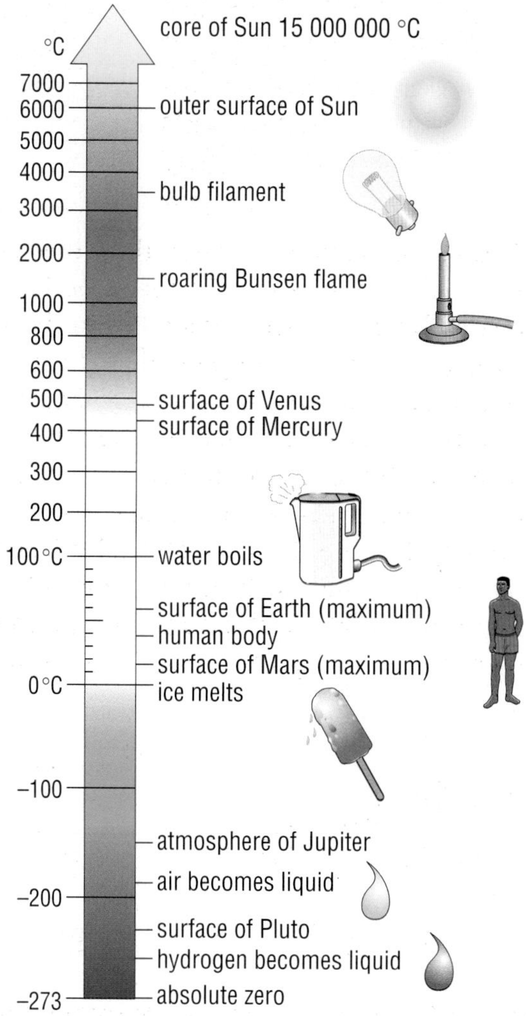

Figure 5.1 The Celsius scale of temperature.

Heat and internal energy

The 'heat' in a substance is really a measure of the total kinetic energy of the atoms and molecules of a substance, due to its internal energy (see page 64). The total amount of heat in a substance is related to its mass. A large mass of a substance holds a larger amount of heat – it has more internal energy – than a smaller mass. For example, if 100 cm^3 of water is heated in a beaker with a Bunsen burner on a roaring flame it will take less time to reach 100 °C than 200 cm^3 of water would because it has a smaller mass.

Figure 5.2 When heating two masses of water, more heat energy needs to be supplied to the larger mass to reach the same temperature.

When a substance is heated the (thermal) energy supplied increases the internal kinetic energy which means the atoms and molecules in the substance move faster and further (see page 64). If the temperature of the substance is taken with a thermometer, kinetic energy from the substance passes to the atoms or molecules from which the thermometer liquid is made and causes them to move faster too. This leads to an expansion of the liquid in the thermometer tube (see page 98). The thermometer measures the (average) kinetic energy of the particles hitting the bulb and not the total kinetic energy of all the particles in the substance.

3 Why does it take a full kettle longer to boil than a half-full kettle?

4 Which do you think contains more internal energy, a teaspoon of boiling water or a pan full of water at 50 °C?

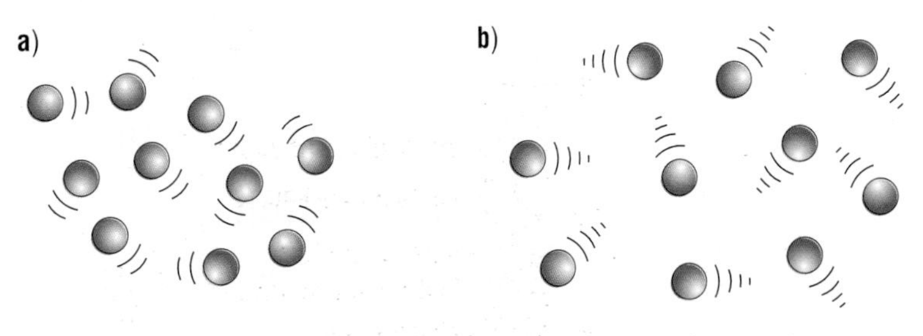

Figure 5.3 Particles in motion in **a)** a cool substance and **b)** a hot substance.

Measuring the amount of heat energy

The amount of heat (thermal) energy given to a substance can be measured by heating the substance with an electric heater. The quantity of electrical energy used can be measured by a joulemeter and this equals the amount of heat (thermal) energy supplied.

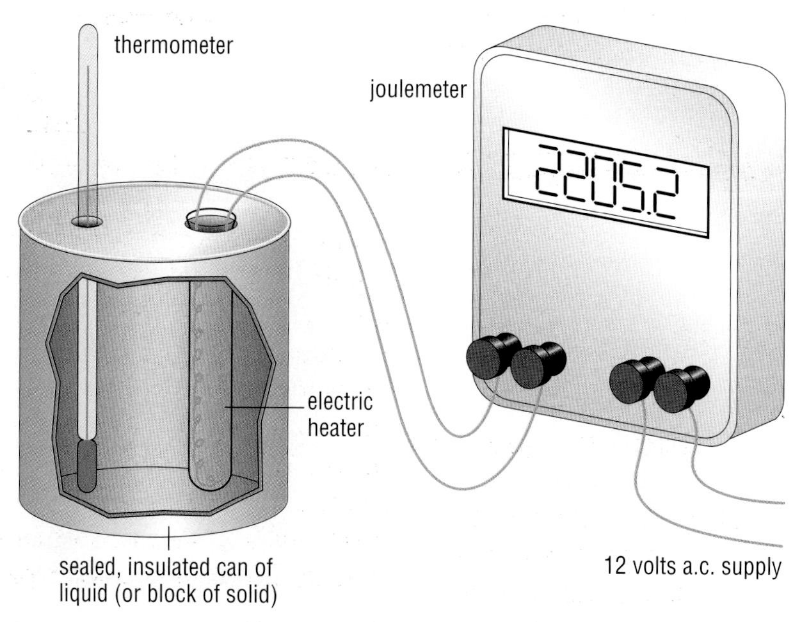

Figure 5.4 Measuring heat energy supplied with a joulemeter.

The equipment in Figure 5.4 can be used to compare how the heat supplied to a liquid or solid affects its temperature. It is found that some substances, such as water, take up large amounts of heat energy but their temperature only rises a few degrees, while the same mass of other substances needs only a small amount of heat energy to raise their temperature by the same amount.

How heat energy travels

There are three ways in which heat energy can travel. They are conduction, convection and radiation. Together they are known as thermal energy transfer.

Conduction

The heat energy is passed from one particle of a material to the next particle. For example, when a metal pan of water is put on a hot plate of a cooker the atoms in the metal close to the hot plate receive heat energy and vibrate more vigorously. They knock against the atoms a little further into the bottom of the pan and make them vibrate more strongly too. These atoms knock against other atoms a little further up and the kinetic energy is passed on. Eventually the inner surface of the pan, which is next to the water, becomes hot too.

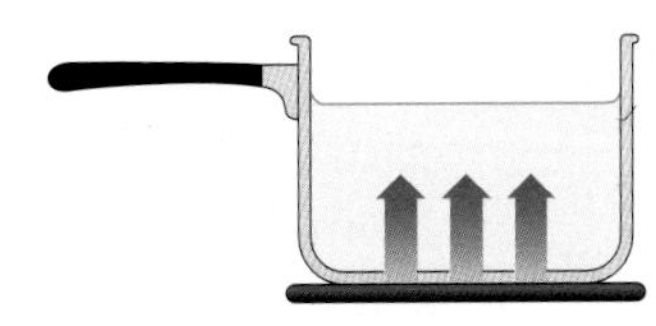

Figure 5.5 The conduction of heat through the bottom of a pan.

Conduction can occur easily in solids, less easily in liquids but hardly at all in gases because the gas atoms are too far apart to affect each other. It cannot occur in a vacuum, such as outer space, where there are no particles to pass on the heat energy. Conduction is fastest in metals because they have electrons that are free to move. When a metal is heated the electrons in that part move about faster and pass on heat energy to nearby electrons and atoms, so that the heat energy spreads quickly through to cooler parts of the metal.

Convection

The heat energy is carried away by the particles of the material changing position. For example, the water next to the hot surface at the bottom of the pan receives heat from the metal. The molecules of water next to the metal move faster and further apart as their kinetic energy increases. This makes the water next to the pan bottom less dense than the water above it and the warm water rises. Cooler water from above moves in to take the place of the rising warmer water. The cool water is also warmed and rises. It is replaced by yet more cool water and convection currents are set up as shown in Figure 5.7.

Figure 5.7 The convection currents in a pan of water heated from below.

5 A metal rod had drawing pins stuck to it with wax and was heated at one end as shown in Figure 5.6.

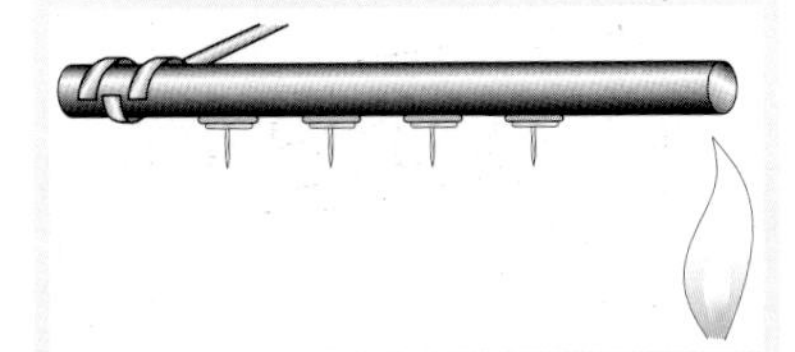

Figure 5.6

a) What do you think will happen in this experiment? Explain your answer.

b) How could this experiment be adapted to compare the conducting properties of different materials?

6 Imagine that a football represents heat energy and football players represent particles in a material. Which of the following events is like
a) conduction and
b) convection?
Explain your answers.
i) The players pass the ball to each other to move it up the field.
ii) A defender receives the ball and runs up field with it into an attacking position.

7 When coal burns, particles of soot rise up above the fire and make smoke. Why doesn't the smoke move along the ground?

8 a) The temperature of the land surface is higher than the temperature of the sea surface during the day. Use the ideas of convection currents to suggest what happens to air above the land and above the sea. Which way do you think the wind will blow across the promenade in Figure 5.8? Explain your answer.

Figure 5.8

b) At night the land surface is cooler than the sea surface. Does this affect the wind direction? Explain your answer.

Convection can only occur in liquids and gases. It cannot occur in solids where the particles are not free to move about, nor in a vacuum such as outer space.

Radiation

Energy can travel through air or through a vacuum as electromagnetic waves (see page 65). For example, as the pan of water gets hotter you can put your hand near its side and feel the heat on your skin even though you are not touching the metal. The sides of the pan are radiating infrared waves. These carry the heat energy from the surface of the pan to the surface of your skin, which is warmed by them.

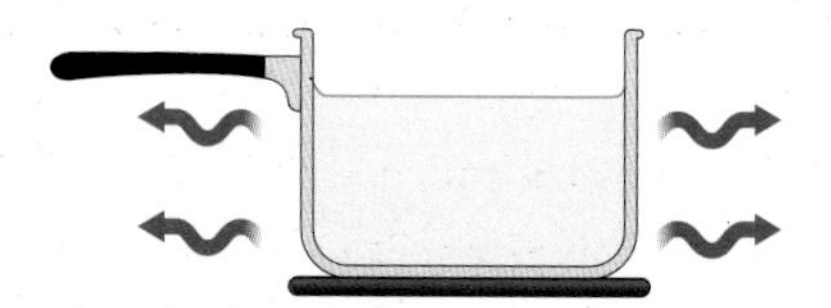

Figure 5.9 Heat radiation from a hot pan.

All objects radiate infrared, but the hotter the object the more infrared energy it radiates and the shorter the wavelength of the waves.

Some infrared radiation can pass through certain solids such as glass. For example, the infrared radiation from the Sun can pass through glass in a greenhouse but the (longer wavelength) infrared radiation from the ground and the plants inside the greenhouse cannot pass back out through the glass. This infrared radiation is trapped and warms the contents of the greenhouse.

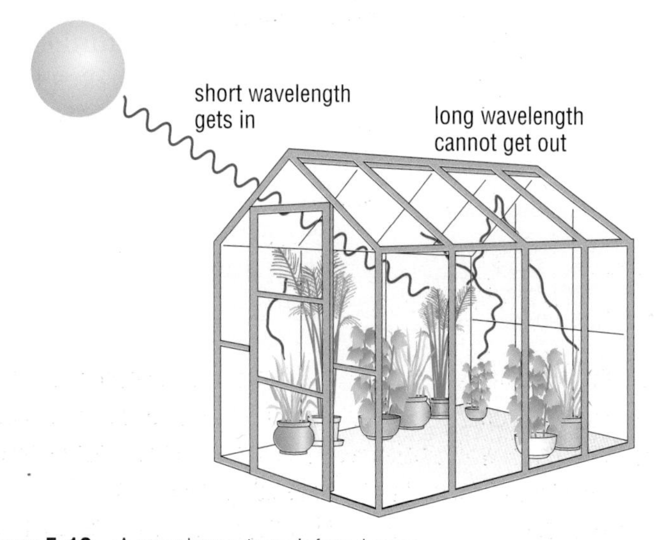

Figure 5.10 A greenhouse traps infrared energy.

9 In question 6 the energy was transferred by particles (players). How is the transfer of heat energy by radiation different?

10 How does the type of surface of an object affect the way it radiates and absorbs heat energy?

The type of surface affects the amount of heat energy radiated from an object in a given time. Darker colours radiate energy more rapidly than lighter colours and black surfaces radiate the most rapidly. The surfaces which radiate the energy least rapidly are light shiny surfaces, like the surface of polished metal.

The type of surface also affects the amount of radiated energy absorbed by the surface in a given time. For example, a light shiny surface absorbs energy the least rapidly, while a black surface absorbs energy the most rapidly.

The Thermos flask

Sir James Dewar (1842–1923) studied how gases could be turned into liquids. Liquid oxygen has a boiling point of −182.9 °C. When the liquid oxygen was made it needed to be stored in a container which would prevent heat from the surroundings entering and causing the liquid to boil. In 1892 Dewar invented a flask called a Dewar flask which allowed him to keep the liquid oxygen cool for his experiments. The Dewar flask is now more widely known as the Thermos flask (Figure A) and is used mainly to keep drinks hot.

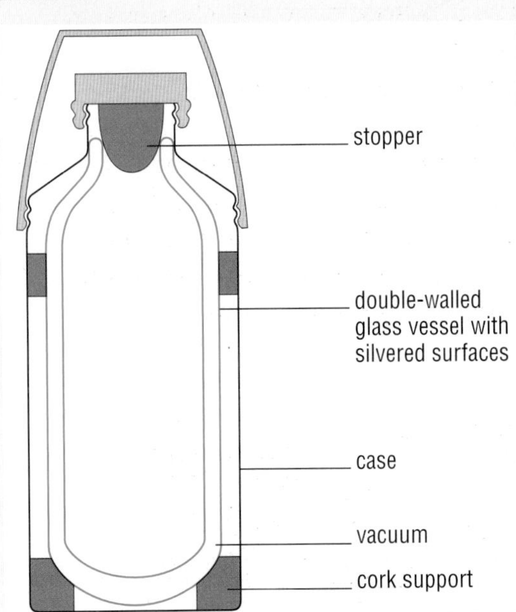

Figure A Structure of a Thermos flask.

The walls of the flask are made of glass, which is a poor conductor of heat, and are separated by a vacuum. The glass walls themselves have shiny surfaces. The surface of the inner wall radiates very little heat and the surface of the outer wall absorbs very little of the heat that is radiated from the inner wall. The cork supports are poor conductors of heat and the stopper prevents heat being lost by convection and evaporation in the air above the surface of the liquid.

1 Which forms of energy transfer does the vacuum prevent?

2 Why are the glass walls shiny? How would the efficiency of the flask be affected if the walls were painted black? Explain your answer.

3 How could a warm liquid lose heat if the stopper was removed? Explain your answer.

How materials change with temperature

Changes in solids

When a solid is heated it expands and when it cools it contracts (see *Chemistry Now! 11–14* page 24). For example, when it is cool a metal bar fits inside a metal gauge (Figure 5.11). Its end will also fit through the hole in the gauge. When the bar has been heated it will no longer fit in the gauge or in the hole. When the bar cools down it will fit in the gauge and hole again.

11 In which ways did the metal bar expand?

12 If the gauge was heated instead of the bar, would the length of the bar fit in the gauge? Explain your answer.

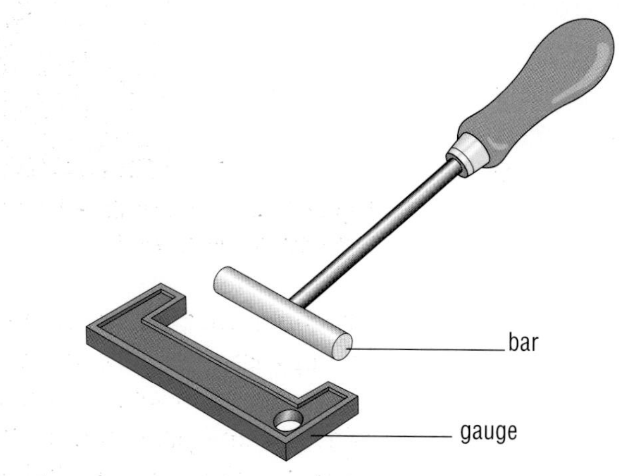

Figure 5.11 This apparatus shows that metals expand when heated.

The expansion of materials due to heating must be taken into account whenever the materials are likely to encounter changes in temperature. For example, metal pipes carrying hot water in large central heating systems are connected together by expansion joints (Figure 5.12) which allow the pipes to lengthen without pushing into each other.

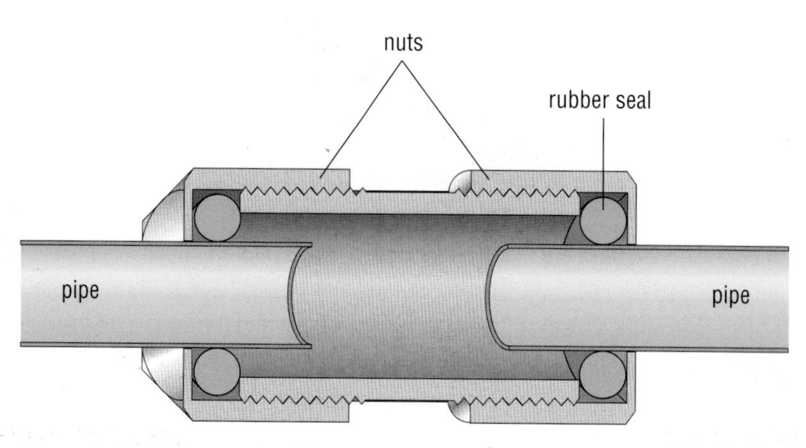

Figure 5.12 An expansion joint.

The temperature changes due to the weather can also cause expansion and contraction. The end of a bridge, for example, may be set on rollers so that as it lengthens it simply moves over its support and does not push into the adjoining roadway.

Figure 5.13 Rollers in the wall of a foot bridge prevent any damage when the bridge expands in hot weather.

The lines on the first railways were made of short lengths of rail that had gaps between their ends. These allowed the rails to expand in hot weather without buckling. When trains passed over the junctions they made a clickety-click sound. Today the lengths of metal used in railways lines are much longer than those used in the past and a very large gap would be needed if they were to be joined together in the same way. The longer rails have tapered ends which overlap each other (Figure 5.14). This arrangement allows the ends to slide past each other when the metal expands, without affecting the safety of the train running along them.

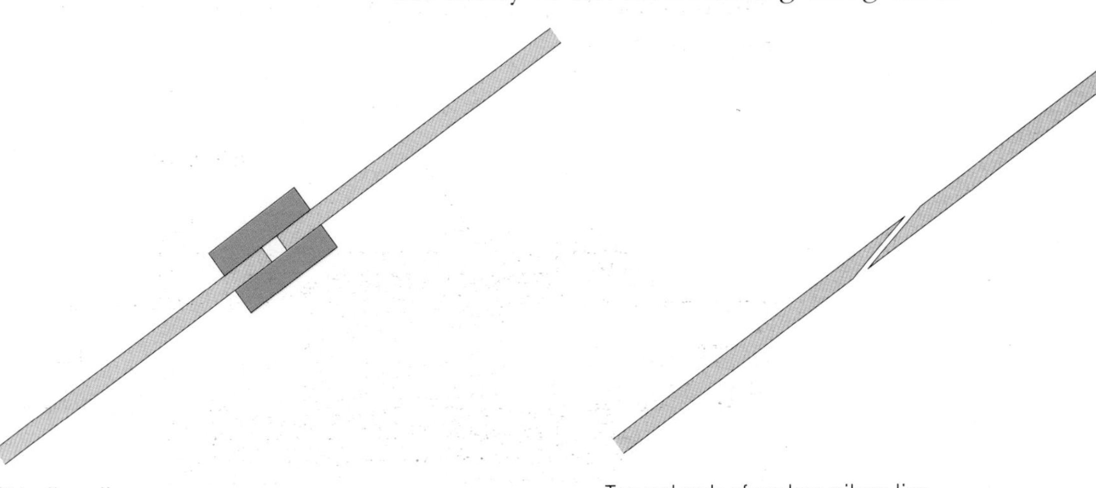

Figure 5.14

13 Figure 5.15 shows an overhead power cable in winter. Draw how it might appear in summer. Explain your answer.

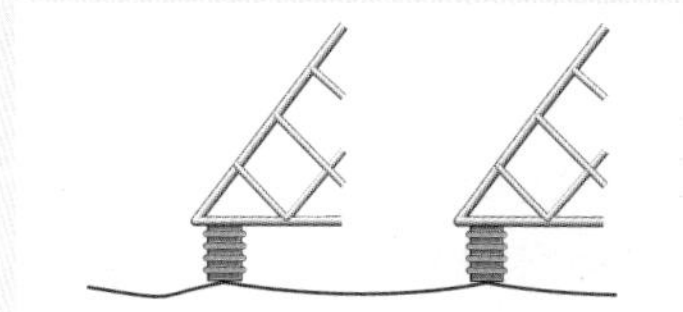

Figure 5.15

Different solids expand by different amounts for a given temperature rise. For example, brass expands more than iron. When strips of these two metals are stuck together they form a bimetallic strip. If the bimetallic strip is heated it bends because the length of the brass strip becomes greater than the length of the iron strip, as Figure 5.16 shows.

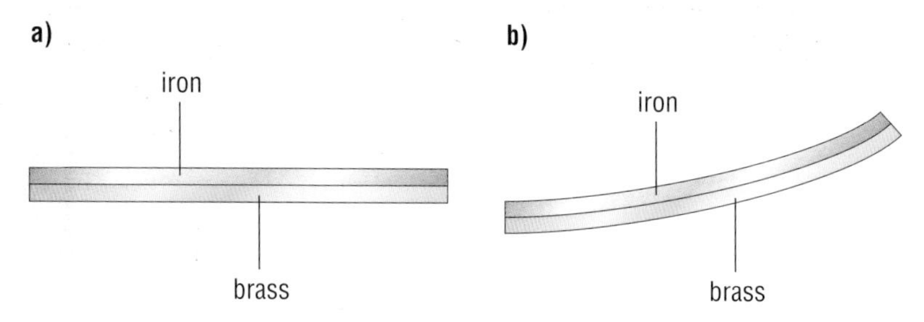

Figure 5.16 A bimetallic strip **a)** when cold and **b)** when hot.

A bimetallic strip may be used in a fire alarm and as a thermostat (temperature regulator) in an electric iron. The bending of the metal as the temperature rises makes or breaks the electrical circuit.

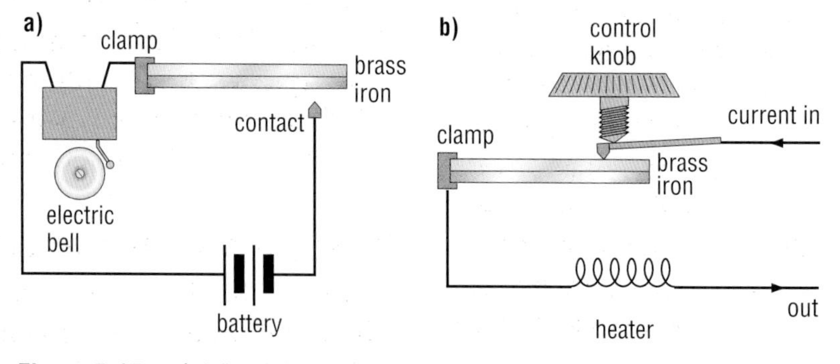

Figure 5.17 **a)** A fire alarm circuit and **b)** a circuit in an electric iron.

14 Why will the fire alarm in Figure 5.17a ring when there is a fire?

15 a) How does turning the screw down on the iron in Figure 5.17b alter the temperature at which the circuit is broken?

b) When the screw is set at the bottom the iron can be used on linen fabrics. When the screw is set at the top the iron can be used for nylon fabrics. Which fabric needs most heat?

16 Metal expands more than glass when both are heated. How can this fact be used to help open a metal screw top on a glass bottle which appears to be stuck?

Changes in liquids

When liquids are heated they generally expand much more than solids for a given temperature rise. They also contract to their original volume when they are cooled. The expansion and contraction of a liquid can be demonstrated by setting up the apparatus in Figure 5.18. When the water gets hot it expands and rises up the glass tube. When the water is allowed to cool the level of water in the tube falls.

However, water has a strange property – as it is cooled it expands again when its temperature drops below 4 °C and continues to expand until it reaches 0 °C (see opposite).

17 How could you use the apparatus in Figure 5.18 to compare the expansion of different liquids? What precautions would you have to take when testing flammable liquids such as alcohol and paraffin?

Figure 5.18 Demonstrating the expansion of water.

18 Which thermometer, one containing mercury or one containing alcohol, could be used in a polar region where the temperature reaches below −40 °C? Explain your answer.

19 Which type of thermometer could be used to measure the boiling point of water? Explain your answer.

Liquids in thermometers

Two liquids that are commonly used in thermometers are mercury and alcohol. Mercury has a freezing point of −39 °C and a boiling point of 360 °C. Alcohol has a freezing point of −112 °C and a boiling point of 78 °C.

When water is cooled

Almost all liquids contract when they are cooled and when they freeze they contract further to form a denser solid. When water cools down it initially contracts like other liquids, but this changes when it reaches 4 °C. As it cools from 4 °C to 0 °C it expands. Water below 4 °C is, therefore, less dense than water at 4 °C. When water has a range of temperatures close to 0 °C, the colder water rises above the warmer water and collects at the water surface. If the cooling of the water continues the water at the surface turns to ice at 0 °C and expands even more. The ice is, therefore, less dense than the water below it so the ice floats on the surface of the cold water.

In very cold winter weather this means that the water in a lake or pond freezes from the surface downwards because the coldest water is at the surface. Fish can remain alive and active in the warmer, denser water at the bottom of the pond while the surface is frozen (see Figure 5.19).

20 a) If water behaved like other liquids, how would a pond freeze in winter?

b) How would fish be affected by the way the pond froze?

21 Explain what has happened to the milk in Figure 5.20.

Figure 5.20

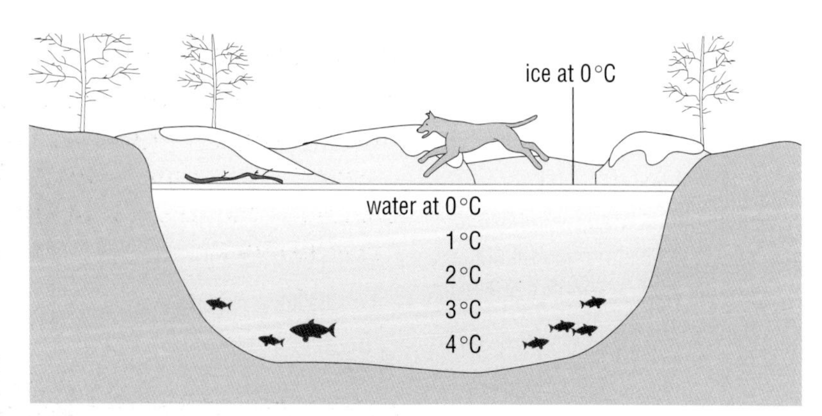

Figure 5.19 Section through a pond in winter.

The cold water in pipes in a building may freeze in very cold winter weather if they are not insulated. The water expands as it freezes, pushing on the walls of the pipes and bursting them. You do not find out that this has happened until the water thaws again.

Changes in gases

Like most liquids and solids, gases expand when they are heated and contract when they are cooled. If a gas and a liquid undergo the same temperature rise the gas expands about ten times more than the liquid.

Hot air balloons

When the air in a hot air balloon is heated it expands and fills the balloon. The density of the air in the balloon falls. It becomes less dense than the air around it. The surrounding air then exerts an upthrust force which is greater than the combined weight of the balloon, basket, pilot and passengers. The density of the surrounding air decreases with an increase in height. The balloon will continue to rise until it reaches air that is sufficiently less dense for the weight and upthrust to balance. If the air in the balloon is allowed to cool it contracts and its density increases. The upthrust is now less than the weight so the balloon sinks until it reaches air that has the same density. The pilot must heat the air with the gas burners to make the balloon rise again.

Figure 5.21 Hot air balloons make use of the fact that air expands when heated.

Explosions

An explosion occurs when a gas is made to expand very strongly and very quickly. This creates large forces that push on everything around. Explosives are used in quarries – the force of the expansion is strong enough to break up rocks.

Figure 5.22 Explosives are breaking up the rocks in this quarry.

Inside a car engine

A car engine has cylinders in which small explosions occur. A mixture of air and petrol vapour is ignited by a spark plug, and the hot gases, which expand quickly, push down a piston. The downward force of the piston is changed into a turning force by other parts of the engine, and this is used to turn the car's wheels.

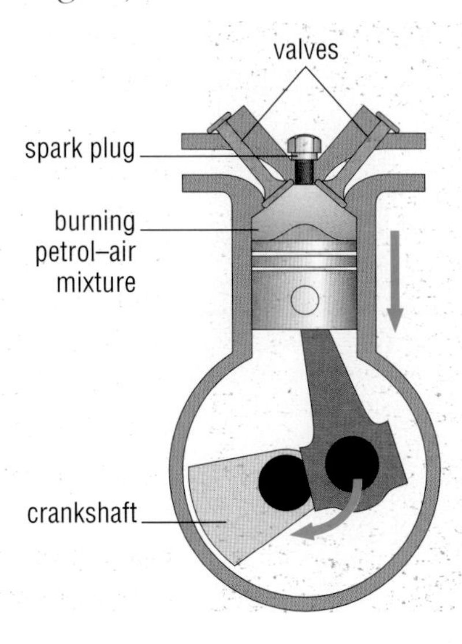

Figure 5.23 A cylinder in a car engine.

22 How does the size and speed of expansion of a gas compare with the size and speed of expansion of a solid?

♦ SUMMARY ♦

- ♦ Temperature is a measure of the hotness or coldness of a substance (*see page 90*).
- ♦ When a substance is heated its internal energy increases and its particles move faster (*see page 91*).
- ♦ A thermometer measures the average kinetic energy of the particles hitting the thermometer bulb (*see page 91*).
- ♦ Heat energy supplied can be measured with a joulemeter (*see page 92*).
- ♦ Heat energy is passed from particle to particle by conduction (*see page 92*).
- ♦ Heat energy is carried by moving particles in a convection current (*see page 93*).
- ♦ Heat energy is carried by electromagnetic waves in radiation (*see page 94*).
- ♦ Solids expand when they are heated and contract when they are cooled (*see page 96*).
- ♦ Liquids expand when they are heated and contract when they are cooled (*see page 98*).
- ♦ Gases expand when they are heated and contract when they are cooled (*see page 100*).

End of chapter questions

An investigation was carried out to see if useful amounts of heat energy from the Sun could be trapped in trays of water.

Three metal trays were used. Each one was 25 cm long, 20 cm wide and 5 cm deep and was filled with 1500 cm^3 of water.

Tray 1 had a glass plate cover and the water in it was untreated.
Tray 2 had some black ink added to the water before the glass plate cover was put over it.
Tray 3 had some black ink added to the water before the glass plate cover was put over it, then the sides and base were packed with vermiculite – a spongelike, rocky material.

The trays were exposed to sunlight during the day for seven hours and the air temperature and the temperature of the water in each tray were taken every hour. Table 5.1 shows the data that were collected.

(continued)

Table 5.1

Time	Air temperature/°C	Water temperatures/°C		
		colourless (without insulation)	black (without insulation)	black (with insulation)
11.15 am	18.7	17.5	17.5	17.5
12.15 pm	19.0	18.9	20.0	20.4
1.15 pm	20.5	22.4	25.1	26.0
2.15 pm	18.3	21.0	23.0	24.9
3.15 pm	18.9	21.5	23.4	25.6
4.15 pm	20.6	24.5	28.3	29.1
5.15 pm	20.2	28.5	31.8	33.2
6.15 pm	19.2	26.0	28.1	31.5

1 Did the water fill the trays to the top? Explain your answer.
2 Plot lines of the data for the air temperature and the temperature of each tray, on the same graph.
3 Compare the graphs you have drawn.
4 What was the purpose of the ink and the vermiculite? Explain your answers.
5 What is the maximum temperature rise? When was it achieved and in which tray?
6 What can you conclude from this investigation?

6 Static electricity

You may have seen a balloon stuck to the wall or ceiling, or received a slight shock when touching a car door, or heard a crackle when taking off your jumper.

To understand any of these you have to think about the structure of the atom and the electric charges on the particles in it.

Figure 6.1 These balloons are held in place by electrostatic forces.

The structure of the atom

An atom has a central nucleus surrounded by electrons. Each electron carries a negative electric charge (see also *Chemistry Now! 11–14* page 52). In the nucleus are particles called protons. Each proton carries a positive

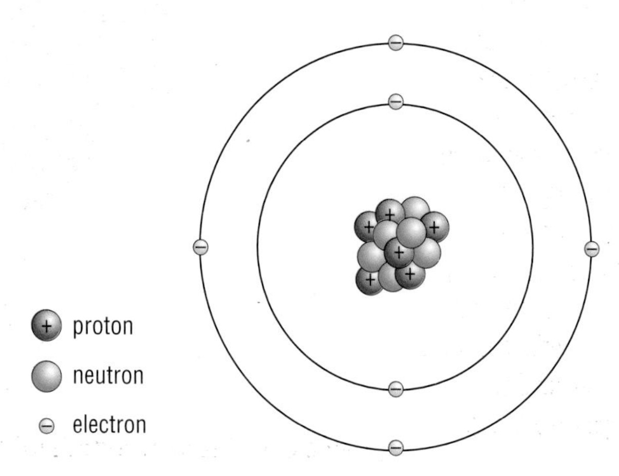

Figure 6.2 The structure of an atom.

electric charge. Usually the number of positive charges carried by the protons is balanced by the number of negative charges carried by the electrons. For example, if an atom has six protons in its nucleus it has six electrons orbiting the nucleus. When the positive charges on the protons are balanced by the negative charges on the electrons in this way the atom is described as being neutral.

As you can see in Figure 6.2, there are also particles called neutrons in the nucleus. They do not have electrical charge.

Charging materials

In the party trick with the balloon, it must be rubbed on clothing, such as a woollen sleeve, before it will stick to the wall. When some dry materials are rubbed in this way they gain electrons from the atoms in the material they are being rubbed against. Other materials lose electrons to the material they are being rubbed against. It depends upon the particular pair of materials involved. When a material that is an electrical insulator (see page 108) gains or loses electrons in this way, it is left with excess charge and the charge stays in place when the materials are separated. The material has been charged with static electricity.

1 When a piece of polythene is rubbed with a dry woollen cloth, electrons move from the cloth to the polythene. Which material becomes **a)** positively charged and which **b)** negatively charged?

2 When a piece of perspex is rubbed with a dry woollen cloth, electrons move to the cloth. Which material becomes **a)** positively charged and which **b)** negatively charged?

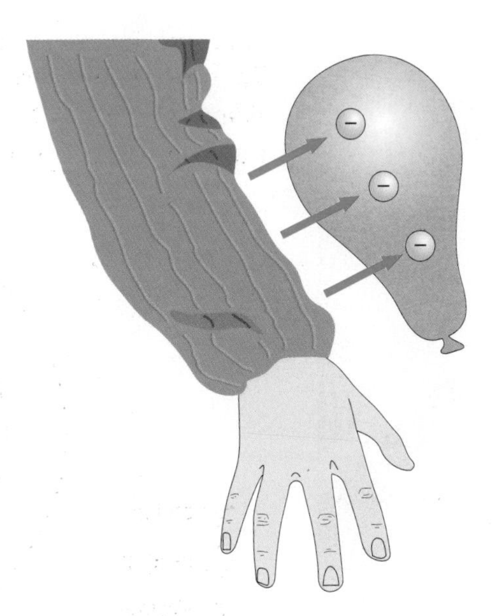

Figure 6.3 Electrons are transferred from the wool to the balloon and stay there.

3 If a charged piece of polythene is set up as shown in Figure 6.5 and a charged piece of perspex is brought close to it, will the polythene swing towards the perspex or away from it? Explain your answer.

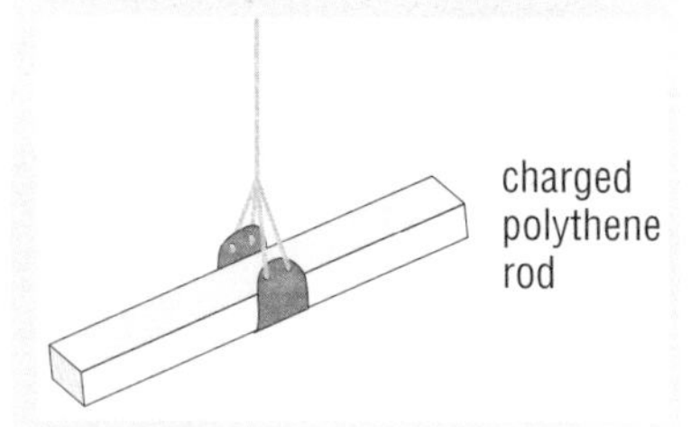

Figure 6.5

4 If a charged strip of polythene is set up as shown in Figure 6.5 and a charged polythene rod is brought close to it, will the polythene strip swing towards the polythene rod or away from it? Explain your answer.

5 a) When long dry hair is brushed the strands often move away from each other as shown in Figure 6.6. Why do you think this happens?

b) The strands of hair also get attracted to the brush. Why do you think this happens?

Figure 6.6

A material that gains electrons when it is rubbed has more negative charges than positive charges and so is said to be negatively charged. A material that loses electrons when it is rubbed has fewer negative charges than positive charges and so is said to be positively charged. Protons are never transferred in this charging process since they are effectively locked in place in the nuclei of the atoms of the material.

When the balloon is rubbed on a sleeve it receives electrons from the material in the sleeve and its surface becomes negatively charged. If two balloons, suspended on nylon threads, are charged and placed close to each other they move apart. The negative charges on the balloons repel each other.

If a positively charged material is placed close to a negatively charged balloon hanging on a nylon thread the balloon moves towards the material because the different charges on the two materials attract each other.

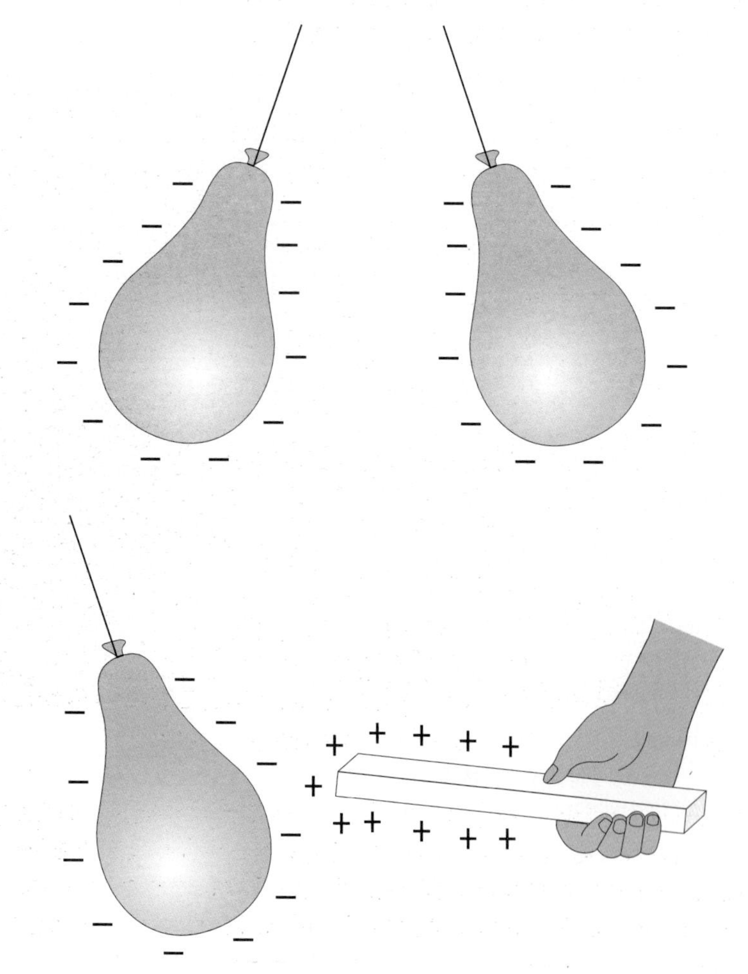

Figure 6.4 Similar charges repel (*top*) and different charges attract (*bottom*).

Early studies of electricity

For millions of years there have been certain kinds of trees which produce sap that turns to a clear yellow fossilised substance called amber. In Ancient Greece amber was used in items of jewellery. Thales (624–546BC), the earliest Greek 'scientific' philosopher, noticed that if amber was rubbed it developed the power to pick up small objects like dust, straw and feathers. The Greek word for amber is elektron so, much later, its attractive power became known as electricity.

William Gilbert (1544–1603), an English scientist, discovered that a few other materials, such as certain gemstones and rock crystal, could also attract small objects when they were rubbed. He called these materials 'electrics'.

Otto von Guericke (see page 56) used an 'electric' called sulphur to make a machine that could generate sparks. He made the sulphur into a ball and attached it to an axle which could be turned quickly by a crank handle. As the ball spun it was rubbed and built up a charge of static electricity which produced sparks. Electric machines became popular as a form of amusement and entertainment. Some people made their living by travelling through European countries, demonstrating their machines.

1 Where did the word 'electricity' come from?
2 How did Gilbert extend the observations of Thales?
3 Why do you think electric machines amused people?

Figure A Using an electric machine to ignite a sample of wine!

Stephen Gray (1696–1736), another English scientist, investigated electricity by rubbing a glass tube that had corks in the ends, and discovered that the corks became charged with static electricity even though they had not been touched. He had discovered that electricity behaved as if it could flow like a liquid.

(continued)

Charles Du Fay (1698–1739), a French scientist, repeated Gray's experiments and extended them by comparing the way in which the objects were charged with electricity. He discovered that if he charged a cork ball using a glass rod that had been rubbed, it was attracted to a cork ball that had been charged using sealing wax that had been rubbed. He also discovered that two cork balls charged by either the rubbed glass or sealing wax repelled each other. From his investigations he believed that electricity was made from two different liquids. They were called 'vitreous electricity' (from rubbing glass) and 'resinous electricity' (from rubbing sealing wax).

4 How was Gray's idea developed by Du Fay?

5 How was Du Fay's work developed by Franklin?

6 How is Franklin's idea of electric charge **a)** similar to and **b)** different from the ideas that we use today?

Figure B An electric machine built in about 1762.

Benjamin Franklin (1706–1790), an American statesman and scientist, refined Du Fay's idea of two electrical fluids by deciding that when substances were charged they received either too much fluid and became positively charged or they had some fluid taken away and became negatively charged.

Insulators and conductors

A material that can become charged with static electricity is called an insulator. If electrons are added to the material they stay in place and the insulator is negatively charged. If the electrons are removed from the material more electrons do not flow into the material and it remains positively charged.

A metal cannot be charged with electricity by rubbing in the way an insulating material can because electrons flow easily through metals. A material through which electrons can flow is called a conductor. The human body is a very good conductor of electricity.

Induced charges

If a material has an electric charge it can make or 'induce' an electric charge on the surface of a material close by without touching the material. For example, if a piece of plastic, such as a pen, is rubbed and held above a tiny piece of paper, the positive charge on the plastic draws electrons to the surface of the paper nearest the plastic. This makes the uppermost surface of the paper negatively charged. When the pen is brought very close to the paper the force of attraction between the two surfaces is strong enough to overcome the weight of the paper and the paper springs up to the surface of the pen.

The underside of the paper is left with a positive charge but since this is further away from the pen the force of repulsion it experiences is weaker than the attractive force and the paper is held.

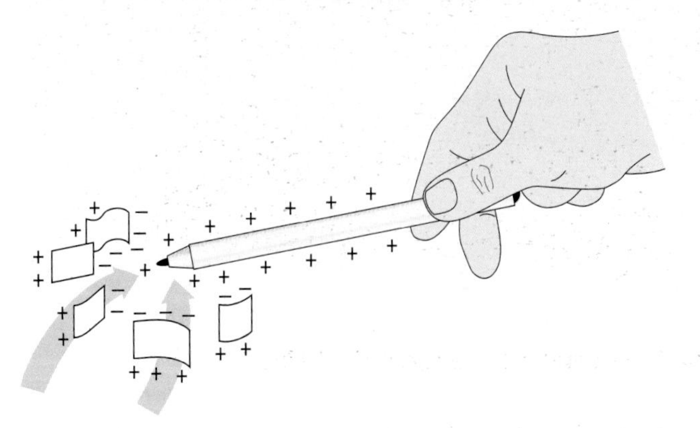

Figure 6.7 The charged pen induces charges on the surfaces of the paper.

6 When a negative charge is induced on one surface of a piece of paper what is induced on the other surface of the paper? Why does this happen?

7 Why does a rubbed balloon stick to the wall?

In a similar way a charged balloon induces an opposite charge on the surface of a wall it is brought close to. When the balloon touches the wall, the force of attraction between the two surfaces is greater than the weight of the balloon and the air inside it so the balloon sticks to the wall (see Figure 6.1).

This way of charging a material without touching it is called charging by induction.

Sparks and flashes

Air is a poor conductor of electricity but if the size of the charge on two oppositely charged surfaces is very large the air between them may conduct electricity as a spark or a flash, like a flash of lightning. This happens when the molecules in the air are split. They form negatively charged electrons and positively charged ions. The electrons move towards the positively charged surface and ions move towards the negative surface (Figure 6.8). As the electrons move they collide with other molecules in the air and split them. The ions and electrons from these molecules also move towards the charged surfaces and split more molecules as they go. This process occurs very quickly and produces a spark. When the charged particles in the air meet the charged surfaces the positive and negative charges cancel out each other and the surfaces lose their charge. They are said to have been discharged.

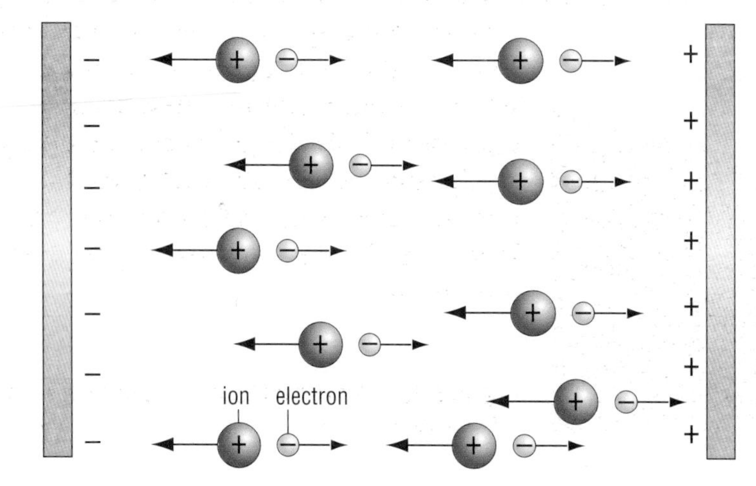

Figure 6.8 The strong electric field between the charged plates ionises the air between them.

The spark plug

In petrol engines there are spark plugs. A spark plug has a small gap in which a spark is generated. This is done by charging up the surfaces on either side of the gap until the air produces a spark. The heat from the spark ignites the petrol vapour in the engine and causes a combustion reaction which produces hot gases. As the gases expand they produce a force which is used by the engine to turn the car's wheels. The sparks are produced hundreds of times a minute when the engine is running.

Figure 6.9 A spark plug.

Preventing an explosion

When an aircraft flies through the air its surfaces are rubbed by air particles and become charged with static electricity. If the aircraft was equipped with non-conducting tyres, such as those used on most vehicles, the charge would remain on the aircraft when it landed. This charge could cause a spark during refuelling. The heat from the spark would be sufficient to cause the fuel vapour to combust which would result in a devastating explosion. This danger is prevented by equipping the aircraft with tyres that conduct electricity. When the aircraft lands the charge it possesses passes to the ground.

Figure 6.10 Sparks must be prevented when an aircraft is being refuelled.

Lightning

When a storm cloud develops, strong winds move upwards through the cloud and rub against large raindrops and hail stones. This rubbing causes the development of charged particles in the cloud. Positively charged particles collect at the top of the storm cloud and negatively charged particles collect at the base. The size of the different charges in each part of the cloud may become so large that lightning, called sheet lightning, is produced between them.

The negative charge at the base of the storm cloud induces a positive charge on the ground below. If the charges become large enough a flash of lightning, called forked lightning, occurs between them.

Figure 6.11 Forked lightning.

The lightning conductor

A lightning conductor is a metal rod that may be attached to the top of a tall building. It is connected by a thick strip of metal which runs down the side of the building to a metal plate buried deep in the ground. When a storm cloud approaches the conductor, the top of the conductor becomes positively charged. The charges collect on the tips of the spikes of the conductor and split some of the molecules in the air into electrons and ions. The positively charged ions move upwards and reduce the negative charge on the cloud base. This in turn reduces the induced charge on the ground and reduces the chance of a lightning strike. If lightning does strike it hits the conductor rather than the building, and the current of electricity passes down the metal strip and passes out into the ground through the plate. If the metal strip was not present the current would pass through the walls of the building, causing damage to the materials and making the walls unsafe.

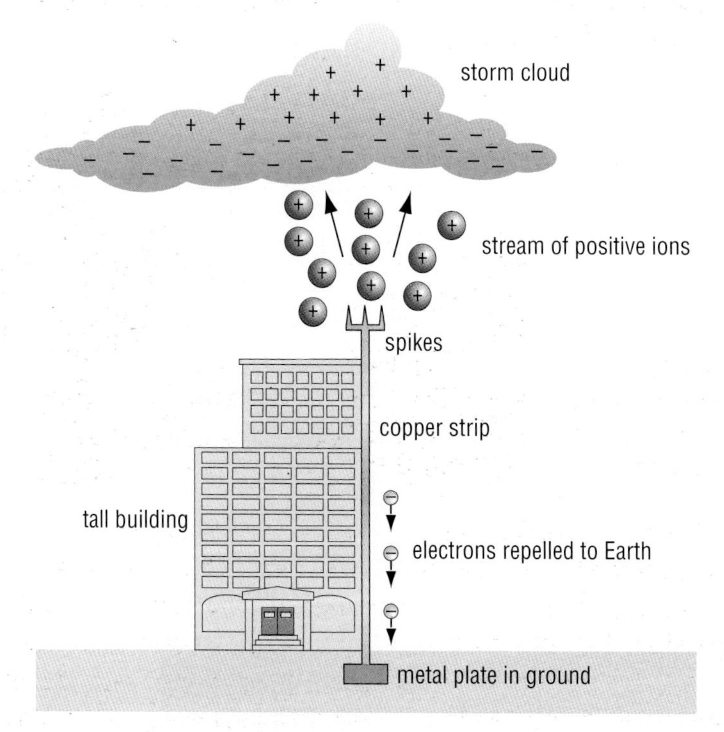

Figure 6.12 The action of a lightning conductor.

If lightning strikes a tree the heat produced by the flow of electricity turns some of the water in the tree into steam. The steam expands quickly and pushes its way out of the tree by ripping off a branch or splitting open the trunk.

8 a) How are sheet lightning and forked lightning **i)** similar and **ii)** different?
b) Which is more dangerous to people on the ground?

9 How does a lightning conductor protect a tall building?

Investigating lightning

The 'electric' machine invented by von Guericke (see page 107) was developed by others. For example, Francis Hauksbee (c.1670–c.1713), an English scientist, invented a machine with a glass globe which produced a much greater charge more easily.

Figure A Hauksbee's electric machine.

The electric charge could be drawn from the globe by a metal rod suspended on insulating threads but the charge could not be built up and stored on the rod. In 1746 Pieter von Musschenbroek (1692–1761) invented a device for storing electricity, after thinking about ways to store electricity like water in a bottle. It was named the Leyden jar after the town in Holland where he lived. Musschenbroek stored so much electricity in his jar that the first time he used it he got a large shock from it!

1. The symbol c. is short for circa, meaning about. Why do you think it was used with the years of Hauksbee's birth and death?
2. Why do you think Musschenbroek thought about water in a bottle when he investigated storing electricity? (See *Early studies of electricity* page 107 before you answer.)

Figure B Von Musschenbroek collecting charge in his Leyden jar.

The devices we use today to store electricity are called capacitors.

It was generally believed in the early 18th Century that lightning was caused by exploding gases, but Benjamin Franklin (see page 108) studied the spark he obtained from a charged Leyden jar and wondered if lightning was caused in a similar way – by a discharge of electricity. He tested his idea by flying a kite in a thunderstorm. The kite had a metal wire attached to it and the damp rope by which Franklin held it acted as a conductor. He attached a metal key to the rope and when he put his hand near the key a spark jumped from it to his knuckle. He was also able to collect electricity from the storm cloud in his Leyden jar then discharge the electricity in the same way as that collected from an electric machine. He reasoned that the electricity had come from the storm cloud and that lightning was produced by a huge discharge

(continued)

3 How did Franklin's experiment change people's ideas about lightning?
4 Why was Franklin lucky?
5 If the general belief had been correct would Franklin's experiment have been as dangerous?

Figure C Franklin's dangerous experiment with a storm cloud. Nobody should try this today.

from the storm cloud. Franklin was very lucky in carrying out his experiment – the next two scientists to repeat his experiments were killed.

Franklin discovered that electricity could be drawn out of a Leyden jar by placing a piece of pointed metal close to the top of the jar. From this observation he performed experiments which led to the development of the lightning conductor.

The van de Graaff generator

In 1931 Robert van de Graaff invented a machine which produced a huge charge of static electricity. The machine is called the van de Graaff generator.

In the generator is a rubber belt which runs over two rollers. One roller is made of perspex and the other is made of polythene. The belt is driven by an electric motor. When the perspex roller is placed at the base of the generator, the belt running over it becomes negatively charged (Figure 6.13). The charged part of the belt rises to the polythene roller at the top of the generator where there is a device that transfers the negative charge to the hollow metal dome. The belt moves over the roller in the dome and back to the roller at the base, where it becomes negatively charged again.

When the rollers are reversed and the polythene roller is placed at the base of the generator, the belt becomes positively charged and the positive charge is transferred to the dome.

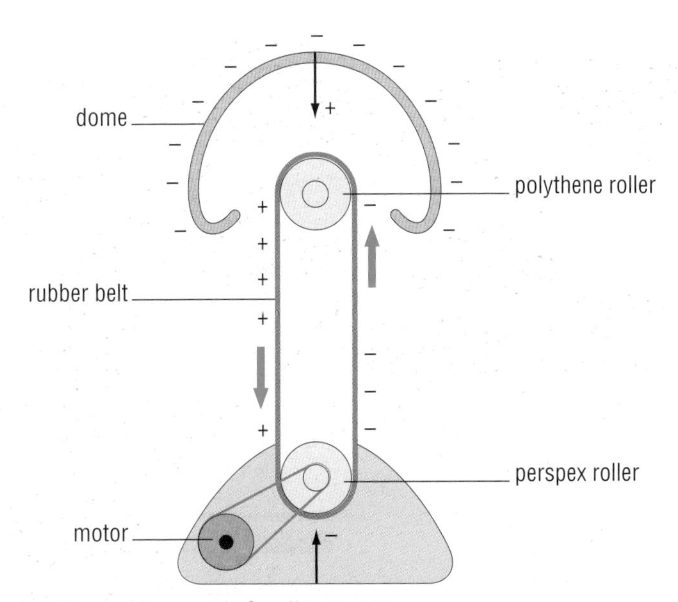

Figure 6.13 Inside a van de Graaff generator.

Very high charges can be stored in the dome and released during investigations. In the past huge van de Graaff generators were used as particle accelerators to investigate atomic structure but they were replaced by other devices (see *Breaking up atoms* page 118). Today they are used in schools and colleges to generate quite large electrostatic charges for demonstration lessons.

Figure 6.14 Demonstrating a large electrostatic charge with a van de Graaff generator.

10 a) Explain what you see in Figure 6.14.

b) Why must the pupil be standing on a sheet of insulating material?

If a wire from a positively charged dome of a van de Graaff generator is connected to the head of an insulated nail and the nail tip is brought near a candle flame, the flame appears to be blown by a wind. The positive charge from the dome collects at the pointed tip of the nail. The presence of this charge attracts electrons from air molecules close by. This results in the air molecules becoming positively charged (positively charged ions). They are repelled by the charge at the nail tip and form an electric wind which blows the candle flame.

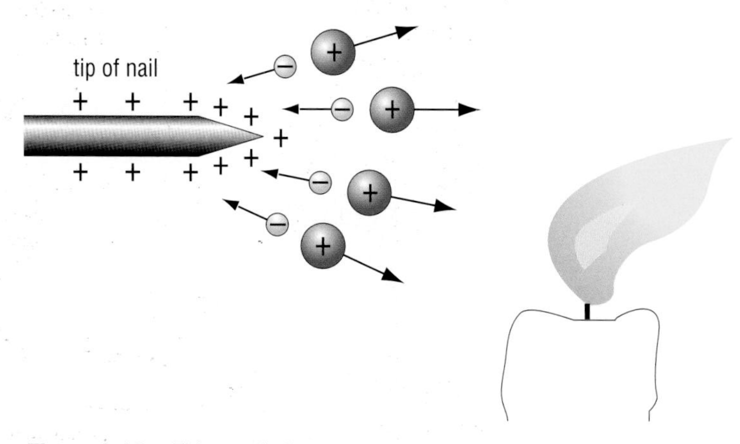

Figure 6.15 This candle flame is being blown by an electric wind.

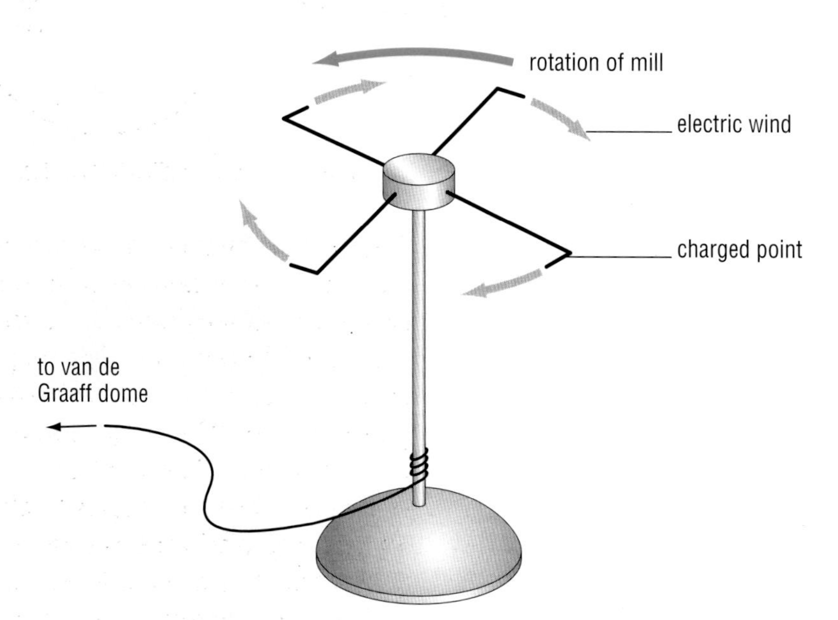

Figure 6.16 Hamilton's mill.

A Hamilton's mill is shown in Figure 6.16. It is free to rotate. When a wire is attached to it from a positively charged van de Graaff generator dome the points on the mill generate an electric wind, like the nail in the previous demonstration. The force on the positive ions producing the electric wind is paired with a reaction force (see page 36) which makes the mill turn round.

The van de Graaff generator can also be used to show that moving electric charge makes a current of electricity. The apparatus is set up as shown in Figure 6.17.

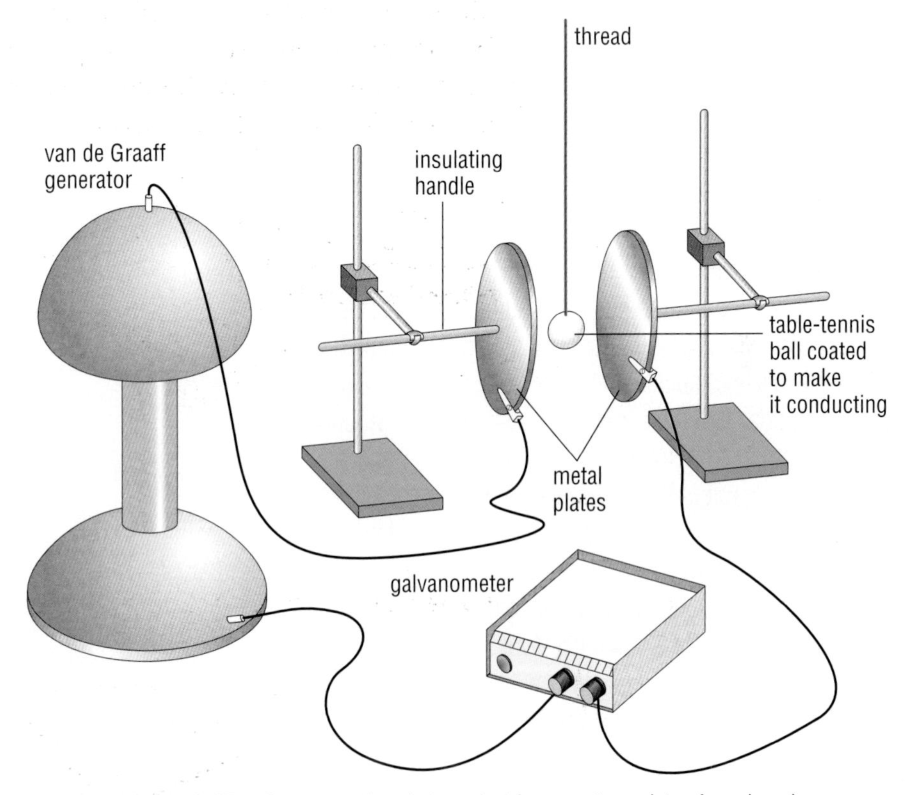

Figure 6.17 Demonstrating that an electric current consists of moving charges.

A galvanometer is an instrument that detects electric current. In this demonstration a circuit is set up which is broken by a gap between two metal plates. A metal-coated table-tennis ball is suspended between the plates and can move to and fro between them, touching each plate in turn. When the dome builds up a charge this is passed to the plate connected to it. The nearby table-tennis ball has the opposite charge induced in it and is attracted to and moves towards the plate. On making contact with the plate it becomes charged from the plate and is immediately repelled. It therefore swings across and hits the other plate to which it gives its charge. It then returns to the rest position and the process repeats itself. As it swings to and fro it repeatedly carries the charge across the gap. When the ball carries the charge in this way the sensitive meter shows that a current is passing round the circuit.

Breaking up atoms

Ernest Rutherford (1871–1937) was born in New Zealand but worked in England. He studied radioactivity at the same time as the Curies (see page 78) and identified two kinds of radiation, called alpha rays and beta rays. It was later discovered that the rays were really charged particles which moved very fast; they then became known as alpha and beta particles.

Rutherford used alpha particles, which are positively charged, to investigate the structure of atoms. He directed a beam of alpha particles at a thin sheet of gold and detected where the particles emerged with a photographic plate placed behind the sheet. Each particle left a mark where it hit the plate. Most of the particles passed straight through the gold sheet, suggesting that it mostly consisted of space through which the particles could pass. Some particles, however, were deflected from the main beam. Rutherford believed these particles had hit other particles inside the gold sheet. From his work Rutherford concluded that atoms had a small central positively charged nucleus which contained most of the atom's mass. He also concluded that there was almost empty space around the nucleus in which electrons were found.

John Cockcroft (1897–1967) was an English physicist who worked with Ernest Walton (1903–1995), an Irish physicist, to find out more about the structure of the atom. They wanted to crash faster-moving particles than alpha particles into the nuclei of atoms to try and split up the nuclei. It had been discovered that hydrogen atoms could be split up into a proton and an electron, so Cockcroft and Walton invented a device to shoot protons at high speed at atomic nuclei. This device was called a particle accelerator. It used a large charge of electricity (like the charge generated by the van de Graaff generator, see page 114) to move the protons in a straight line towards the target. Cockcroft and Walton broke up lithium atoms to produce helium atoms with their particle accelerator.

1. How would Rutherford's photographic plate have appeared if none of the alpha particles had passed through the gold? Explain your answer.
2. Where do you think most marks were found on the photographic plate? Explain your answer.
3. Which part of an atom did the deflected alpha particles hit?
4. Particle accelerators were commonly known as atom smashers. How accurate was this description? Explain your answer.

Figure A Cockcroft and Walton's particle accelerator.

(continued)

In 1930 Ernest Lawrence (1901–1958), an American physicist, invented a circular particle accelerator. The beam of particles was directed in a circle by electromagnets. Each time the particles travelled round the accelerator they were given a push by an electrical device. Eventually the beam of fast-moving particles was directed onto the target atoms.

Figure B The particle accelerator at CERN, Geneva.

The first circular particle accelerator was just over 30 centimetres in circumference but scientists soon began to build larger ones. Today the largest accelerator is at Geneva in Switzerland and is 27 kilometres in circumference (Figure B). By using very high-speed particles, atoms have been broken up to reveal over 200 subatomic particles. They are detected by a range of devices as they speed away from a shattered nucleus. They may be detected by photographic film, semiconductor devices, or a chamber containing liquid hydrogen. When a particle passes through the chamber it leaves a track of bubbles. The angles and lengths of the tracks are used to help identify the particles.

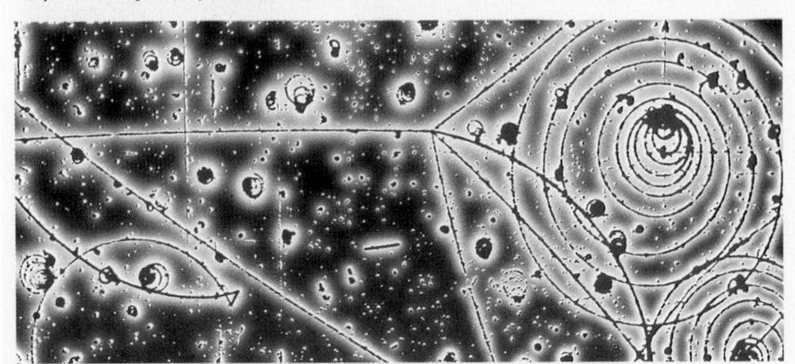

Figure C Tracks in a bubble chamber. The spiral tracks are made by lightweight particles such as electrons.

From breaking up atoms it has been found that protons and neutrons are each made from three particles called 'quarks', held together by 'gluons'.

5 What advantages do you think the circular accelerator had over the one that fired particles in a straight line?

6 Why have circular particle accelerators become larger and larger?

For discussion

'We have survived quite successfully without knowing that we are made of many different kinds of subatomic particles, so why spend large amounts of money on more expensive investigations when the money could be put to better use helping people in many different ways?'

In what different ways could the money be used?

How far do you agree with the question? Explain your reasoning.

♦ SUMMARY ♦

- ♦ An atom has two kinds of electrically charged particles. They are protons and electrons (*see page 104*).
- ♦ Static electricity may be generated by rubbing insulators (*see page 105*).
- ♦ Charged materials can have either a positive or a negative charge (*see page 106*).
- ♦ Materials that hold charges of static electricity are called insulators, materials that allow electricity to pass through them are called conductors (*see page 108*).
- ♦ A material may become charged by induction (*see page 109*).
- ♦ Static electricity can be discharged through the air as a spark or a flash (*see page 109*).
- ♦ The van de Graaff generator can produce large charges and may be used to study the effects created by static electricity (*see page 114*).

End of chapter question

1 How could you use your knowledge of the structure of the atom to explain how a plastic pen that has been rubbed can pick up tiny pieces of paper?

7 Current electricity

Circuits

If you set up this equipment and close the switch, the lamp comes on.

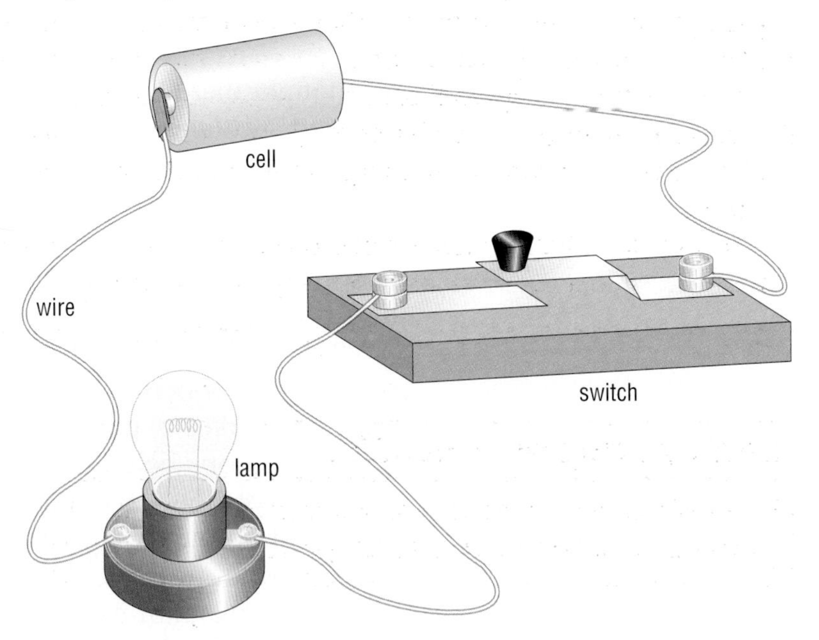

Figure 7.1 A simple electric circuit.

The wires of the circuit are composed of atoms that are held tightly together but around them are many electrons that are free to move. The metal filament in the lamp and the metal parts of the switch also have free electrons. When the switch is closed, the wires on either side of the switch are linked by metal contacts and a path is made along which the electrons can flow. When you open the switch, the lamp goes out. The path is broken and the electrons cannot flow.

The energy to move the electrons comes from the cell. The chemical reactions that take place in the cell make the electrons leave the cell at the negative terminal when the circuit is completed. They push their way into the wire and move the other electrons along, creating a flow or current of electricity. At the positive terminal electrons are drawn back inside the cell. The wire in the lamp filament is more resistant (see page 124) to the flow of electrons than the other wires in the circuit. As the current moves through the filament some of its electrical energy is transferred to heat energy and light energy.

1 Describe the path of an electron round the circuit in Figure 7.1 when the switch is pressed down.

2 a) How does the wire in the filament behave differently to other wires in the circuit when the current flows?

b) What property of the wire accounts for this difference?

In time the chemicals which take part in the reaction inside the cell are used up. They can no longer release energy to make the electrons move and the current stops. The number of electrons in the circuit does not change, it is the chemical energy released by the cell that changes.

When Benjamin Franklin (see page 108) described substances as having positive or negative electric charges he thought that electricity flowed from a positively charged substance to a negatively charged one. His idea was taken up by other scientists until it was discovered that it was the flow of negatively charged electrons that produced a current. Franklin's idea is still used today, however; it is known as the conventional current direction.

When circuits are drawn, symbols are used for the parts or components. The use of symbols instead of drawings makes diagrams of circuits quicker to make and the connections between the components are easier to see. The symbols have been standardised like the SI units described on page 2 and are recognised by scientists throughout the world. The circuit in Figure 7.1 is shown as a circuit diagram using symbols in Figure 7.2a. The components for the circuit are the wires, cell, lamp and switch (Figure 7.2b).

3 In Figure 7.1 (page 121), the base of the cell (on the right) is the negative terminal and the cap (on the left) is the positive terminal. How can you distinguish between the positive and negative terminals in a cell in a circuit diagram?

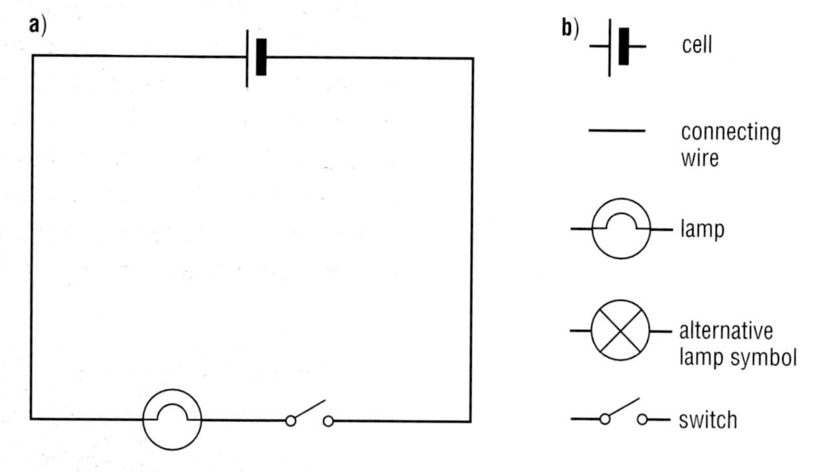

Figure 7.2 **a)** A circuit diagram and **b)** the symbols used.

In everyday life, cells are almost always called batteries but this is scientifically incorrect. In science a battery is made of two or more cells joined together. The symbols for a battery of two cells, three cells or more cells are shown in Figure 7.3a–c.

Figure 7.3 **a)** Two cells, **b)** three cells and **c)** any number of cells.

The lining up of cells next to each other, in a row, end to end as shown in Figure 7.3, is described as arranging them in series. Other electrical components can also be arranged in series, for example, lamps may be arranged in series as Figures 7.5c and 7.6a–f on the next page show.

The voltage of a cell

The ability of the cell to drive a current is measured by its voltage. This is indicated by a figure on the side of the cell with the letter V after it. The volt, symbol V, is the unit used to measure the difference in electrostatic potential energy (see page 63), usually just referred to as 'potential', between two points. The voltage written on the side of the cell refers to the difference in potential between its positive and negative terminals. It is a measure of the electrical energy that the cell can give to the electrons in a circuit.

When cells are arranged in series with the positive terminal of one cell connected to the negative terminal of the next cell, the current-driving ability of the combined battery of cells can be calculated by adding their voltages. For example, two 1.5 V cells in series produce a voltage of 3 V. The two cells together give the electrons in the circuit twice as much electrical energy as each one would provide separately.

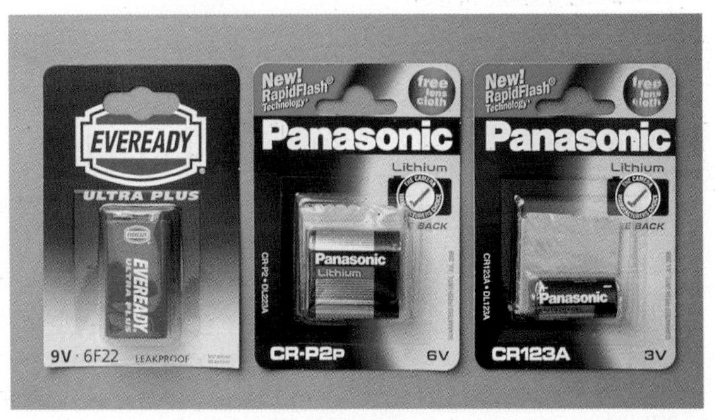

Figure 7.4 The voltage is clearly displayed on the packaging of cells and batteries.

4 A wire carrying a current of electricity can be described as being similar to a stream carrying a current of water. In what ways are the wire and the stream similar?

5 Predict the brightness of the lamps in the circuits in Figure 7.6 compared with that of a single lamp in a circuit with one cell. Use one of the following words in each case:

very dim, dimmer, the same, brighter, very bright

(All the lamps are identical and all the cells have the same voltage.)

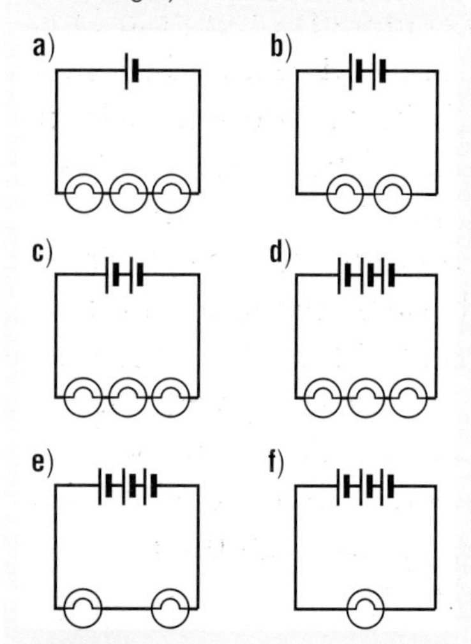

Figure 7.6

6 Compare the circuit in Figure 7.7 with the one in Figure 7.6b. Do you think the lamps will glow with the same brightness? Explain your answer.

Figure 7.7

Resistance

The material through which a current flows offers some resistance to the moving electrons. A material with a high resistance only allows a small current to pass through it when a certain voltage is applied. A material with a low resistance allows a larger current to pass through it for the same applied voltage.

The wires connecting the components in a circuit have a low resistance while the wires in the filaments of the lamps have a high resistance. When the lamps are connected in series their resistances combine in the same way as the voltages of the cells in series – they add. They therefore offer a greater resistance to the current than each lamp would separately.

Lamps and current size

The size of the current flowing though a circuit can be estimated by looking at the brightness of the lamps in the circuit. A lamp shines with normal brightness when it is connected to one cell as shown in Figure 7.5a. The lamp shines more brightly than normal when it is in a circuit with two cells (Figure 7.5b) and shines less brightly when it is in a circuit with one cell and another lamp as shown in Figure 7.5c.

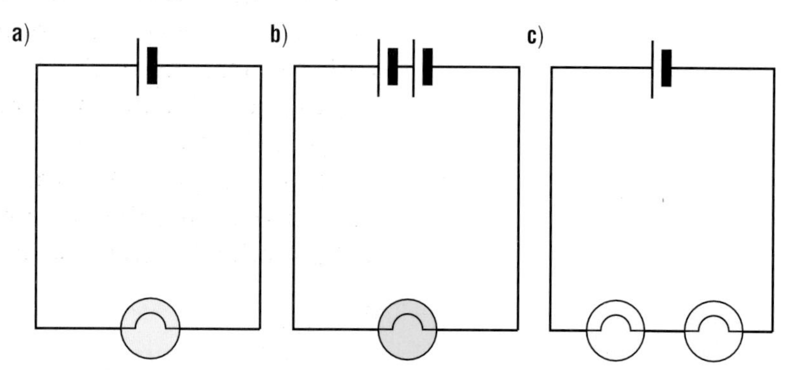

Figure 7.5 Three arrangements of cells and lamps in series.

Parallel circuits

Lamps can be arranged in a circuit 'side by side' rather than end to end. This kind of circuit is called a parallel circuit (Figure 7.8). The resistances of the lamps do not combine to oppose the flow of current in the same way as they do in a series circuit. Each lamp receives the same flow of electrons as it would if it were on its own in a circuit with the cell.

7 How do you think the brightness of two lamps arranged in parallel compares with the brightness of two lamps arranged in series (both arrangements having one cell)?

8 If current flows through two lamps arranged
a) in series,
b) in parallel,
and the filament of one lamp breaks, what happens to the other lamp? Explain your answers.

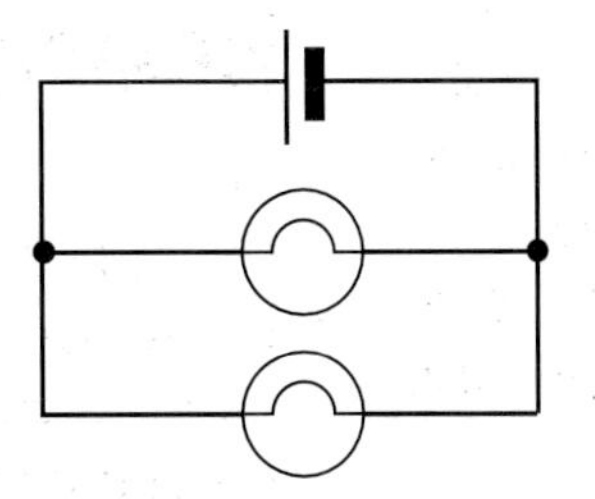

Figure 7.8 Two lamps in parallel.

Measuring electricity

Measuring current

The rate at which electrons flow through a wire is measured in units called amperes. This word is usually shortened to amps and the symbol for it is A. One amp is equal to the flow of 6 million, million, million electrons passing any given point in the wire in a second!

The current flow in a circuit is measured using an instrument called an ammeter. This is a device which has a coil of wire set between the north and south pole of a magnet. The coil has a pointer attached to it and it turns when a current passes through it. The amount by which the coil turns depends on the size of the current and is shown by the movement of the pointer across the scale.

When an ammeter is used it is connected into a circuit with its positive or red terminal connected to a wire that leads towards the positive terminal of the cell, battery or power pack. It is always connected in series with the component through which the current flow is to be measured (Figure 7.9). Ammeters usually have a very low resistance so that the current passes through them without affecting the rest of the circuit.

9 How many electrons are flowing per second past a point in a circuit in which there is a current of **a)** 0.5 amps, **b)** 5 amps and **c)** 30 amps?

10 Towards which terminal of the power supply should the negative or black terminal of an ammeter be connected?

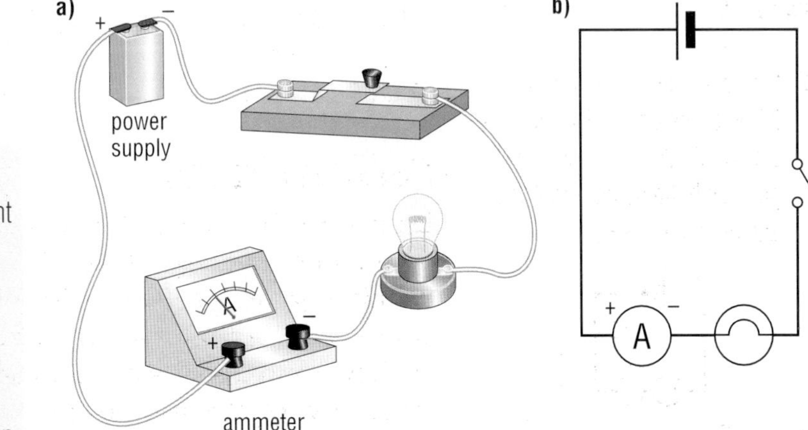

Figure 7.9 **a)** An ammeter connected in a circuit and **b)** the circuit diagram showing its symbol.

When an ammeter is to be used to measure the current flowing through a series circuit such as that shown in Figure 7.10a, the ammeter is placed at a position such as A or B.

When an ammeter is to be used to measure the current flowing through a parallel circuit such as that shown in Figure 7.10b, the ammeter should be placed at A, B and C in turn.

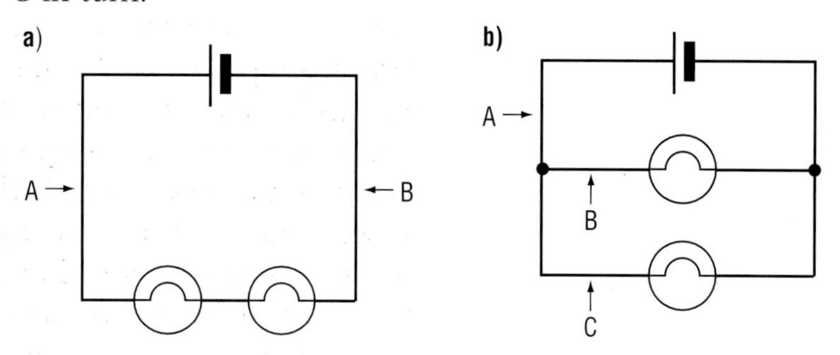

Figure 7.10 Measuring current in **a)** series and **b)** parallel circuits.

Measuring voltage

The potential difference or voltage between two points in a circuit is measured by a voltmeter. The units used are volts (V).

The voltmeter is connected into a circuit with its positive or red terminal connected to a wire that leads towards the positive terminal of the cell, battery or power pack. The negative or black terminal must be connected to a wire that leads towards the negative terminal of the source of the current. However, unlike the connection of an ammeter, the wires are attached to either side of the part of the circuit being tested – it is arranged in parallel with this part of the circuit. Voltmeters generally have a very high resistance, so when connected in parallel they take little current and do not affect the rest of the circuit.

11 Compare how an ammeter and a voltmeter are connected into a circuit.

Figure 7.11 **a)** A voltmeter connected in a circuit and **b)** the circuit diagram showing its symbol.

Switches

In Chapter 6 on static electricity we saw how air could conduct electricity between surfaces which had large positive and negative charges. A high electrostatic potential difference, or voltage, has to build up for the air to conduct electricity. At the voltages used in simple electrical circuits the air does not conduct electricity, so if there is a gap in the circuit a spark does not cross it. The current simply stops flowing and devices in the circuit, such as lamps and motors, stop working.

As you know, the stopping and starting of current flow in a circuit can be controlled by a switch. When a switch is switched on, or closed, a gap in the circuit is bridged by a conducting material through which the current flows. When the switch is switched off, or opened, the conducting material is moved so that a gap is formed and the current stops flowing.

Types of switch

The on/off switch and the push button switch are well known. Their symbols are shown in Figure 7.12.

Figure 7.12 Symbols for **a)** an on/off switch and **b)** a push button switch.

The on/off switch is also known as the single-pole single-throw switch or SPST switch. The part that moves to close the gap is called the pole, and the action of moving the pole so it makes contact to complete the circuit is called the throw.

Some switches are called single-pole double-throw switches or SPDT switches. They can close a gap to complete a circuit in two ways, as Figure 7.13 shows.

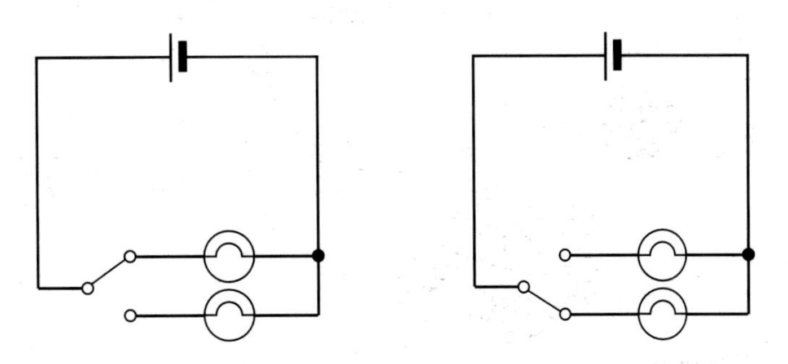

Figure 7.13 Circuit with a single-pole double-throw switch.

Switches that rely on electromagnetism are described on pages 144–146.

Controlling components with switches

Two switches may be used in a circuit to control the operation of an electrical device. They may be arranged in series or parallel.

When the switches are arranged in series they make an AND circuit. This means that you must close switch 1 AND switch 2 for a current to flow (Figure 7.14).

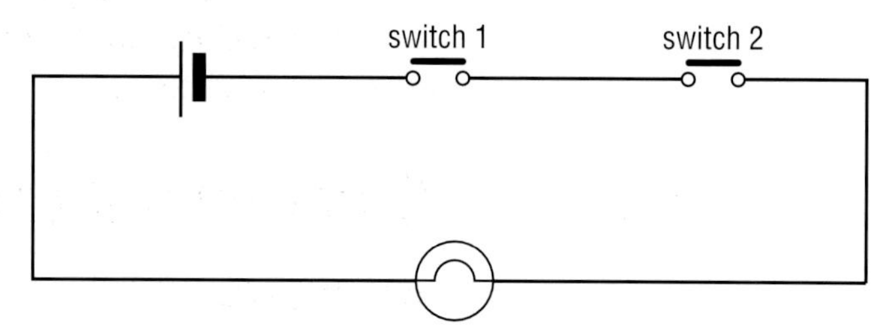

Figure 7.14 AND circuit.

When the switches are arranged in parallel they make an OR circuit. This means that you must close switch 1 OR switch 2 OR both for the current to flow (Figure 7.15).

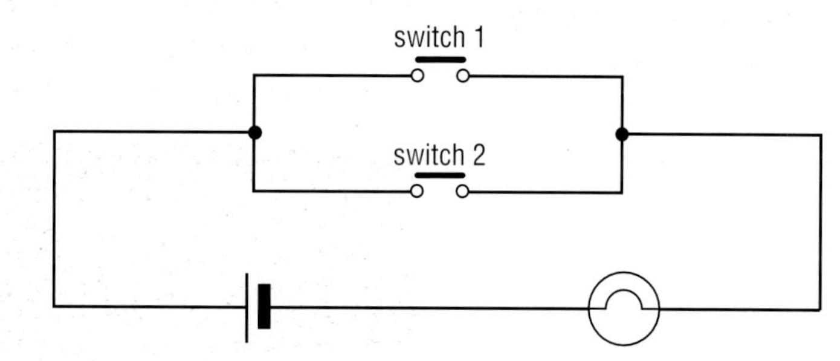

Figure 7.15 OR circuit.

The position of the switches in a circuit and the action of the electrical component, such as a motor or an LED (see page 131), can be given in a truth table. A truth table for the AND circuit is shown in Table 7.1.

Table 7.1 Truth table for the AND circuit.

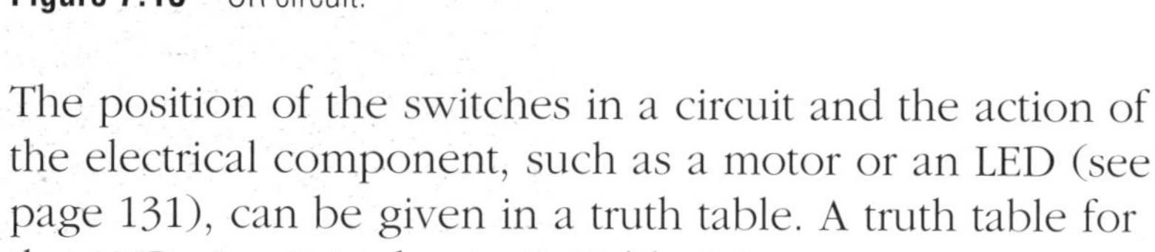

Switch 1	Switch 2	Component
open	open	off
open	closed	off
closed	open	off
closed	closed	on

12 Construct a truth table for the OR circuit of Figure 7.15, using Table 7.1 as a guide.

13 a) Which circuit would you use if two switches are required to be closed in sequence for an electric motor to open a bank vault door?

b) Draw a circuit diagram (see Figure 8.20 on page 146 for the motor symbol).

14 a) How could you use an OR circuit to protect two windows with a burglar alarm?

b) Draw a circuit diagram (see page 132 for the buzzer symbol).

Truth tables are very useful for describing the positions of switches and the action of components in the complicated circuits in microprocessors.

An AND circuit is used in a pedestrian crossing control. The length of time the traffic lights show is controlled by a timer and a switch. When the green traffic light has shown for a certain length of time, the timer closes one switch. If you then press the pedestrian button, a second switch is closed and the circuit to make the red traffic light come on is activated.

Street lighting may be controlled by a switch that can be operated manually or by a light dependent resistor, using an OR circuit.

Other circuit components

Resistors

The property of resistance was discussed on page 124. If a short piece of wire which has a high resistance is included in a simple circuit with a cell, a switch and a lamp, the lamp will shine less brightly than before. If a longer length of high resistance wire is included in the circuit the light will shine even more dimly.

A component that is designed to introduce a particular resistance into a circuit is called a resistor.

15 How does the length of a high resistance wire affect the flow of current through the circuit?

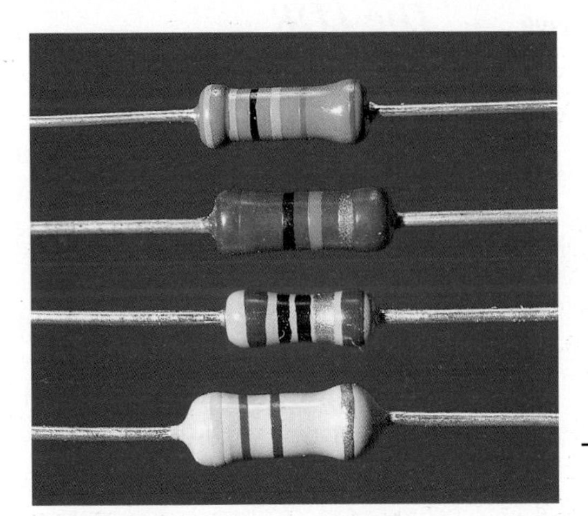

Figure 7.16 Four resistors and the symbol for a resistor.

A variable resistor can be made in which a contact moves along the surface of a resistance wire and brings different lengths of the wire into the circuit. This device is sometimes called a rheostat. In order to make it more compact, the length of the wire is wound in a coil and the contact is made to move freely across the top of the coil.

16 In Figure 7.17, which way should the contact be moved to
a) increase and
b) decrease the resistance in the part of the wire included in the circuit between A and B?

17 Figure 7.18 shows a variable resistor in a dimmer switch. How would you turn the switch to make the lights
a) brighter and **b)** dimmer? Explain your answer.

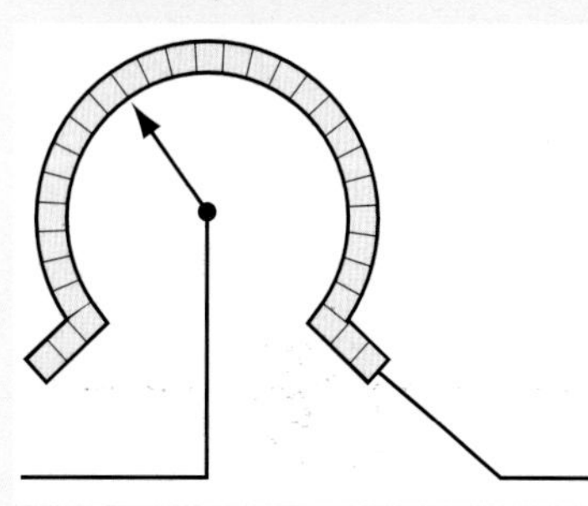

Figure 7.18

For discussion

Which pieces of equipment in your home do you think have resistors which control the flow of electricity?

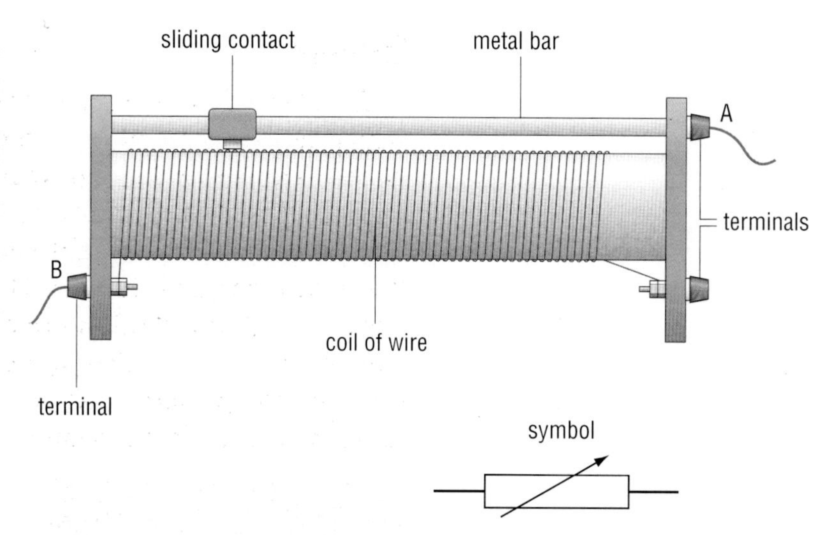

Figure 7.17 A variable resistor and its symbol.

In Figure 7.17 the current passes through terminal A, along the bar, through the sliding contact and coil of wire to terminal B. When the contact is placed on the far left the current passes through only a few coils of the wire. As the contact is moved to the right the current flows through more of the wire and encounters greater resistance. When the contact is moved from the right to the left the current flows through fewer coils of the wire and encounters less resistance.

The LDR

An LDR is a light dependent resistor. It is made from two pieces of metal which are joined together by a semiconductor. A semiconductor is a material that has just a few electrons which can move freely. Silicon and germanium are two elements that are widely used as semiconductors.

When the LDR receives light energy, more electrons are released in the semiconductor to move freely through it, and the resistance of the LDR becomes lower. When the amount of light shining on it is reduced, fewer electrons can flow and the resistance increases.

18 Some bedside clocks have a display which glows dimly when the room is dark yet shines brightly if the room is light. How could an LDR be responsible? How may the LDR make it easier for you to get to sleep?

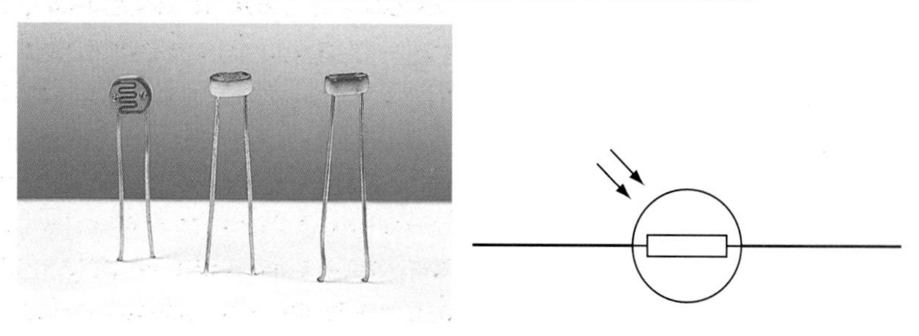

Figure 7.19 Three LDRs and the symbol for an LDR.

Diodes

A diode is a device made from a semiconducting material which has been given two impurities, phosphorus and boron. The current can flow from the part of the semiconductor with boron in it (called p-type semiconductor) to the part with phosphorus in it (called the n-type semiconductor). This allows the current to pass through the diode in one direction only. Diodes are used to control the direction of the flow of a current through complicated circuits, such as those used in a radio, which have components in series and parallel.

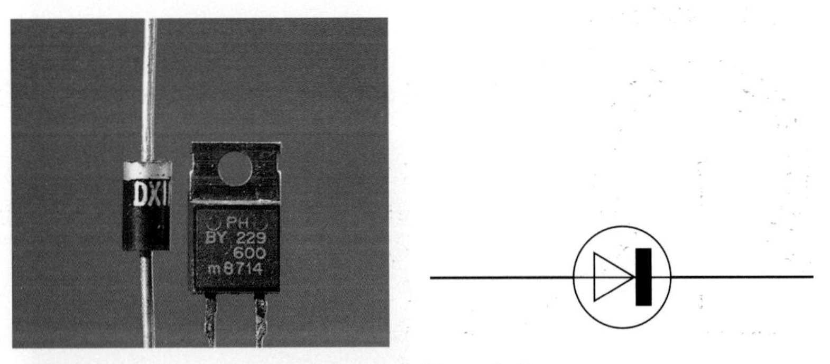

Figure 7.20 Two diodes and the symbol for a diode.

Diodes have a band marked at one end. When the diode is connected into a circuit the end with the band on must be connected to a wire coming from the negative terminal of the cell or battery for the current to flow. When a diode symbol is drawn in a circuit diagram the symbol should be drawn with the straight line facing the negative terminal of the source of the current.

19 Compare the action of a resistor and a diode.

The LED

An LED is a light emitting diode. In simple circuits we often use a lamp to show that a current is flowing. In electronic circuits an LED performs the same task more efficiently. An LED is a semiconductor diode, allowing a current to flow in only one direction through it, and it produces light. It does not produce light in the same way as a filament in a lamp (see page 121). It is made from semiconductors such as gallium arsenide and gallium phosphide, and when a current passes through these materials their electrons move between distinct energy levels and release some of their energy as light. An LED can emit red, yellow or green light. The colour emitted depends on the semiconductor materials used to make the LED.

20 How is an LED **a)** similar to and **b)** different from a lamp?

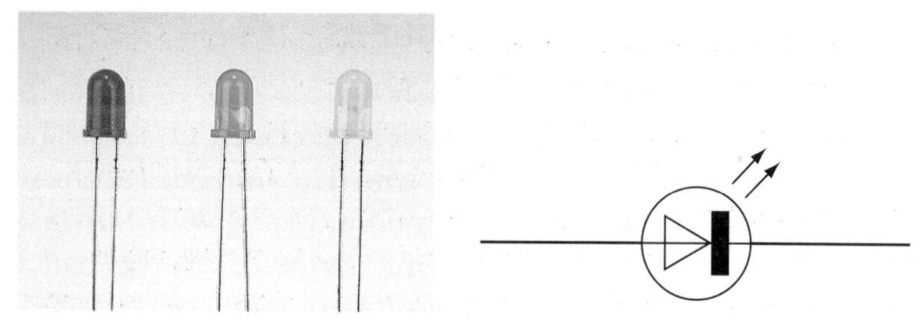

Figure 7.21 Three LEDs and the symbol for an LED.

Buzzers

A buzzer is an electrical device in which one part vibrates strongly when a current of electricity passes through it. The vibrations produce the sound (see also page 174).

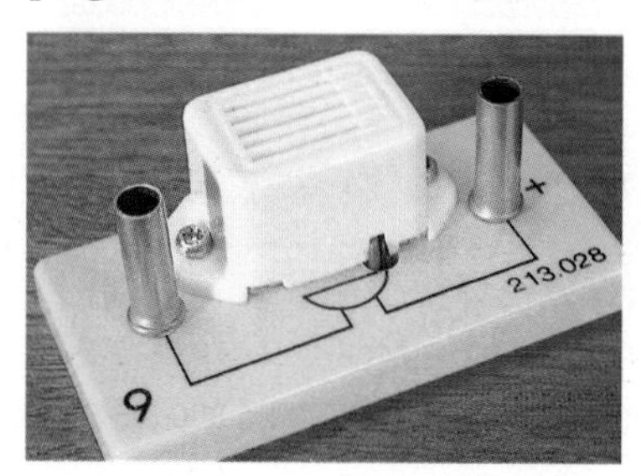

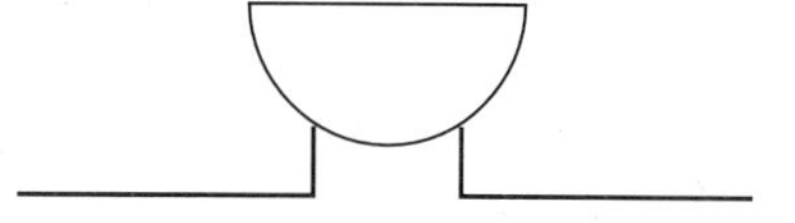

Figure 7.22 A buzzer and its symbol.

Superconductors

Heike Kamerlingh-Onnes (1853–1926) was a Dutch physicist who studied how gases behaved as they turned into liquids. He was particularly interested in helium, which has a boiling point of −269 °C. In 1908 Kamerlingh-Onnes cooled helium gas so much that it turned into a liquid. He set up the cryogenic laboratory at the University of Leyden and began studying how other materials behaved at low temperatures. In 1911 he cooled mercury to a temperature of almost −273 °C and passed electricity through it. He found that the metal offered no resistance to the current. The property of a material that offers no resistance to a current is called superconductivity and the material is called a superconductor. Other metals that behave as superconductors at very low temperatures are aluminium and lead.

When a current is passed through a normal conductor energy is needed to overcome the conductor's resistance. When a current is passed through a superconductor no energy is needed to overcome resistance because the resistance does not exist.

Figure A The magnetic field around the superconducting plate makes the magnetic cube float in the air.

1. What was Kamerlingh-Onnes' first interest in scientific investigations?
2. Why did his interest in helium lead him to study materials at low temperatures?
3. Compare the behaviour of a superconductor with that of an ordinary conductor.
4. What extra equipment is needed if a superconductor is to be used in a circuit?
5. In what year did Muller and Bednorz make their discovery?

(continued)

Since Kamerlingh-Onnes' time scientists have studied many materials and tested them for superconductivity. They have found some materials that behave as superconductors at higher temperatures. In 1988 Alex Muller (b.1927), a Swiss physicist, and J. Georg Bednorz (b.1950), a West German physicist, shared the Nobel Prize for Physics for their discovery a year earlier that a ceramic material containing barium and copper oxide behaves as a superconductor at −238 °C. Since then more materials have been discovered that are superconductors at higher temperatures but until superconductors can be used at normal temperatures, their use will remain limited. Today thcy are used in particle accelerators (see page 119) and certain types of body scanners used in hospitals. If a superconductor was found to work at normal temperatures it could be used to transport electricity more cheaply.

For discussion

Why could transporting electricity be made cheaper if superconductors could be used at normal temperatures?

How would the use of superconductors at normal temperatures affect the use of energy resources?

♦ SUMMARY ♦

- ♦ A closed or complete circuit is needed for an electric current to flow (*see page 121*).
- ♦ The ability of a cell to drive a current round a circuit is indicated by its voltage (*see page 123*).
- ♦ The material through which a current flows offers resistance to the current (*see page 124*).
- ♦ Lamps and other components may be arranged in series or in parallel (*see page 124*).
- ♦ An ammeter measures the rate of flow of the current (*see page 125*).
- ♦ A voltmeter measures the difference in potential between two parts of a circuit (*see page 126*).
- ♦ The starting and stopping of current flow in a circuit is controlled by one or more switches (*see page 127*).
- ♦ Variable resistors and light dependent resistors can be used to control current flow (*see pages 129–130*).
- ♦ A diode is used to control the direction of current flow through a circuit (*see page 131*).
- ♦ A buzzer vibrates when a current passes through it (*see page 132*).

End of chapter question

1 A circuit contains a cell, an LDR, an LED and a switch. When the switch is closed and the circuit is left in daylight the LED glows, but when the closed circuit is left in the dark the LED no longer glows. Explain what is happening in the circuit in both the light and the dark.

8 Magnetism

Three metals can show magnetic properties. They are iron, cobalt and nickel. Steel is a metal alloy which can show magnetic properties. It is made from iron and carbon (see *Chemistry Now! 11–14* pages 129–130). Steel can also be mixed with other metals to make an alloy which does not show magnetic properties. For example, stainless steel is made from steel, chromium and nickel and it does not show magnetic properties.

Materials that show magnetic properties do not show them all the time. For example, steel paper clips do not generally attract and repel each other. When a material is showing magnetic properties it is said to be magnetised and is known as a magnet. The most widely used magnets used to be made from steel but most magnets are now made of mixtures of the magnetic metals. Alnico is an example.

1 Which three metals do you think might be present in Alnico? Explain your answer. Which ones are magnetic?

Figure 8.1 Magnets not only hold messages on fridge doors but a magnetic strip in the fridge door is used to hold it closed.

It is thought that the word 'magnet' comes from the name of the ancient country of Magnesia which is now part of Turkey. In this region large numbers of black stones were found which had the power to draw pieces of iron to them. The black stone became known as lodestone or leading stone because of the way it could

be used to find directions (see *Early discoveries about magnetism* page 140). Today it is known as the mineral called magnetite and it has been found in many countries.

Figure 8.2 Magnetite is a naturally occurring magnet.

The behaviour of magnets

Magnets can attract or repel other magnets and can attract any magnetic material even if it is not magnetised. When suspended from a thread, a bar magnet aligns itself in a north–south direction.

Non-magnetic materials, such as wood, paper, plastic and most metals, cannot be magnetised and so can do none of these things. Some, such as paper and water, can let the force of magnetism pass through them while other materials, such as a steel sheet, do not let the force of magnetism pass through them.

2 How do magnetic materials differ from non-magnetic materials in **a)** what they are made of and **b)** their properties?

The strength of the magnetic force

At each end of a bar magnet is a place where the magnetic force is stronger than at other places in the magnet. These places where the magnetic force is strongest are called the poles of the magnet. The end of the magnet which points towards north when the magnet is free to move is called the north-seeking pole or north pole. At the other end of the magnet is the south-seeking pole or south pole.

When the north pole of one magnet is brought close to the south pole of another magnet that is free to move, the south pole moves towards the north pole. Similarly, a north pole is attracted to a south pole. However, two south poles repel each other, as do two north poles. These observations can be summarised by the phrase 'different poles attract, similar poles repel'.

If you bring a steel paper clip (which is not magnetised) towards either pole of a magnet you will feel the pull of the magnetic force become stronger as the paper clip gets closer to the pole. As you move the paper clip away again you will feel the pull of the magnet become weaker.

When a material that can show magnetic properties, such as a steel paper clip, is attracted to the end of a magnet it also becomes a magnet and can attract other magnetic materials to it. The paper clip has been made into a magnet by a process called induction. When the paper clip is moved away from the magnet it loses its magnetism.

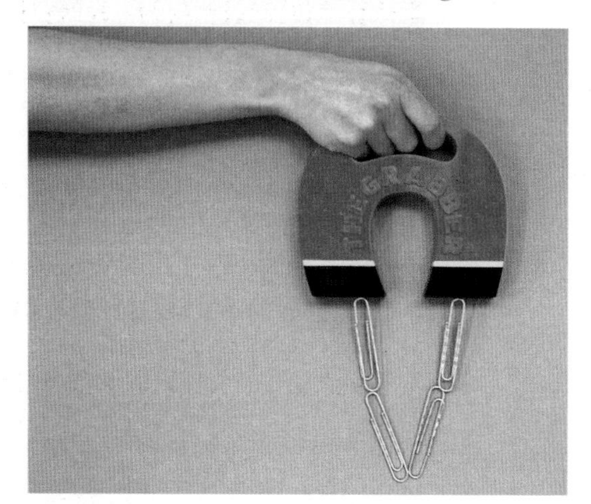

Figure 8.3 Paper clips attracted by the magnetic force of a magnet are themselves magnetised.

3 What is the relationship between the distance from the magnet and the strength of the magnetic force?

4 If you have studied induced electric charge (page 109), compare it with magnetic induction by answering these questions. What happens when:
   a) a charged rod is brought near a small piece of paper and the end of a magnet is brought near a paper clip?
   b) the charged rod touches the paper and the end of the magnet touches the paper clip?

5 A nail is magnetised by being in contact with one end of a magnet. Can it still attract magnetic materials to it when it has left the magnet? Explain your answer.

6 If three steel paper clips are attached in line to the bottom of a magnet the lowest paper clip is attached less strongly to the middle one than the middle paper clip is attached to the top one. A fourth paper clip cannot be added. Look at your answer to question 3 and explain why the paper clips behave in this way.

Inside a magnet

Groups of particles from which a magnetic material is made form tiny regions called domains. Each domain behaves like a tiny magnet. If the domains are arranged at random (Figure 8.4a) the material does not attract other magnetic materials to it although it can be attracted to a magnet. It also does not point north–south when it is free to move.

Magnetic domains can be made to arrange themselves in line. When this is done all their north poles face in one direction and all their south poles face in the opposite direction. This arrangement produces a north and a south pole in the material as a whole (Figure 8.4b). When the material is in this condition it has been magnetised – it is now a magnet.

Some materials, such as steel, are magnetically 'hard' and once domains have been aligned they tend to stay put. Others, such as iron, are magnetically 'soft' and domains soon rotate again to random positions, so the material loses its magnetism.

7 If you cut a magnet in half does each half become a magnet? Explain your answer.

8 A piece of steel can be made into a magnet by repeatedly stroking it with a magnet as shown in Figure 8.5. How does this affect the domains?

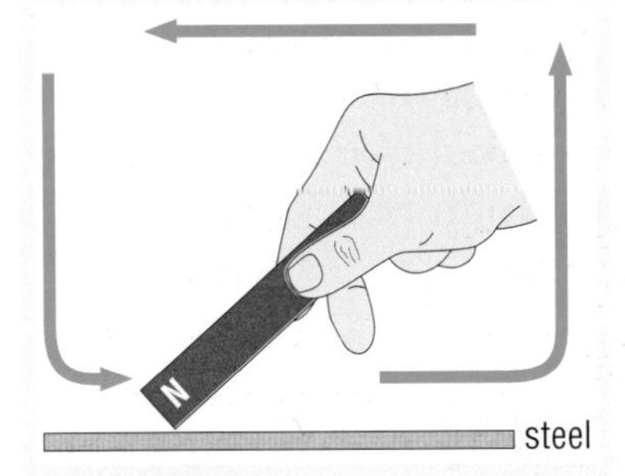

Figure 8.5

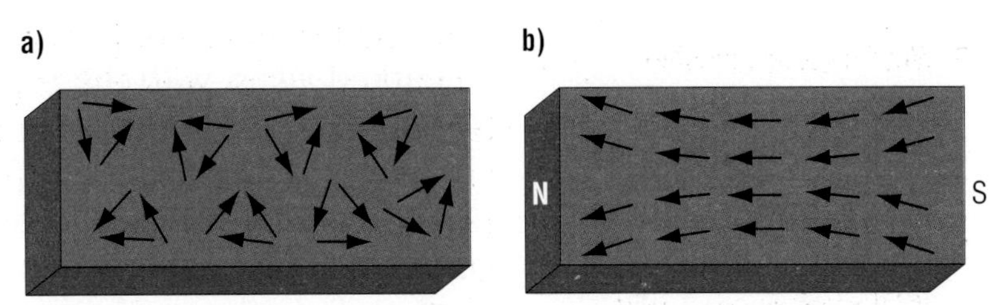

Figure 8.4 **a)** Domains in an unmagnetised material and **b)** domains in a magnet.

The magnetic field

The region around a magnet in which the pull of the magnetic force acts on magnetic materials is called the magnetic field.

The field around a magnet can be shown by using a piece of card and iron filings. The card is laid over the magnet and the iron filings are sprinkled over the paper. Each iron filing has such a small mass that it can be moved by the magnetic force of the magnet if the paper is gently tapped. The iron filings line up as shown in Figure 8.6. The pattern made by the iron filings is called the magnetic field pattern.

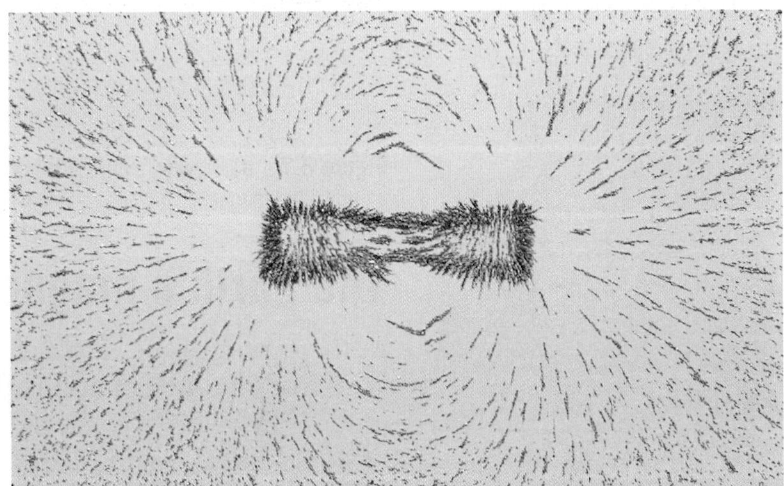

Figure 8.6 The magnetic field pattern of a bar magnet shown by iron filings.

The iron filings appear to form lines around the magnet. This phenomenon can be checked by using a plotting compass and a piece of paper and pencil. The magnet is placed in the centre of the paper and the plotting compass is placed on one side of the magnet close to its north pole. The north pole of the compass will point away from it. The position of the north pole of the compass is marked on the paper and the plotting compass is then moved so that its south pole is over the mark made on the paper. The position of the north pole is marked again with the plotting compass in the new position and the process is repeated until the plotting compass reaches the south pole of the magnet. If the points marking the positions of the north pole of the compass are joined together by a line running from the north pole to the south pole of the magnet (Figure 8.7a), this will represent one of the magnetic 'lines of force' forming the field pattern. Arrows should be drawn on the lines, pointing from the magnet's north pole to its south pole (Figure 8.7b).

9 How does the information from the activity with the plotting compass compare with the field pattern produced by the iron filings?

10 Figure 8.8 shows iron filings spread out when in contact with the end of a bar magnet. Make a drawing of how you think the field lines are arranged all around the magnet.

Figure 8.8

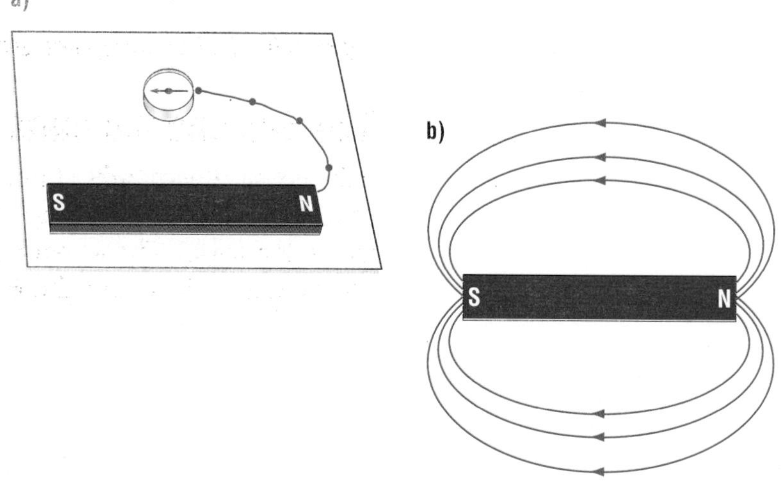

Figure 8.7 **a)** Drawing a magnetic line of force and **b)** the magnetic field pattern around a bar magnet.

The Earth's magnetic field

At the centre of the Earth is the Earth's core. It is made from iron and nickel and is divided into two parts – the inner core made of solid metal and the outer core made of liquid metal. As the Earth spins the two parts of the core move at different speeds and this is thought to generate the magnetic field around the Earth and make the Earth seem to have a large bar magnet inside it.

The Earth spins on its axis which is an imaginary line that runs through the centre of the planet. The ends of the line are called the geographic north and south poles. Their positions on the surface of the Earth are fixed. Magnetic north – towards which the free north pole of a magnet points – is not at the same place as the geographic north pole (Figure 8.9), and it changes position slightly every year.

11 a) Look at the field pattern around the Earth in Figure 8.9. Which pole of the imaginary bar magnet inside the Earth coincides with magnetic north?

b) Draw a bar magnet inside the Earth and label its poles. Also label the position of south pole on the Earth's surface.

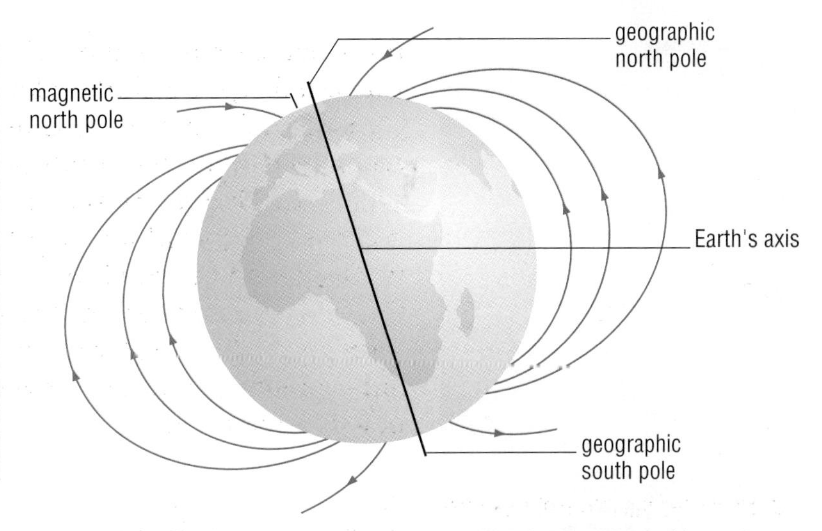

Figure 8.9 The Earth's geographic and magnetic poles do not coincide.

The Sun and the Earth's magnetic field

Billions of electrically charged particles leave the Sun every second. They stream out through space and form the solar wind. Those particles that approach the Earth or pass close to it distort the Earth's magnetic field.

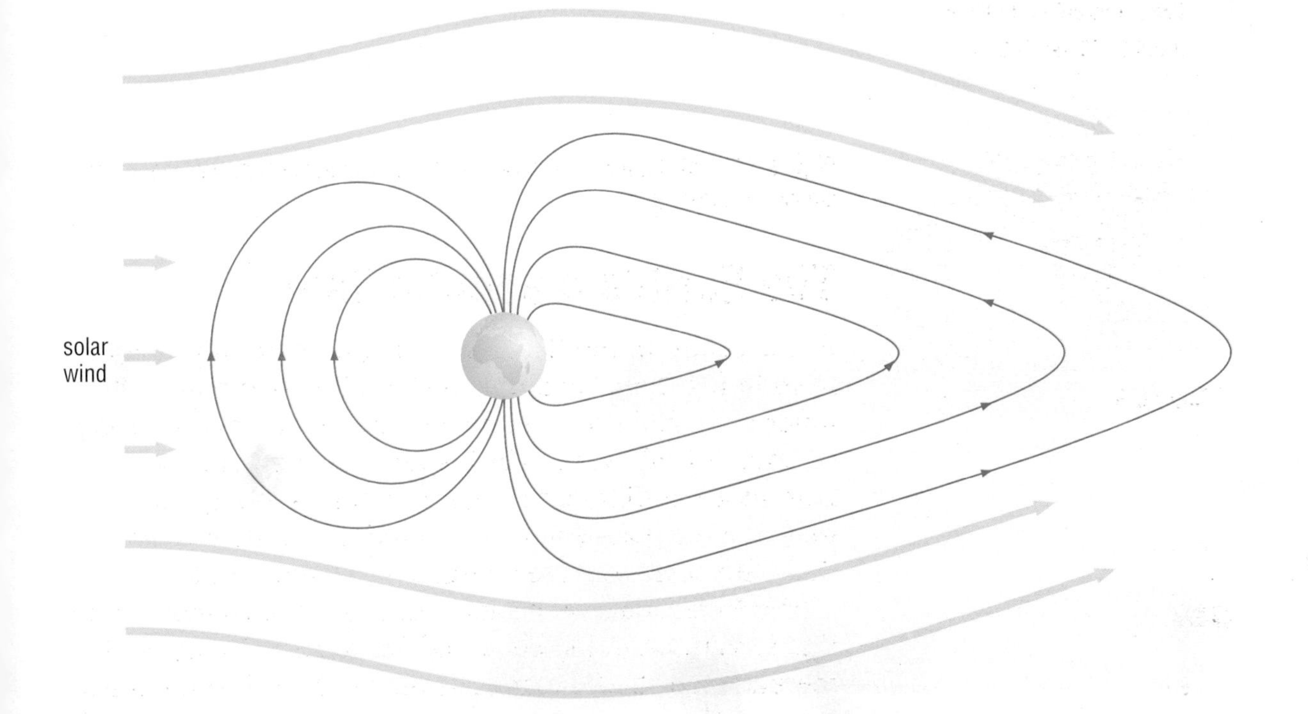

Figure 8.10 Charged particles in the solar wind distort the Earth's magnetic field.

12 How does the solar wind affect the Earth's magnetic field?

Some of the particles in the solar wind are drawn in towards the Earth's poles and when they enter the upper atmosphere they collide with particles of gas. Light

Figure 8.11 The aurora borealis.

energy is released as a result of these collisions. It appears like a shimmering curtain of colour which is known as the northern lights (aurora borealis) and the southern lights (aurora australis). The intensity of the light emitted varies with the strength of the solar wind.

Early discoveries about magnetism

The discovery of how magnetite can be used to identify the direction of north and south is thought to have occurred in China over 4500 years ago. It is thought that the discovery may have come about in the following way.

In ancient China people were concerned about where they were buried. They took advice from people who spun an object on a board to find the best direction for the grave. As the practice continued the people who used the boards and spinners charged more money and used more expensive and unusual materials, such as magnetite, to attract even higher fees for their work. When magnetite was used as a spinner it always settled in a north–south direction, while the other objects settled in any random direction. The importance of magnetite in direction finding led to the development of the compass.

1 How did magnetite become used for direction finding?
2 How is the knowledge about the compass thought to have spread?

Figure A An early Chinese compass.

The knowledge of using magnetite for direction finding is believed to have slowly passed to other countries as they traded with one another. It reached Europe some time after AD950.

(continued)

Petrus de Peregrinus (also known as Peter the Pilgrim) was a French engineer who lived in the 13th Century. He experimented on the way magnets could attract and repel each other and how they could point north and south. He believed that the magnet pointed to the outer sphere of the heavens (see *Early ideas on forces* page 19). Compasses at that time were made by floating the magnetic needle on water but Peregrinus showed that attaching the needle to a pivot made the compass easier to use.

Figure B An Italian mariner's compass made in 1580, using a pivot originally designed by Peregrinus.

3 How did the work of Peregrinus help Gilbert with his scientific modelling?

4 How did Gilbert's explanation of the reason for magnets pointing north–south differ from the explanation of Peregrinus?

William Gilbert (1544–1603) was an English scientist and doctor to Elizabeth I, who made many experiments on magnets and disproved beliefs, such as garlic destroys magnetism and rubbing a diamond on a piece of iron makes the iron into a magnet.

Gilbert suspended a magnetic needle so that it could move both horizontally and vertically and discovered that the needle also dipped as it pointed north–south. He extended his investigation by using a model of the Earth made out of a sphere of lodestone (magnetite). He put a compass with a pivot at different places on the surface of his model Earth and showed that the dip varied with the position of the compass on the sphere, just as it did with compasses at different places on the surface of the Earth. From this investigation Gilbert described the Earth as behaving as if it contained a huge magnet.

Figure C William Gilbert.

For discussion

Was the ancient Chinese practice of grave positioning a scientific process? Explain your answer.

The link between magnetism and electricity

Hans Christian Oersted (1777–1851) was a Danish physicist who studied electricity. In one of his experiments he was passing an electric current along a wire from a voltaic pile (see *Chemistry Now! 11–14* page 113) when he noticed the movement of a compass needle which had been left near the wire. This chance observation led to many discoveries of how magnetism and electricity are linked together, and many modern applications.

When an electric current passes through a wire it generates a magnetic field around the wire. A compass can be placed at different places on a card around the wire, as shown in Figure 8.12, and lines of force can be plotted.

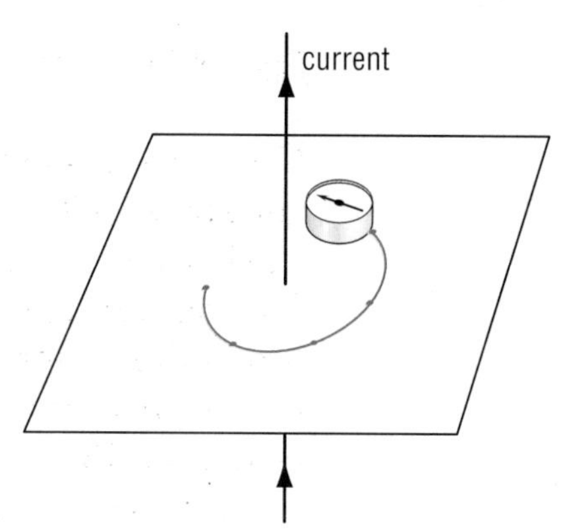

Figure 8.12 Plotting magnetic field lines around a current-carrying wire.

When the current flows up through the card, the field shown in Figure 8.13a is produced. When the current flows down through the card, the field shown in Figure 8.13b is produced.

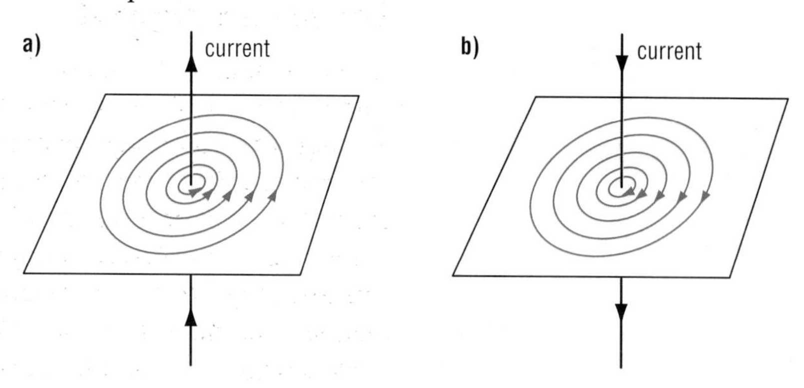

Figure 8.13 The magnetic field around a current-carrying wire.

Lines of force on diagrams of magnetic fields show not only the direction of the field as given by a plotting compass but also the strength of the field in different places. The lines of force are close together where the field is strong and wider apart where the field is weaker.

If the wire is made into a coil and connected into a circuit, a magnetic field is produced around the coil as shown in Figure 8.14.

13 How are the fields in Figure 8.13a and b different?
14 How does the strength of the magnetic field around the wire coil vary?
15 Compare the magnetic field of a bar magnet (Figure 8.7b) with that produced by a current in a wire coil (Figure 8.14).

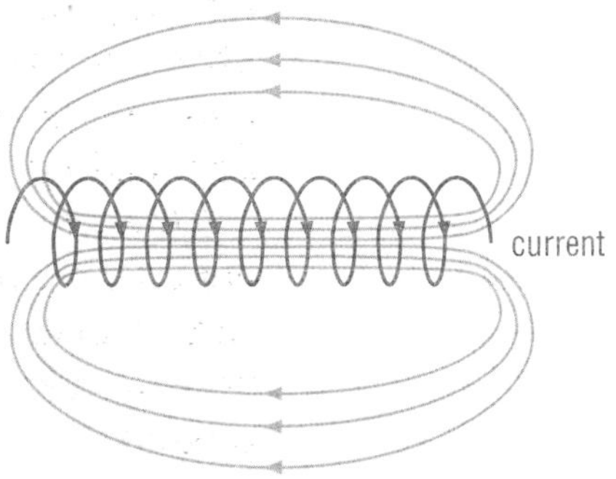

Figure 8.14 The magnetic field around a current-carrying coil.

If a piece of steel is placed inside the wire coil and the current is switched on the magnetism of the coil and the steel is stronger than that of the coil alone. The current flowing through the coil induces magnetism in the steel. When the current is switched off the steel keeps some of the magnetism it acquired because it is magnetically hard (see page 136).

If a piece of iron is placed inside the coil it makes an even stronger magnet when the current is switched on than the steel did. When the current is switched off the iron loses its magnetism completely because it is magnetically soft (see page 136).

The electromagnet

An electromagnet is made from a coil of wire surrounding a piece of iron. When a current flows through the coil magnetism is induced in the iron, and the coil and iron form a strong electromagnet. When the current is switched off the electromagnet loses its magnetism completely, straight away. This device, which can instantly become a magnet then instantly lose its magnetism, has many uses. For example, a large electromagnet is used in a scrapyard to move the steel bodies of cars.

16 Describe how you think an electromagnet can be used to make a stack of scrapped cars three cars high.

Figure 8.15 An electromagnet in a scrapyard.

The reed switch

A reed switch (Figure 8.16) is a magnetic switch. It has two pieces of soft iron, called the reeds, supported by metal which has a springy property. The reeds are enclosed in a glass container which is filled with an inert gas. This gas is used instead of air because the metal does not react with it and so does not corrode.

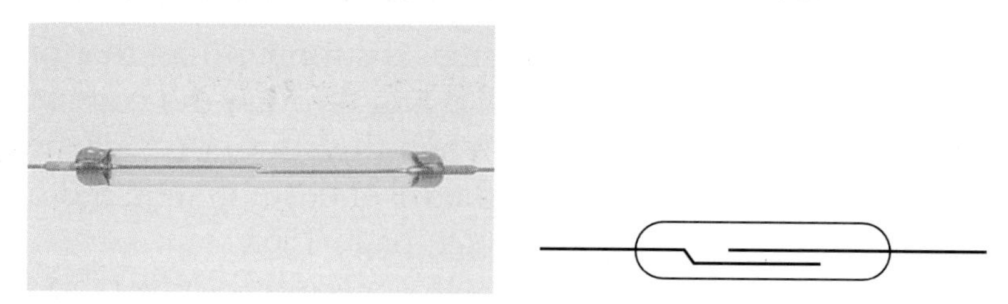

Figure 8.16 A reed switch and its symbol.

When a magnet is brought close to the reed switch it makes the soft iron reeds become magnets (Figure 8.17). The opposite poles on the free ends of the reeds attract each other. The magnetic force between them bends the two pieces of springy metal so that the two reeds touch and close the circuit, allowing the current to flow. When the magnet is taken away the soft iron reeds lose their magnetism and the tension force in the springy metal pulls the reeds apart.

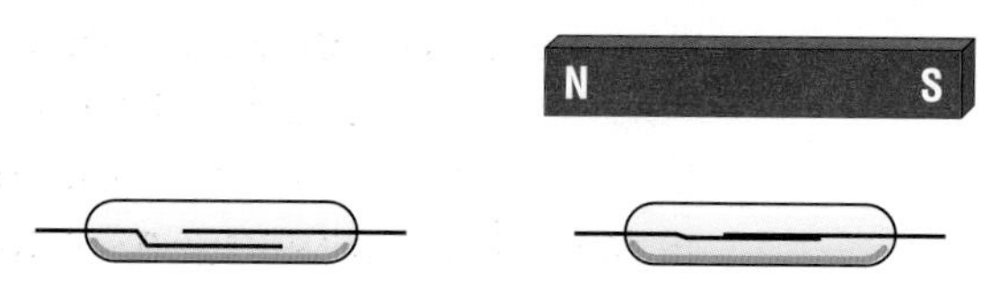

Figure 8.17 How a reed switch works.

17 How would metal corrosion affect a reed switch? Explain your answer.

18 If a door is fitted with a burglar alarm as in Figure 8.18, how is the alarm set off when the door is opened?

This type of reed switch is used in burglar alarms where the reed switch is placed in the door frame and magnets are placed in the door and the door frame.

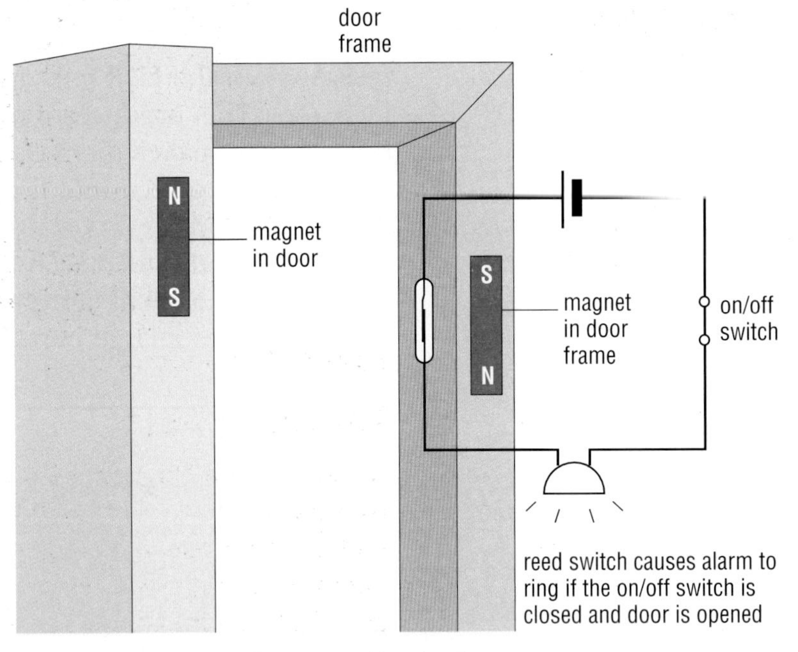

Figure 8.18 A reed-switch operated burglar alarm.

The reed relay

A reed relay is a reed switch like the one shown in Figure 8.16 but with a coil of wire wrapped round it.

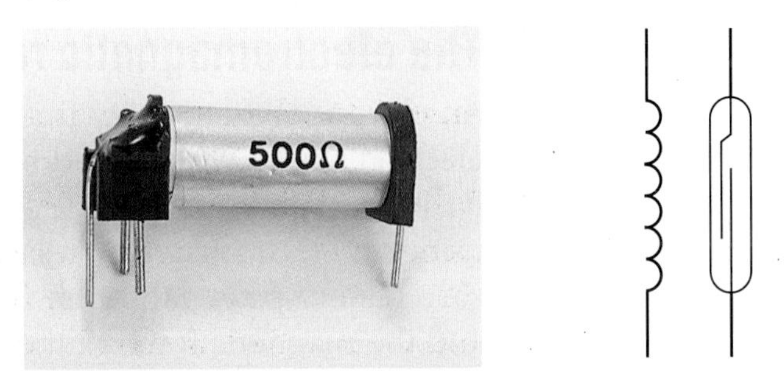

Figure 8.19 A reed relay and its symbol.

When an electric current flows through the coil, a magnetic field is produced in and around the coil (see page 143) which causes the reeds to move. The coil and reeds are connected in separate circuits. Only a small current is needed by the coil to move the reeds but a large current can be conducted in the other circuit by the reeds. This allows a circuit through which a large current passes to be controlled by a circuit in which a small current flows.

A motor can be controlled by light by using the circuits shown in Figure 8.20. When it is dark, the high resistance of the LDR allows only a very small current to flow in circuit A. It is not enough to produce a magnetic field around the reeds in the relay. When it is light the resistance of the LDR falls and the size of the current increases. This produces a magnetic field around the reeds which makes them come together and close circuit B. A much larger current flows through circuit B to make the motor work.

The use of the reed relay allows a component which only requires a small current to control a component which requires a large current.

19 What happens in circuits A and B when it becomes darker again?

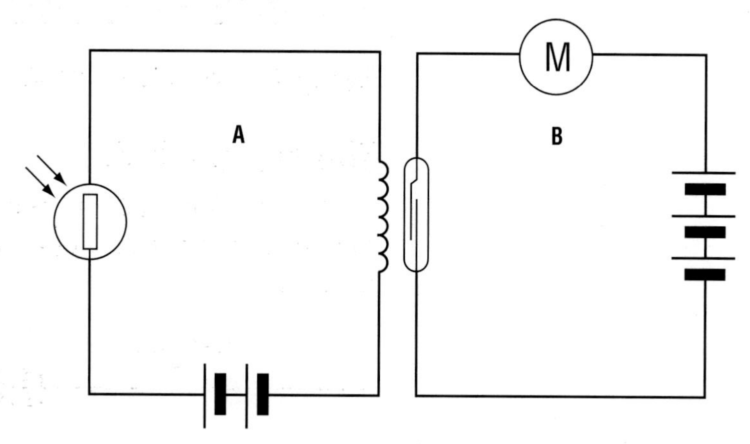

Figure 8.20 A light-operated motor circuit using a reed relay.

The electromagnetic relay

An electromagnetic relay is a switch operated by an electromagnet. When the driver of a car puts the key in the dashboard and twists it, the ignition switch is turned on using an electromagnetic relay. A small current from the car's battery passes through the coil of an electromagnet and the magnetic force of the electromagnet pulls on a piece of iron called an armature (Figure 8.21). An armature is a part of an electrical device which moves when a magnetic field develops around it. The magnetic force is strong enough to overcome the forces in the attached spring and it is squashed. The armature moves towards the electromagnet and the end of the armature pushes down on the contacts of springy metal. The contacts touch and close the switch in a circuit through which a very large current flows. This current is used to turn the starter motor which starts the engine running. The big current only goes a short distance. It does not need to go all the way to the key and back.

20 When the driver hears the engine start running he or she stops twisting the ignition key and the current no longer flows to the relay's electromagnet. What happens to the **a)** spring, **b)** armature and **c)** contacts?

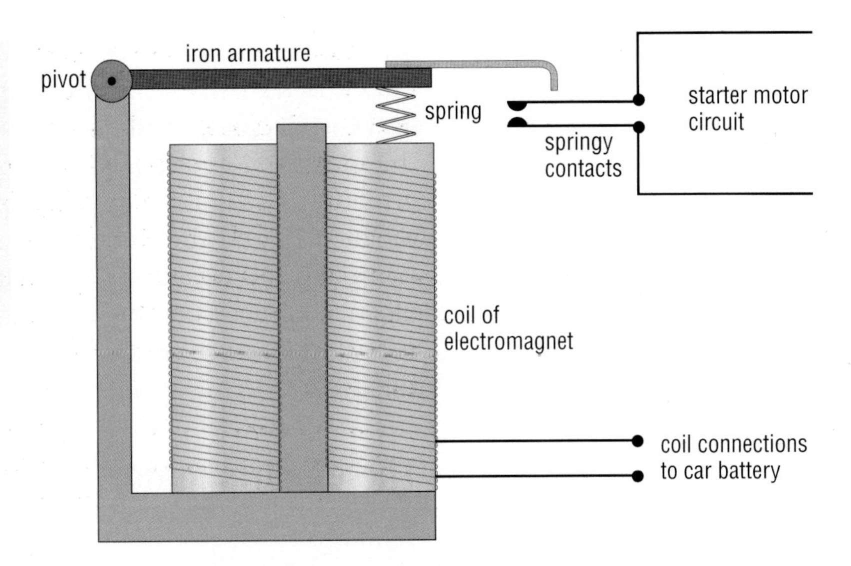

Figure 8.21 An electromagnetic relay operating a starter motor circuit.

The electric bell

Look at Figure 8.22 and see if you can work out the path the current takes through the circuit when the switch is pushed.

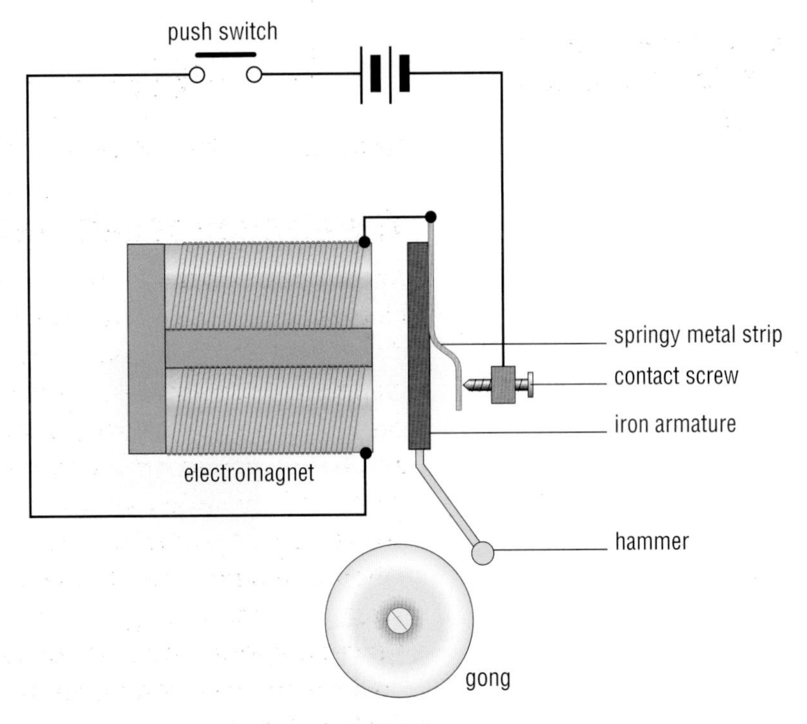

Figure 8.22 The circuit of an electric bell.

When the switch is pushed the current passes through the coil and the electromagnet pulls the armature to it. This makes the hammer strike the gong. When the

21 Describe the changes that take place in the springy metal strip holding the armature when the current **a)** flows and **b)** stops flowing. Use the term strain force in your description.

armature is pulled to the electromagnet a gap develops between the springy metal strip and the contact screw and the circuit is broken. The current stops flowing and the electromagnet loses its magnetism. This makes the armature swing back to its original position. The springy metal strip and the contact screw now touch again and complete the circuit so the armature is pulled to the electromagnet once more. The bell is made to ring by the repeated beating of the hammer until the push switch is released.

The electric motor

Joseph Henry (1797–1878) was an American physicist who developed the electric motor from his studies on electromagnetism.

In a very simple electric motor there is a coil of wire which is free to turn on a shaft between the poles of a magnet. An electric current is passed into the coil where it makes a magnetic field develop. This interacts with the magnetic field of the magnet and causes the coil to spin. The motor has a sliding contact system connecting it to the rest of the circuit, consisting of brushes and a commutator (Figure 8.23), so that a current can reach the coil when it is rotating. The design of the commutator is such that the current direction in the coil changes every half turn. This keeps the turning forces on the coil acting in the same direction all the time it is going round. The coil spins continuously in one direction and causes the shaft to spin.

For discussion

What can the turning motion of an electric motor be used for?

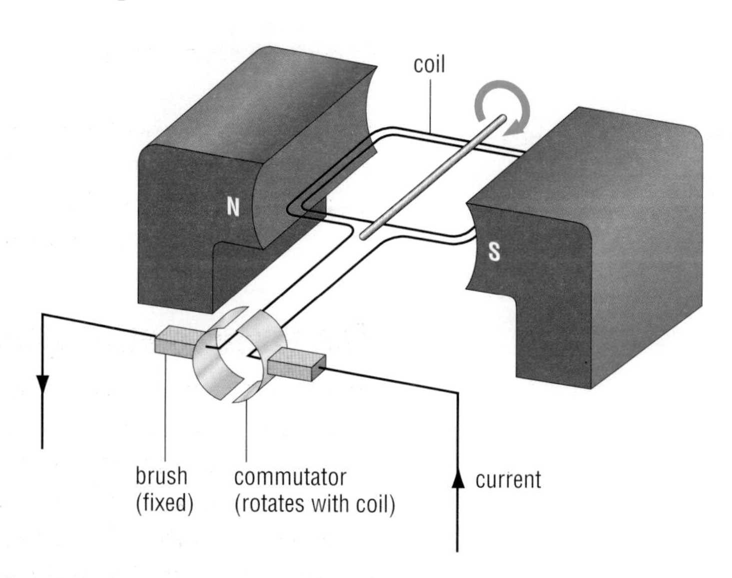

Figure 8.23 A simple electric motor.

Generating electricity

Michael Faraday (1791–1867), an English physicist, discovered that an electric current could be made to flow in a wire if the wire was made to move through a magnetic field. This principle is used to generate electricity in a bicycle dynamo and in a power station generator.

The bicycle dynamo

A bicycle dynamo is an electrical device which is clamped onto the frame of a bicycle close to a tyre. It has a wheel on top which can be made to touch the tyre. The inside of a dynamo is shown in Figure 8.24.

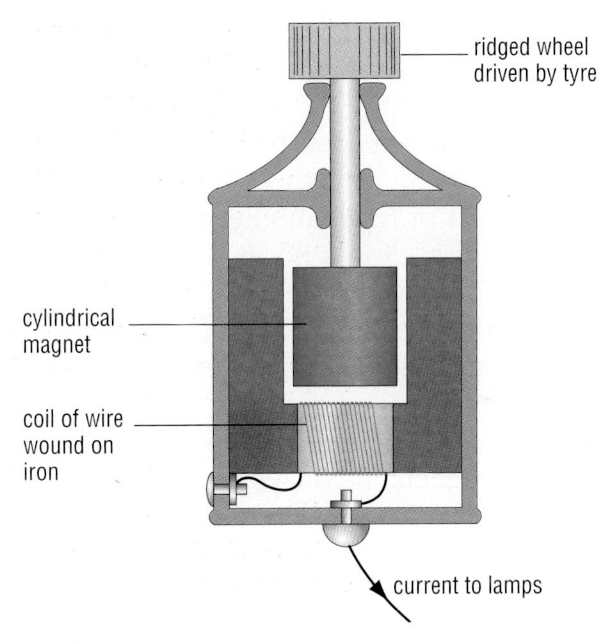

Figure 8.24 Inside a dynamo.

22 What would be the problem if dynamos were the only way electricity was provided in bicycle lamps?

When the dynamo wheel is in contact with the tyre it rotates as the bicycle wheel turns. Inside the dynamo the magnet turns and its field sweeps through the wires, generating an electric current which lights the bicycle's lamps.

The power station generator

Inside a power station generator is a huge electromagnet surrounded by coils of wire. The electromagnet is attached to a shaft to which the turbine blades are attached (Figure 8.25). When the turbine is made to spin (see page 85) the electromagnet also spins, generating a current of electricity in the surrounding coils of wire.

Figure 8.25 Turbine assembly for a power station generator.

♦ SUMMARY ♦

- Magnetic materials are attracted by a magnet; non-magnetic materials are not (*see page 135*).
- A magnet can attract or repel another magnet (*see page 135*).
- A bar magnet aligns itself in a north–south direction when it is free to move (*see page 135*).
- A magnet has a north-seeking pole and a south-seeking pole (*see page 135*).
- A magnet can be made by induction (*see page 136*).
- There are tiny regions called domains inside a magnet (*see page 136*).
- A magnetic field exists around a magnet (*see page 137*).
- The Earth has a magnetic field (*see page 138*).
- A wire with an electric current passing through it has a magnetic field around it (*see page 142*).
- An electromagnet is a magnet whose magnetism can be switched on and off by switching a current on and off (*see page 143*).
- A reed switch is opened and closed by a magnet (*see page 144*).
- An electromagnetic relay is a switch operated by an electromagnet (*see page 146*).
- An electromagnet is used to produce the repeated ringing of an electric bell (*see page 147*).
- An electric motor works because of the interaction between the magnetic fields of a current coil and the poles of a magnet (*see page 148*).
- Electricity can be generated by magnetism (*see page 149*).

End of chapter questions

1 Why do magnets line up in a north–south direction?

2 Assess the importance of magnetism in **a)** providing electricity for the home and **b)** the working of electrical devices in the home.

9 Light

1 What is the luminous object which is providing light for you to read this book?

Light is a form of energy. It is a form of electromagnetic radiation (see page 65). Objects that emit light are said to be luminous while those that do not emit light are said to be non-luminous. Non-luminous objects can only be seen if they are reflecting light from a luminous source. The Moon is a non-luminous body – the 'moonlight' it produces is reflected sunlight.

Luminous objects

Most luminous objects, such as the Sun, stars, fire and candle flames, release light together with a large amount of heat, that is, infrared radiation (see page 66).

Figure 9.1 A bonfire radiates light and heat.

Luminescence

Luminescence is the emission of light from an object without a large amount of heat. The LED (see page 131), for example, produces only a very small amount of heat when it emits light. There are three types of luminescence. They are bioluminescence, phosphorescence and fluorescence.

Bioluminescence

Some living things such as glow worms, fireflies and certain deep sea fish exhibit bioluminescence (see Figure 9.2). They emit light with very little heat because of certain chemical reactions which take place in their bodies. Enzymes act as catalysts (see *Chemistry Now! 11–14* page 67) in these reactions.

Figure 9.2 A cuttlefish with light organs.

2 What might happen if living organisms that emit light energy also produced a large amount of heat energy?

Phosphorescence

Some substances are phosphorescent. When they absorb light of a short wavelength they emit light of a longer wavelength. They continue to emit light in the dark. Luminous paint, which may be used on clock and watch faces, contains a phosphorescent substance. It allows you to tell the time in the dark from the glowing hands and numbers.

Figure 9.3 Phosphorescent materials on a watch face.

3 Compare bioluminescence, phosphorescence and fluorescence.

Fluorescence

A fluorescent material is also one that absorbs light of a short wavelength and emits light of a longer wavelength, but it also absorbs ultraviolet waves (see page 66) then emits visible light waves. For example, when a tubular fluorescent lamp is switched on both visible and ultraviolet light are released by the mercury vapour it contains. The ultraviolet is absorbed by the fluorescent material coating the inside of the tube and is then released as visible light into the air around it.

A fluorescent material stops emitting light as soon as it is prevented from absorbing light or ultraviolet waves, so a fluorescent tube does not glow after it is switched off.

Figure 9.4 Fluorescent tubes provide most of the light in this factory.

Light rays

Light leaves the surface of a luminous object in all directions but if some of the light is made to pass through a hole it can be seen to travel in straight lines. For example, when sunlight shines through a small gap in the clouds it forms broad sunbeams with straight edges. The path of the light can be seen because some of it is reflected from dust in the atmosphere. Similarly, sunlight shining through a gap in the curtains of a dark room produces a beam of light which can be seen when the light reflects from the dust in the air of the room.

Figure 9.5 Although the Sun radiates light in all directions, the sides of sunbeams seem almost parallel because the Sun is a very distant luminous object.

Smaller lines of light, called rays, can be made by shining a lamp through slits in a piece of card.

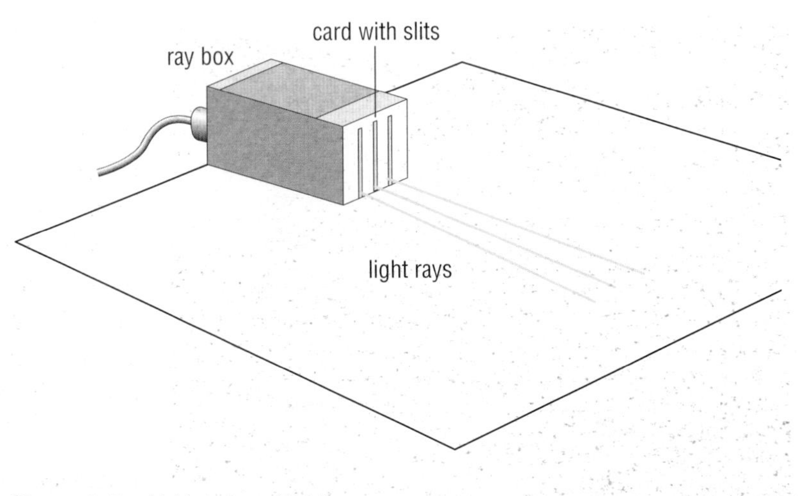

Figure 9.6 Making rays of light.

Classifying non-luminous objects

Non-luminous materials can be classified as transparent, translucent or opaque according to the way light behaves when it meets them. When light shines on a transparent material, such as glass in a window, it passes through it and so objects on the other side of it can be seen clearly.

When light shines on a translucent object, such as tracing paper, some of the light passes through but many light rays are scattered. Objects on the other side cannot be seen clearly unless they are very close to the translucent object.

When light shines on an opaque object none of the light passes through it.

Shadows

When a beam of light shines on an opaque object the light rays which reach the object are stopped while those rays which pass by the edges continue on their path. A region without light, called a shadow, forms behind the object. The shape of the shadow may not be identical to the shape of the object because the shadow's shape depends on the position of the light source and on where the shadow falls.

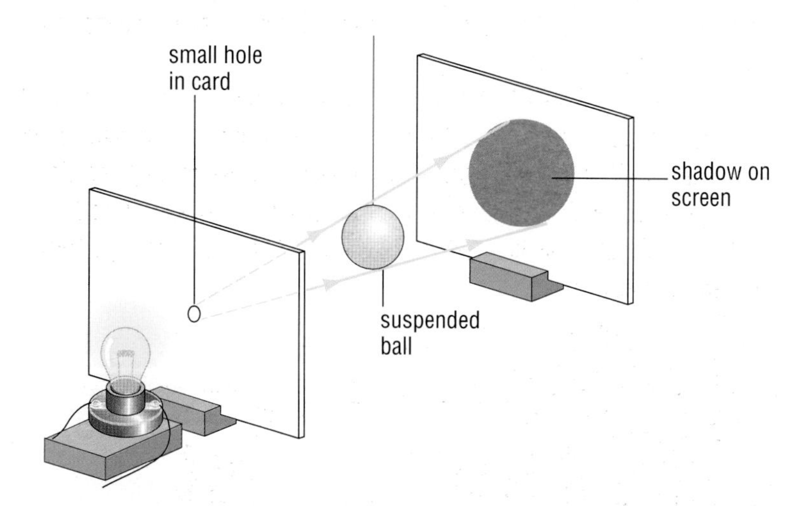

Figure 9.7 Formation of a shadow.

Shadows are also cast by the Moon and the Earth (see page 198).

For discussion

How might the shadow of a brick appear if light travelled in a curve from the light source?

What is light?

Empedocles (c.490–c.430BC) was a Greek philosopher who believed that we see things because our eyes send out rays which touch objects. Plato (427–347BC) built on this idea but believed that objects gave out rays which the eyes' rays intercepted. Democritus (c.470–c.380BC) believed that objects were made of atoms, some of which passed from the objects through the air to the eye and allowed us to see the objects.

1 Was the Sun needed in Empedocles' idea about how we see? How do you think he might have explained seeing in the night?
2 Democritus has been described as being 'ahead of his time'. Why?
3 Why was Newton's work on light preferred to the work of Huygens?

Figure A Democritus thought that sight involved moving atoms.

Christian Huygens (1629–1695), a Dutch physicist, put forward a wave theory of light, in which he claimed that light moved in a similar way to waves of water and sound. The theory required the existence of a substance called the ether which is found everywhere – the ether was needed to enable the light waves to move. He thought the waves were very small and for most experiments they did not affect the light rays which could be considered as travelling in straight lines.

Isaac Newton (1642–1727) believed this to be wrong, as sound can travel round corners but light does not. His theory was similar to that of Democritus – he believed light travelled as tiny particles which moved through the air.

Huygens' explanation did not satisfy many scientists. They preferred Newton's explanation, as his work in other areas of physics (see page 196) had been impressive.

Figure B Did light travel like waves in a puddle?

(continued)

In 1801 Thomas Young (1773–1829), an English physicist, performed an experiment in which he shone a light through narrow, close slits as shown in Figure C. The result could not be explained if light travelled as particles but could be explained by the wave theory. Young believed that the regions where the light was brightest were where the crests of the light waves met together and the regions of darkness were where the troughs of the waves cancelled out the crests (see Figure D).

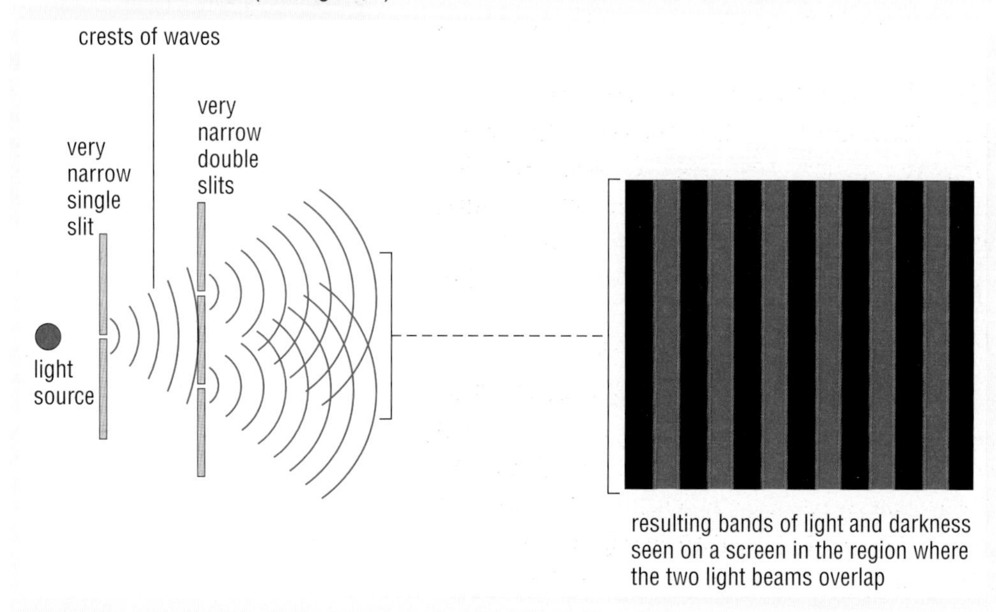

Figure C Young's experiment.

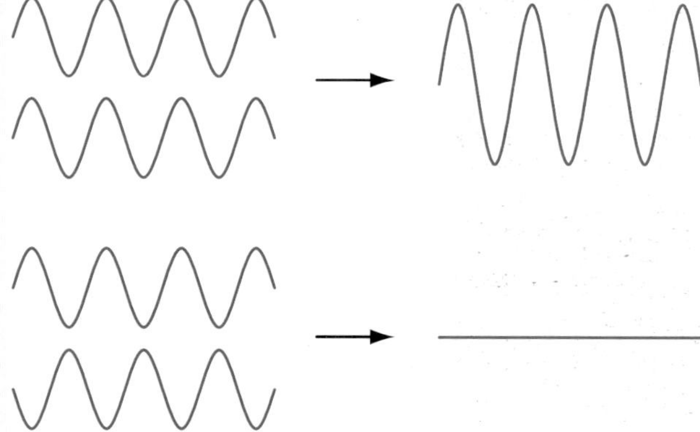

Figure D How the crests and troughs combine.

Michael Faraday (1791–1867), an English physicist and chemist, performed many experiments on electricity and magnetism. James Clerk Maxwell (1831–1879), a Scottish physicist, took some of Faraday's results and showed that electricity and magnetism were so closely related that one could not exist without the other. In 1845 Faraday had performed an experiment in which a magnet affected a beam of light. This showed that light had electromagnetic properties, too.

(continued)

Maxwell predicted that light consisted of electromagnetic waves and calculated the velocity of the waves to be about 300 million metres per second. Later this was found to be true (see page 163).

Philip von Lenard (1862–1947), a Hungarian physicist, discovered that when light is shone onto certain metals, electrons are released from the metal surface. He found that a bright light released a greater number of electrons than a dim light. This suggested to him that light was made from 'particles of energy' which moved the electrons, so Newton's ideas were revived.

Max Planck (1858–1947), a German physicist, proposed that electromagnetic energy could be divided up into small units called quanta. His idea became known as the quantum theory. Albert Einstein (1879–1955) applied Planck's theory to successfully explain Lenard's results. Also, when Einstein developed his theory of relativity, which took into account the results of many other experiments, he showed that the presence of an ether was not required to explain how light moves.

These investigations into the nature of light reveal that it can be considered either to be waves or particles. The form that you consider it to be depends on the work that you are doing with light. For example, if the way light passes through transparent objects is being studied, the light can be considered to be formed of waves. But if the way light makes the solar cells on a calculator generate electricity is being studied, the light can be considered to be made of 'particles' or quanta of energy called photons.

4 How did Faraday contribute to forming Maxwell's idea that light is made from electromagnetic waves?

5 How did Planck's theory fit in with von Lenard's results?

6 What is light?

Figure E This car is powered by photons which strike the solar cells on its surface.

You may have trouble thinking that light can be considered in two different ways. It may help with this problem if you think about how we consider people in different ways. The way you behave with an older person, such as a parent, is different to the way you behave with people of your own age. Both older and younger people see you in different ways. Possibly none of them see the 'real' you!

Reflecting light

Your bedroom is probably full of objects but if you were to wake in the middle of the night you could not see them clearly because they are not luminous. You can only see them by reflected light and unless your room is partially lit by street lights the objects will not be clearly seen until sunrise. The way light is reflected from a surface depends on whether the surface is smooth or rough.

Studying reflections

A few terms are used in the study of light which make it easier for scientists to describe their investigations and ideas. In the study of reflections the following terms are used:

- incident ray – a light ray that strikes a surface
- reflected ray – a light ray that is reflected from a surface
- normal – a line perpendicular (that is at 90°) to the surface where the incident ray strikes
- angle of incidence – the angle between the incident ray and the normal
- angle of reflection – the angle between the reflected ray and the normal
- plane mirror – a mirror with a flat surface
- image – the appearance of an object in a smooth, shiny surface. It is produced by light from the object being reflected by the surface.

The way the incident ray, normal and reflected ray are represented diagrammatically is shown in Figure 9.8. The back surface of a mirror is always shown as here, as a line with short lines at an angle to it.

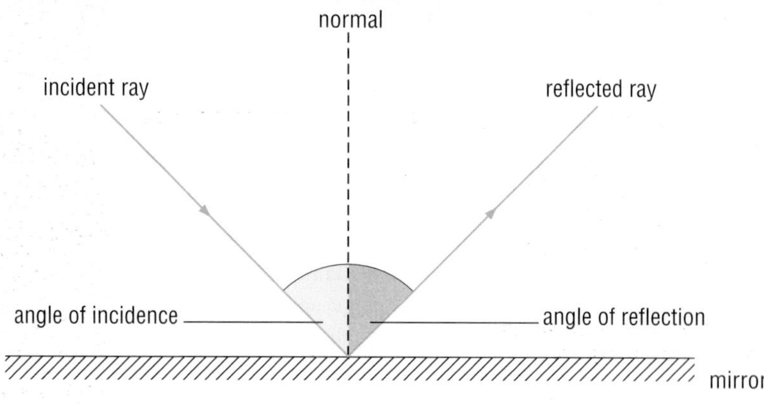

Figure 9.8 Reflection of light from a plane mirror.

4 Figure 9.10 shows three drawings made of the path of incident and reflected rays in an experiment using the apparatus in Figure 9.9. Use a protractor to measure the angle of incidence and angle of reflection. What do these drawings tell you about the process of reflection?

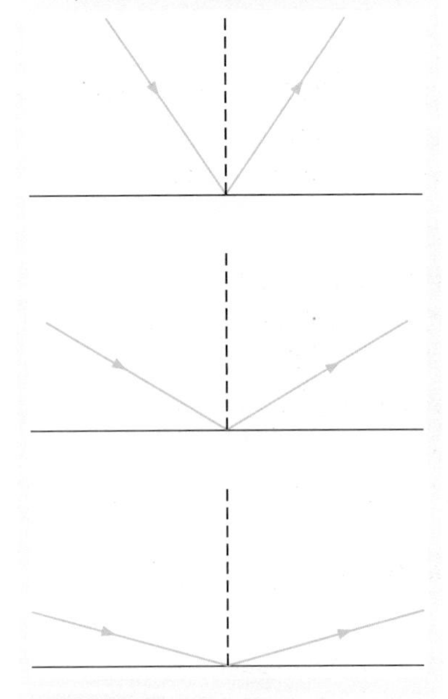

Figure 9.10

The way light rays are reflected from a plane mirror can be investigated using the equipment shown in Figure 9.9.

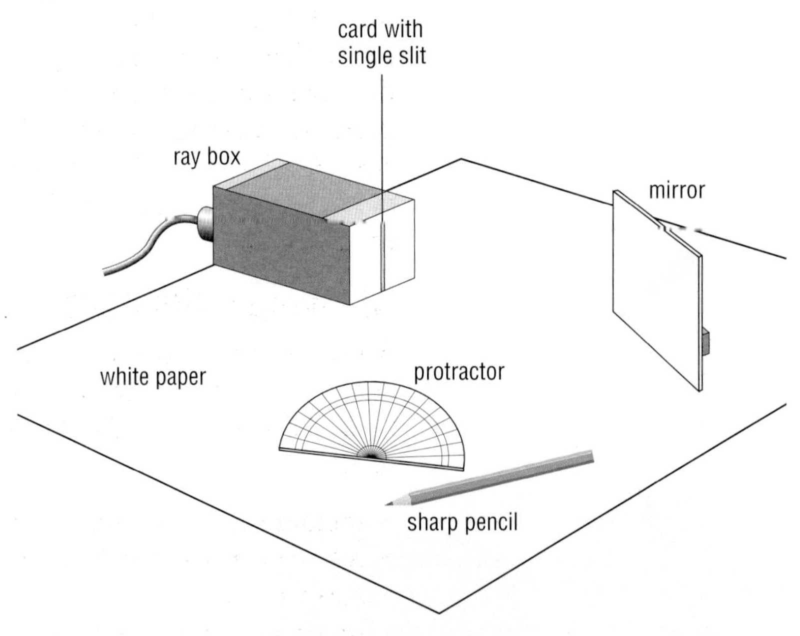

Figure 9.9 Investigating reflection from a plane mirror.

Objects with smooth surfaces

Glass, still water and polished metal have very smooth surfaces. Light rays striking their flat surfaces are reflected as shown in Figure 9.11. The angle of reflection is equal to the angle of incidence. When the reflected light reaches your eyes you see an image (Figure 9.12).

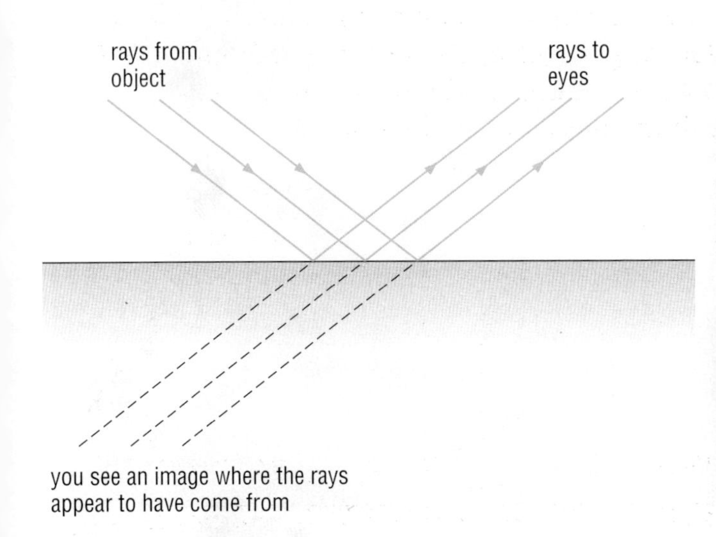

Figure 9.11 Regular reflection from a smooth surface

Figure 9.12 Light reflected from the smooth surface of a lake can produce an image in the water.

Two kinds of images

There are two kinds of images that can be formed with light. They are real images, such as those produced on a cinema screen by biconvex lenses (see pages 165–166) and virtual images, which cannot be projected onto a surface but only appear to exist, such as those in a plane mirror or other smooth, shiny surface.

The virtual image of yourself that you see when you look in a plane mirror is the same way up as you are, is the same size as you are, and is at the same distance from the mirror's surface as you are but behind the mirror instead of in front of it. The main difference between you are and your virtual image is that the virtual image is the 'wrong way round' – for example, your left shoulder appears to be the right shoulder of your virtual image.

Figure 9.13 Your image in a mirror is the wrong way round.

The periscope

Two plane mirrors may be used together to give a person at the back of a crowd a view of an event.

Figure 9.14 Some of the people in this scene are using periscopes to help them see over the crowd.

5 Copy Figure 9.15 and draw in the path of a ray of light travelling from the golfer to the eye.
6 Why is a periscope useful on a submarine?

The arrangement of the mirrors in a periscope is shown in Figure 9.15.

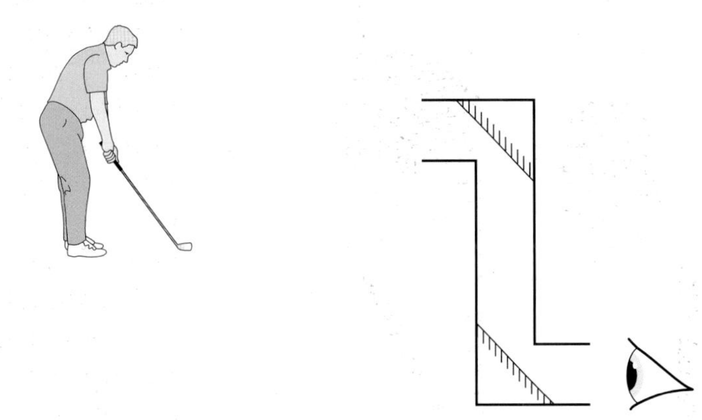

Figure 9.15 Inside a simple periscope.

Objects with rough surfaces

Most objects have rough surfaces. They may be very rough like the surface of a woollen pullover or they may be only slightly rough like the surface of paper. When light rays strike any of these surfaces the rays are scattered in different directions as Figure 9.16 shows.

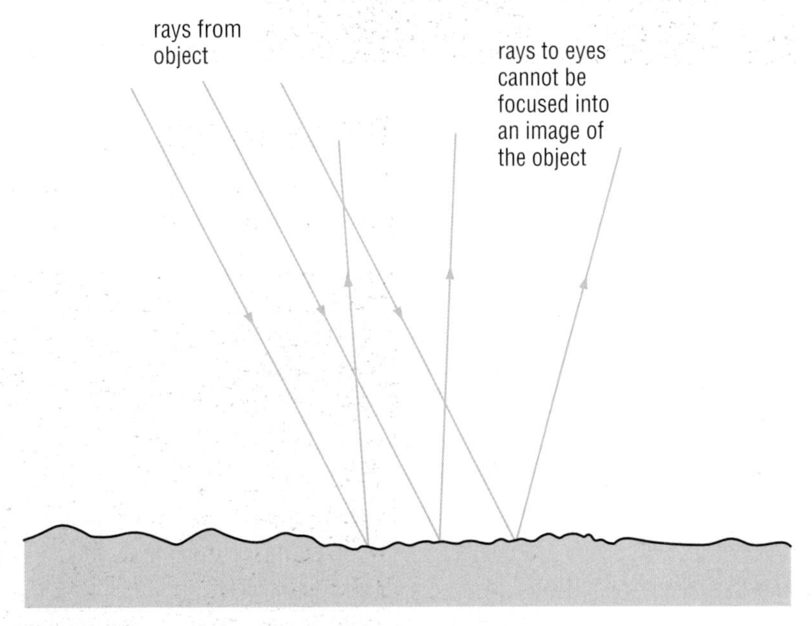

Figure 9.16 Light rays are scattered by a rough surface.

You see a pullover or this page by the light scattered from its surface. You do not see your face in a piece of paper because the reflection of light is irregular, so cannot form an image.

The speed of light

The Ancient Greeks believed that light travelled at infinite speed and this remained unchallenged until Ole Rømer (1644–1710), a Danish astronomer, observed the moons of Jupiter and studied how they travelled around the planet. When Jupiter was between the Earth and one of its moons, the moon could not be seen from the Earth and was said to be eclipsed by Jupiter. The four large moons move around Jupiter quite quickly (see page 195) and other scientists had found it possible to time them. When Rømer studied the eclipses more thoroughly, he discovered that they appeared to occur earlier when the Earth was nearer Jupiter in its orbit than when it was further away (Figure A).

1 Draw the Earth, Jupiter and one of Jupiter's moons to show their positions when one of the moons is eclipsed by Jupiter, as viewed from the Earth (see Figure A).
2 How did Rømer's calculation compare with Bradley's calculation?

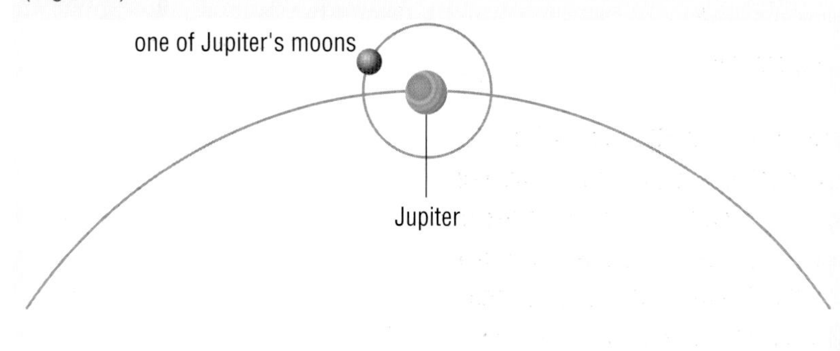

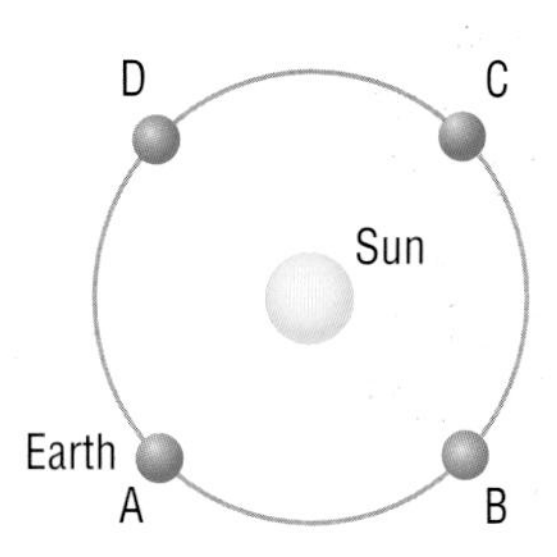

Figure A The positions of the Earth in its orbit when Rømer made his observations.

Rømer did not believe that the moons speeded up at different times of year. He believed the difference was due to light having a finite speed and that it took longer to reach the Earth when the Earth was moving at points A and B than when it was moving at points C and D. By taking measurements and making calculations, Rømer deduced a speed of light which showed that light took 11 minutes to get from the Sun to the Earth.

James Bradley (1693–1762), an English astronomer, studied the position of the stars at different times of year as the Earth moved in its orbit. From his studies he calculated the speed of light. His results showed that light took 8 minutes 11 seconds to travel from the Sun to the Earth.

In 1849 Armand Fizeau (1819–1876), a French physicist, used the device shown in Figure B to measure the speed of light.

(continued)

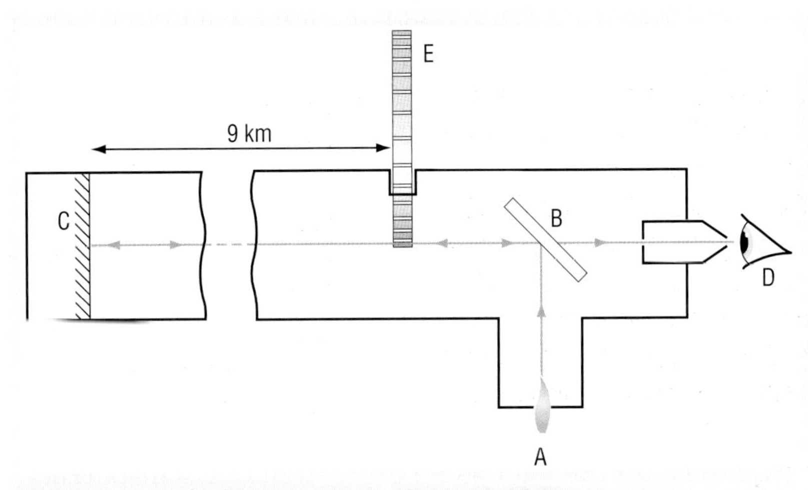

Figure B Fizeau's device for measuring the speed of light.

> **3** How did Fizeau's calculation compare with the speed of light calculated by scientists today?

The light from a flame (A) was reflected by a glass sheet (B) and travelled 9 kilometres to the mirror (C) where it was reflected back through B to the eye (D). A toothed wheel (E) was set to rotate rapidly and its speed was adjusted until the reflected light from C could be seen at D. When this was achieved it meant that the wheel was moving so fast that light passed to C through one gap between the teeth and arrived back at E, having travelled 18 kilometres, just as the next gap moved into place. The speed of the wheel at which the light could be seen was found. This speed and the distance travelled by the light were used to calculate the speed of light. Using this equipment Fizeau found that light travelled between C and D in 1/18 144 of a second. He made many measurements and calculated light to travel at a speed of 314 262 944 metres per second. Many other scientists refined Fizeau's work and today light has been measured at travelling at 299 992 460 metres per second in a vacuum, slightly slower in air and even slower in water and glass. The speed of light in air is often rounded up to 300 000 000 metres per second.

Passing light through transparent materials

If a ray of light is shone on the side of a glass block as shown in Figure 9.17a the ray passes straight through, but if the block is tilted the ray of light follows the path shown in Figure 9.17b.

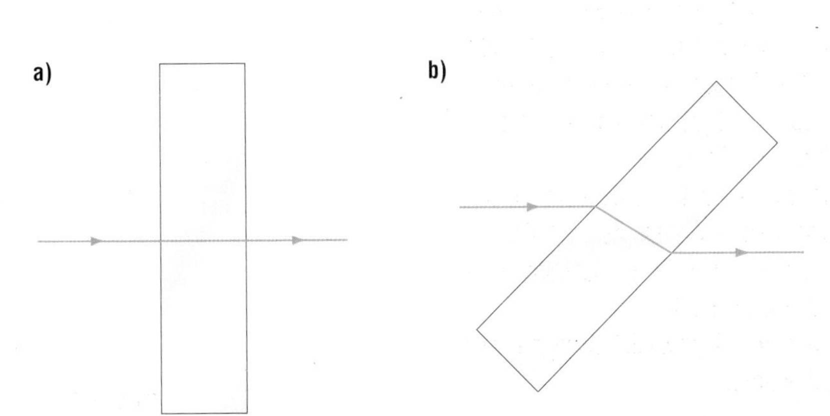

Figure 9.17 Light is refracted if the incident ray is not at 90° to the surface of the transparent material.

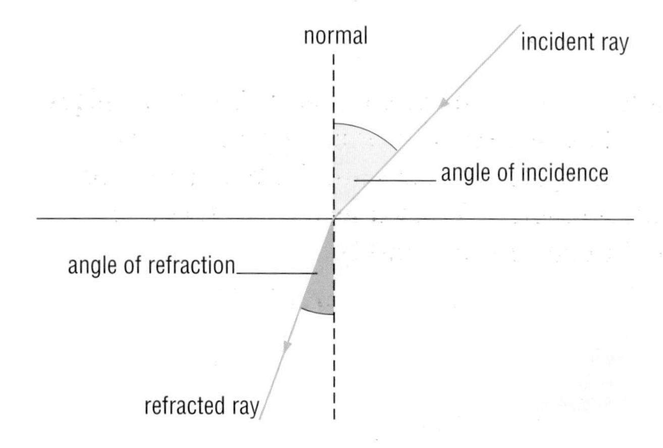

This 'bending' of the light ray is called refraction. The angle that the refracted ray (see Figure 9.18) makes with the normal is called the angle of refraction.

Figure 9.18 The angle of incidence and the angle of refraction.

The refraction of light as it passes from one transparent substance or 'medium' to another is due to the change in the speed of the light. Light travels at different speeds in different media. For example, it travels at almost 300 million metres per second in air but only 200 million metres per second in glass. If the light slows down when it moves from one medium to the other, the ray bends towards the normal. If the light speeds up as it passes from one medium to the next, the ray bends away from the normal.

Light speeds up as it leaves a water surface and enters the air. A light ray appears to have come from a different direction than that of the path it actually travelled (see Figure 9.19a and b). The refraction of the light rays makes the bottom of a swimming pool seem closer to the water surface than it really is. It also makes streams and rivers seem shallower than they really are and this fact must be considered by anyone thinking of wading across a seemingly shallow stretch of water. The refracted light from a straw in a glass of water makes the straw appear to be bent.

7 How is the reflection of a light ray from a plane mirror (see page 158) different from the refraction of a light ray as it enters a piece of glass?

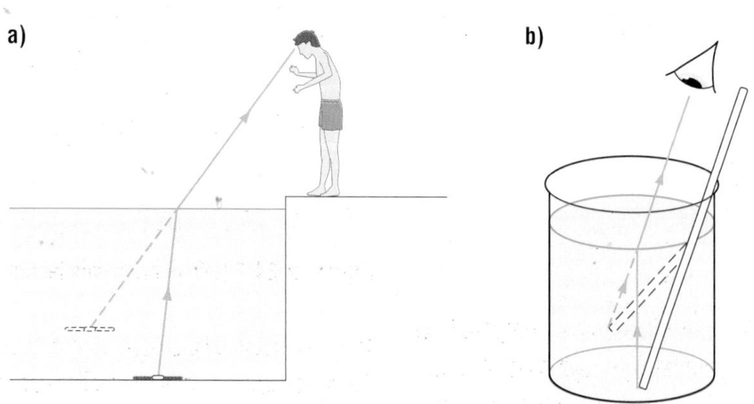

Figure 9.19 Refraction of light as it passes from water to air makes an object appear closer to the surface than it really is.

Lenses

A lens is made from a transparent material, such as glass or plastic, and has one or both of its opposite sides curved. Two examples of lenses are the biconvex lens and the biconcave lens. The two lenses are shown in cross-section in Figure 9.20a and b.

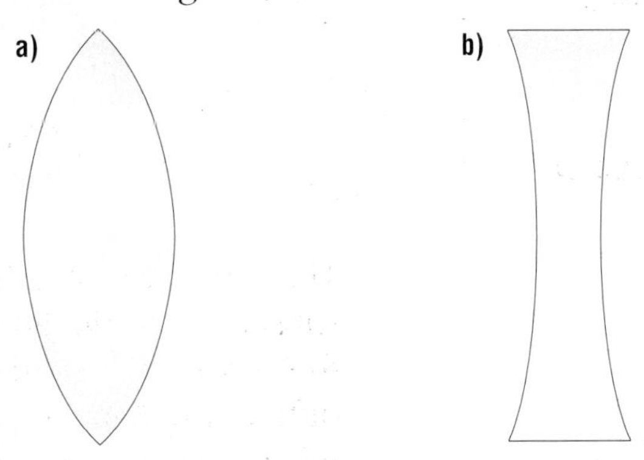

Figure 9.20 **a)** A biconvex lens and **b)** a biconcave lens.

The biconvex lens

When parallel light rays (for example, from a distant object) strike the surface of a biconvex lens almost all are refracted and brought to a point called a focus on the other side of the lens, as Figure 9.21 shows. A thick lens refracts the light more than a thin lens and its focus is nearer the lens than the focus of a thin lens.

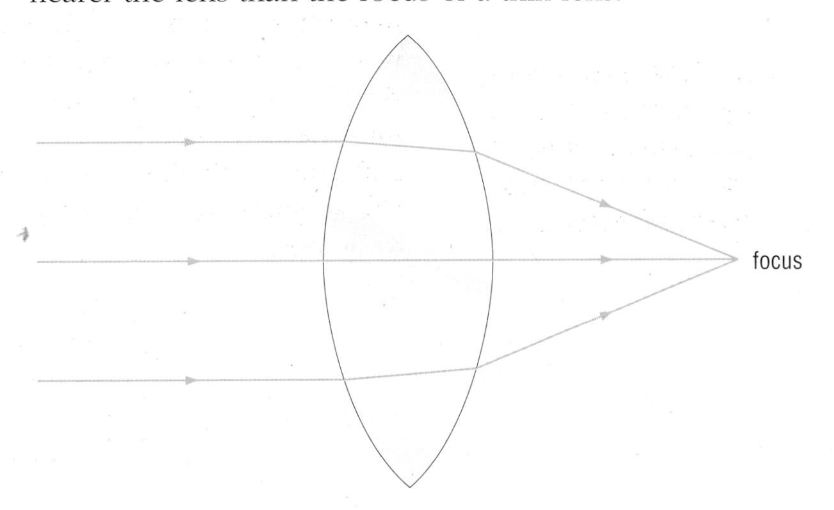

Figure 9.21 Refraction of parallel light rays by a biconvex lens.

8 Draw diagrams to compare how parallel light rays pass through a thick biconvex lens and a thin biconvex lens.

If you look through a biconvex lens at an object that is very close to it you will see a magnified image that is the right way up (Figure 9.22). The image is virtual – it cannot be focused onto a screen.

Figure 9.22 A biconvex lens can be used as a magnifying glass.

However, if you look at a distant object through a biconvex lens you will see an image that is upside down, the wrong way round and smaller than the actual object. This image can be focused onto a screen – it is a real image. A biconvex lens focuses light in the eye (see page 167) in this way, and is used to focus an image onto a film in a camera (see page 168).

The biconcave lens

When parallel rays of light strike the surface of a biconcave lens they pass through it but move apart as shown in Figure 9.23. If you look through a biconcave lens at an object you will see that the image is the right way up, the right way round but smaller than the object. It cannot be focused on a screen.

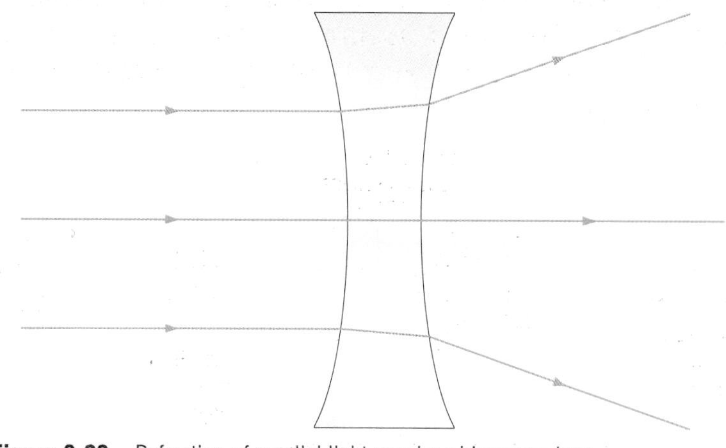

Figure 9.23 Refraction of parallel light rays by a biconcave lens.

9 How is the shape of a biconvex lens different from a biconcave lens?

10 Converging means 'bringing together' and diverging means 'moving apart'. Which type of lens is **a)** a converging lens and which is **b)** a diverging lens? Explain your answer.

11 Why are the middle rays in Figures 9.21 and 9.23 not refracted?

The eye and the camera

The eye

Most of the light rays which strike the curved transparent front of the eye are refracted by it as they pass through. They continue through a chamber filled with transparent liquid (see Figure A), then are refracted by the lens. The rays pass from the lens through a transparent jelly-like substance before striking the retina, a light-sensitive surface at the back of the eye. Here the rays form an image. Some of the energy in the light rays is converted into electrical energy in the nerve endings in the retina. The optic nerve conducts electrical messages or impulses to the brain where we become aware of what our eyes see.

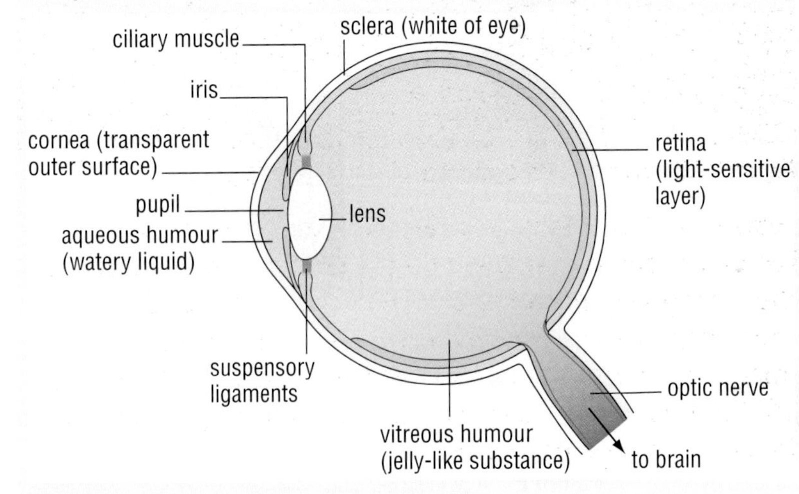

Figure A The structure of the eye.

Two common eye defects are short sight and long sight. They can be treated by the use of lenses (Figure B).

Short sight is caused by either the eye lens being too strong or the eyeball being too long from front to back. It is corrected by using a diverging lens which spreads out the light rays a little before they enter the eye.

Long sight is caused by either the eye lens being too weak or the eyeball being too short. The weakening of the lens can occur with age. It is corrected by using a converging lens which brings the light rays together a little before they enter the eye.

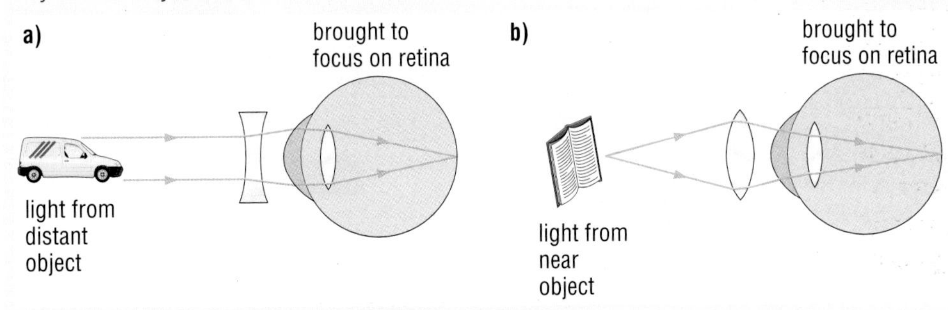

Figure B Correction of **a)** short sight and **b)** long sight.

1 What is the name of **a)** the curved, transparent front surface of the eye, **b)** the watery liquid, **c)** the jelly-like substance and **d)** the light-sensitive layer?

2 Why does the eye lens not have to do all the work of converging incoming light rays?

3 a) Figure C shows light passing into the eye of a short-sighted person. Draw a diagram showing the lens needed to correct the condition. Draw in the path taken by the rays 1 and 2 due to the addition of the lens.

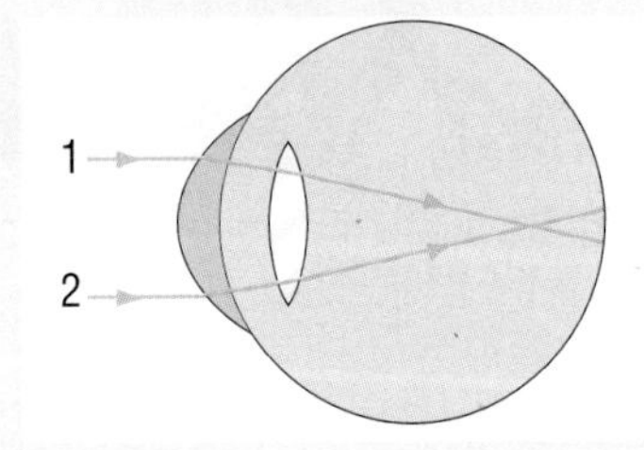

Figure C

b) How would the treatment of a long-sighted person be different to the treatment in part **a)** of this question? Explain your answer.

(continued)

The camera

The first type of camera was the camera obscura. It was a dark room with a small hole in one wall. Light shining through the hole made an image on the opposite wall. The image was of the view on the other side of the hole. The first camera obscura was invented in the 16th Century but by the late 17th Century small camera obscuras were made so that they could be carried and set up outside. They had a translucent wall on which the image fell and were used by artists. An artist could trace the image that was seen on the translucent wall. A small camera obscura, called the pinhole camera, is used today to demonstrate that light travels in straight lines.

4 How does the pinhole camera show that light travels in straight lines?

5 How is the pinhole camera **a)** similar to and **b)** different from the eye?

6 How is the simple lens camera **a)** similar to and **b)** different from the eye?

Figure D A type of portable camera obscura used by artists in the 19th Century.

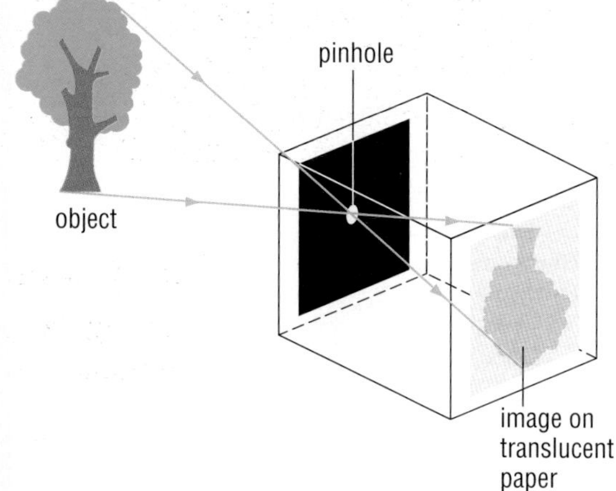

Figure E A pinhole camera.

Joseph Niépce (1765–1833), a French inventor, used a camera obscura to take a photograph. The photographic plate, made of pewter, needed eight hours' exposure to light to form a picture. In 1839 Louis Daguerre (1789–1851), also a French inventor, made a camera containing a plate of copper that needed less than a minute's exposure to form a picture.

A simple modern camera (Figure F) has a lens and a film which contains light-sensitive chemicals. There is a shutter behind the lens which remains closed unless the button is pressed to take a photograph. The shutter usually only opens for a fraction of a second but during that time enough light passes through the lens and is focused to form an image on the film. The light energy causes changes in the chemicals on the film. When the film is treated with more chemicals, in the process called developing, the permanently changed chemicals form a picture of the image. From the developed film, prints are made on light-sensitive paper. These are the photographs we keep as records of events.

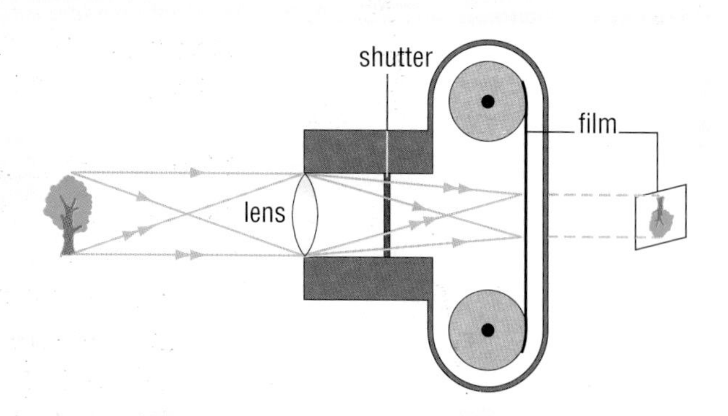

Figure F A simple lens camera.

(continued)

Some cameras today have electronic devices instead of film. The images they record can be transferred to video tape, sent directly to a computer, or be transmitted directly by television.

Figure G News cameras record images electronically.

The prism

A triangular prism is a glass or plastic block with a triangular cross-section.

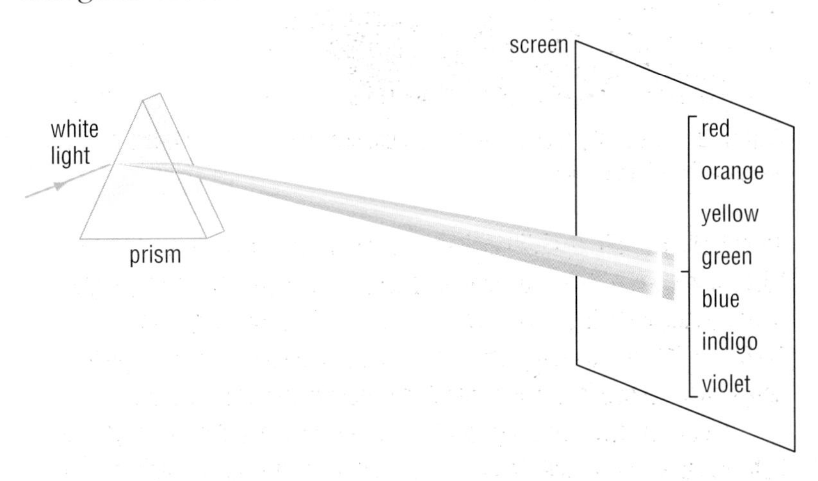

Figure 9.24 White light passing through a prism is split up into its constituent colours, forming a spectrum.

When a ray of sunlight is shone through a prism at certain angles of incidence and its path is stopped by a white screen, a range of colours, called a spectrum, can be seen on the screen.

Light behaves as if it travelled as waves (see page 65). The 'white' light from the Sun contains light of different wavelengths which give different coloured light. When they pass through a prism the light waves of different

12 Look at Figure 9.24 (page 169). Which colour of light has the shortest wavelength? Explain your answer.

wavelengths travel at slightly different speeds and are spread out, by a process called dispersion, to form the colours of the spectrum. The light waves with the shortest waves are slowed down or refracted the most.

The rainbow

If you stand with your back to the Sun when it is raining or you look into a spray of water from a fountain or a hose you may see a rainbow. It is produced by the refraction and reflection of the Sun's light through the water drops. Figure 9.25 shows the path of a light ray and how the colours in it spread out to form the order of colours – the spectrum – seen in a rainbow.

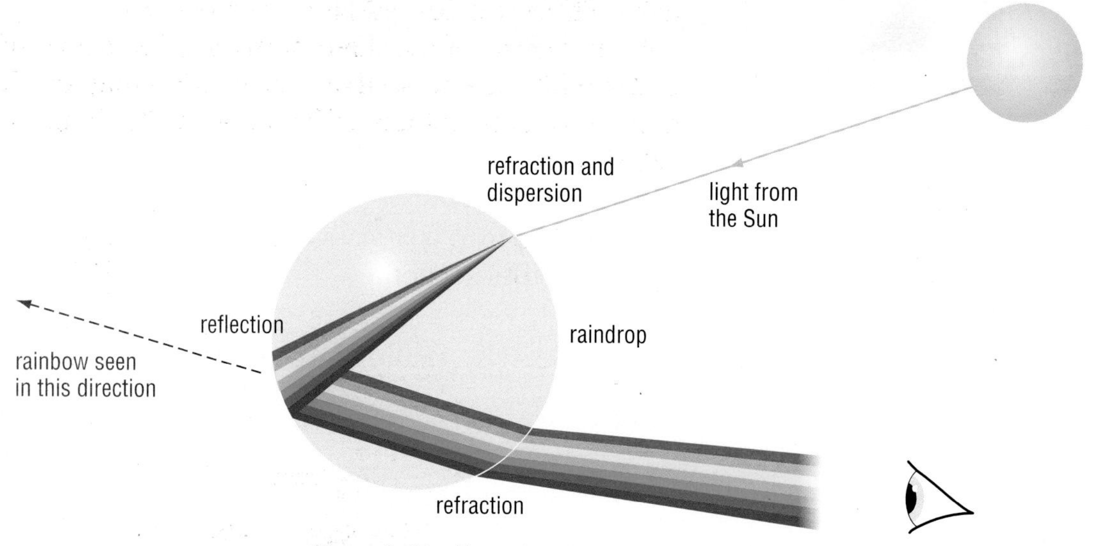

Figure 9.25 Formation of a rainbow.

Sometimes a second, weaker rainbow is seen above the first because two reflections occur in each droplet. In the second rainbow the order of colours is reversed.

Colour

Absorbing and reflecting colours

13 Name some everyday objects which **a)** reflect all the colours in sunlight and **b)** absorb all the colours in sunlight.

When a ray of sunlight strikes the surface of an object, all the different colours in it may be reflected or they may all be absorbed. If all the colours are reflected the object appears white; if all the colours are absorbed the object appears black.

Most objects, however, absorb some colours and reflect others. For example, healthy grass reflects mainly green and absorbs other colours.

14 The colours on a television or computer screen are made by three different colours of substances called phosphors. They glow to release their colour of light. What do you think the colours of the phosphors are? Explain your answer.

15 Which primary colours overlap to produce **a)** yellow, **b)** magenta, **c)** cyan and **d)** white light?

Filtering colours

Sheets of coloured plastic or glass can filter the colours in light. They absorb some of the colours and allow other colours to pass through, producing different coloured light. For example, a blue filter allows only blue light to pass through.

Combining colours

When different coloured lights are combined it is found that all the colours can be made from different combinations of just three colours. They are red, green and blue, and are called the primary colours of light. These are different from the primary colours needed to make different coloured paint (see below).

When beams of the three primary colours are shone onto a white screen so that they overlap they produce three secondary colours of light and white light, as Figure 9.26 shows.

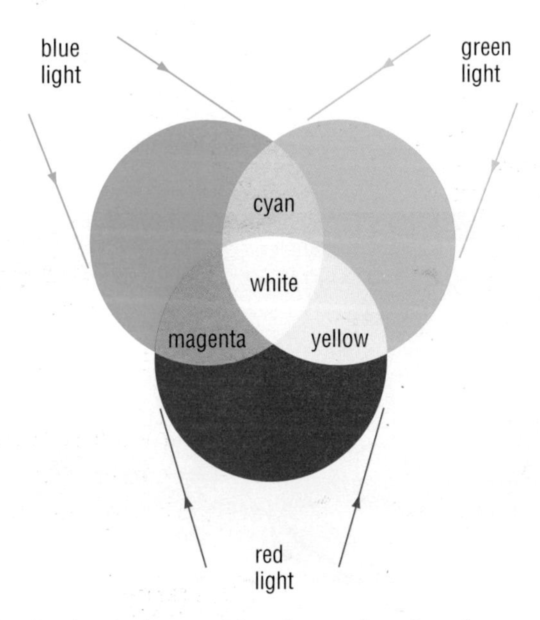

Figure 9.26 Overlapping beams of the primary colours form the secondary colours.

For discussion

Identify the light source you are using for seeing things around you. Choose an object in the room. Describe the changes that take place in the light from its leaving the source until it reaches your eyes from the object. Is it refracted through glass? Is it partially reflected from any surface? Which colours have been absorbed by the object?

Colours and paint

Three different colours of paint, ink or dye can be used to make almost all the other colours. These three colours are yellow, magenta and cyan. They are mixed together in different proportions to produce a wide range of colours, like those in the photographs in this book. Tiny dots of the three colours form the printed picture.

Lasers

Charles Townes (b.1915) worked with microwaves (see Figure 4.10, page 66) which were used in radar to detect the position of aeroplanes. He devised a way of building up a strong beam of microwaves by a process called microwave amplification by stimulated emission of radiation.

Theodore Maiman (b.1922) studied Townes' work and developed it to produce a strong beam of light. This beam was different from natural light beams. Unlike a natural light beam where the light waves are not in step, the waves in the beam he produced were all in step (see Figure A). It is this arrangement of the light waves that gives the laser beam its power.

1 Why do you think Townes' microwave beam generator was called a MASER?
2 What do you think LASER stands for?
3 How is light in a laser beam different from normal light?

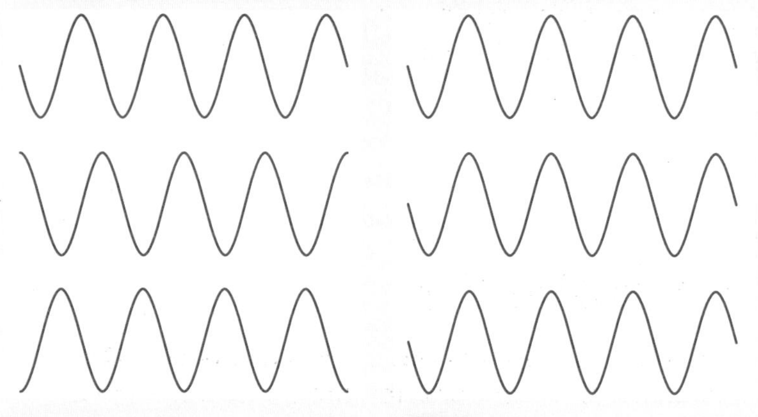

Light waves out of step Light waves in step
Figure A

Figure B The internal structure of a laser beam generator.

The material in which the laser beam is generated has a mirror at one end and a partly silvered mirror at the other. The atoms in the material receive energy by a flash of light or a current of electricity. Some atoms then release light waves which travel up and down the material, being reflected at the ends by the mirrors. As the light waves move through the material they stimulate more atoms to release light waves, which are in step with the incident light waves. Such a large number of light waves build up that they pass through the partially silvered mirror end as a laser beam.

(continued)

Lasers may be used to make holes in metals or to weld them together. They are even used to weld a detached retina back into place in the eye. They are also used to scan bar-codes in shops, to produce holograms and dramatic light shows.

Safety note

Lasers are classified according to the safety hazard they present. Class 1 lasers are enclosed, like the laser in some kinds of computer printer. They are safe to use if the printer is used properly. Class 2 lasers produce a bright light that makes you blink and are safe to use in schools provided that (a) you do not look along the line of light made by the laser, (b) a very bright beam is not reflected into your eye and (c) you do not try to stop yourself from blinking. There are two more classes of laser (Classes 3 and 4) which are too hazardous to use in schools.

4 Look at Figure A on page 167 and make a drawing of the path a laser beam would take through the eye to weld the retina back into place.

5 From the list of the uses of lasers, do you think that they can be made to produce beams of different strengths? Explain your answer.

♦ SUMMARY ♦

- Light is a form of energy that is released from luminous objects (*see page 151*).
- Materials can be classified as opaque, translucent or transparent (*see page 154*).
- A shadow forms when light rays are stopped by an opaque object (*see page 154*).
- We see non-luminous objects by the light they reflect (*see page 158*).
- Light rays are reflected from a smooth surface at the same angle at which they strike it (*see page 158*).
- A real image can be formed on a screen but a virtual image cannot (*see page 160*).
- When light rays strike the surface of a transparent material at an angle to the perpendicular they are refracted (*see page 163*).
- Biconvex and biconcave lenses refract light in different ways (*see pages 165–166*).
- A prism can split up sunlight into different colours of light (*see page 169*).
- The colour of an object we see depends on the colours of light that it absorbs and reflects (*see page 170*).

End of chapter question

1 Describe what happens to light in a beam from the time it reaches the Earth from the Sun and shines upon a leaf, to when it enters your eye.

10 *Sound*

You have probably performed some experiments on sound without knowing it. At some time most people have made a ruler vibrate by holding one end over the edge of a desk and 'twanging' it. The end of the ruler moves up and down rapidly and a low whirring sound is heard which becomes higher as you pull in the ruler from the edge of the desk.

Figure 10.1 Making a ruler vibrate.

From vibration to sound wave

An object can make a sound wave when it vibrates. In practical work on sound you might use an elastic band, a guitar string or a tuning fork because they all vibrate easily. A vibration is a movement about a fixed point. This movement may be described as a to-and-fro movement or a backwards and forwards movement (Figure 10.2).

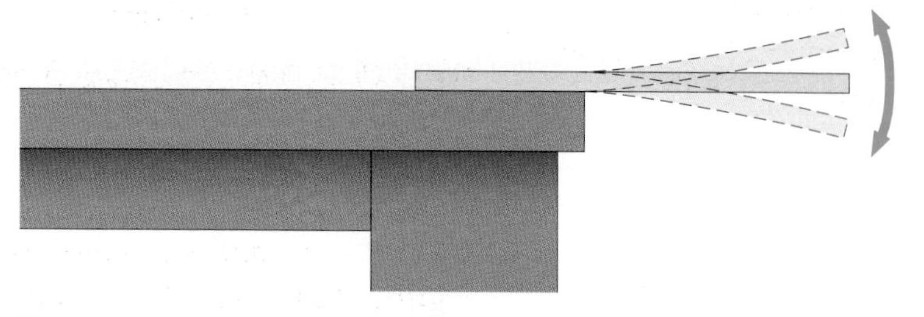

Figure 10.2 Vibration is a to-and-fro movement.

Sound waves can travel in a gas, a liquid or a solid because they all contain particles (see *Chemistry Now! 11–14* page 23). When an object vibrates it makes the particles next to it in the gas, liquid or solid vibrate too. For example, when an object vibrates in air it pushes on the air particles around it.

As the vibrating object moves towards the air particles it squashes them together. The particles themselves are not compressed but the pressure in the air at that place rises because the particles are closer together (Figure 10.3a).

As the object moves away from the air particles next to it, it gives them more space and they spread out and the pressure at that place falls (Figure 10.3b).

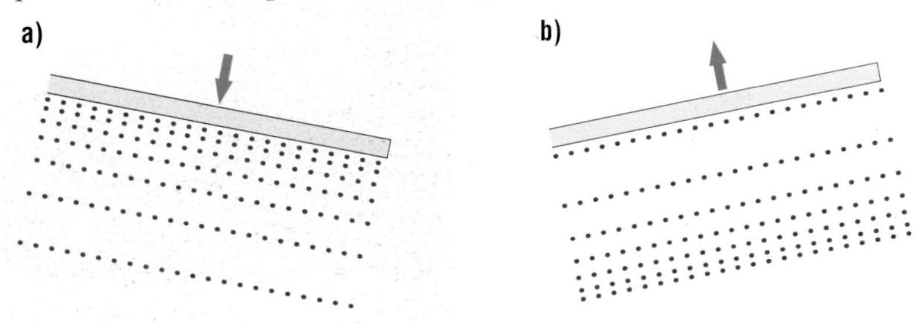

Figure 10.3 A vibrating object causes pressure variations in the air around it.

As the object vibrates the air particles close by also move backwards and forwards and they in turn cause other air particles further away to squash together and then spread out. This makes alternate regions of high and low pressure which travel through the air away from the vibrating object (Figure 10.4).

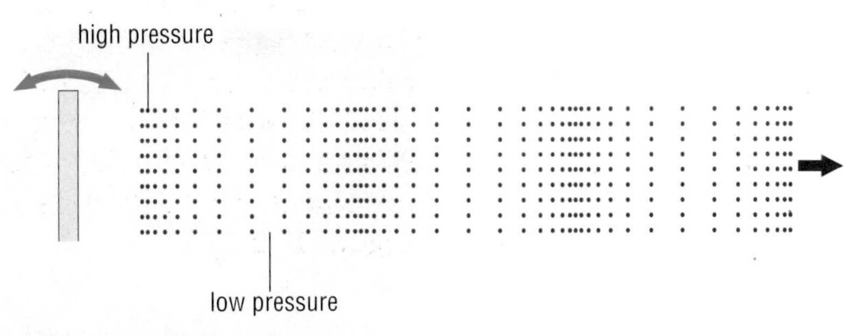

Figure 10.4 Regions of high and low pressure move away from the vibrating object.

1 When a table tennis ball on a thread is made to touch a vibrating prong of a tuning fork the ball swings backwards and forwards. How can this demonstration be used to explain how sound waves are made?

If these changes in pressure were plotted on a graph they would make a waveform similar to that shown in Figure 10.8 (page 177). The waves of sound move out from the vibrating object in all directions.

Sound waves are generated and travel in liquids and solids in the same way as they do in gases. The particles in liquids and solids are held close together by forces of attraction (see *Chemistry Now! 11–14* page 23). In a liquid however the particles are further apart than in a solid and can move over one another. Sound travels very well through a liquid. It moves faster and further than it does in a gas.

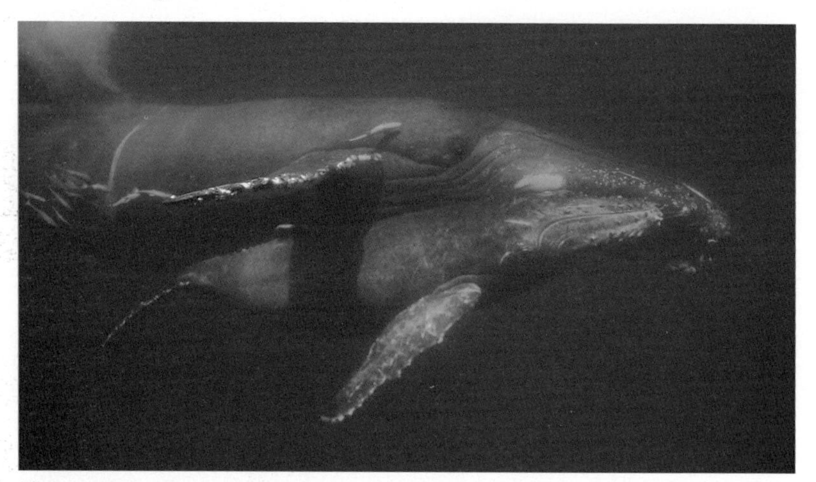

Figure 10.5 These whales communicate by sound waves.

The humpback whale emits a series of sounds called songs which travel thousands of kilometres through the ocean. It uses its songs to communicate with other whales.

When sound travels through a solid it moves even faster than through a liquid because of the close interactions of the particles. However, the sound does not travel so far.

Figure 10.6 This snake is listening for vibrations in the ground.

A snake detects vibrations in the ground with its lower jaw bone. The bone transmits the vibrations to the snake's ears and helps the snake listen for the footsteps of its prey.

Sound waves cannot pass through a vacuum because it does not contain any particles. Figure 10.7 shows an experiment that demonstrates this. As air is drawn out of the bell jar with a pump, the sound of the bell becomes quieter. When a vacuum is established in the bell jar the bell cannot be heard although the hammer can be seen striking it.

2 Why is it that a bell in a sealed bell jar **a)** can be heard when the jar is full of air but **b)** cannot be heard when a vacuum is created in the jar?

Figure 10.7 Sound cannot be heard through a vacuum.

Describing the wave

Figure 10.8 shows the different positions particles can occupy when a sound wave is produced. This type of graph is called a displacement/distance graph.

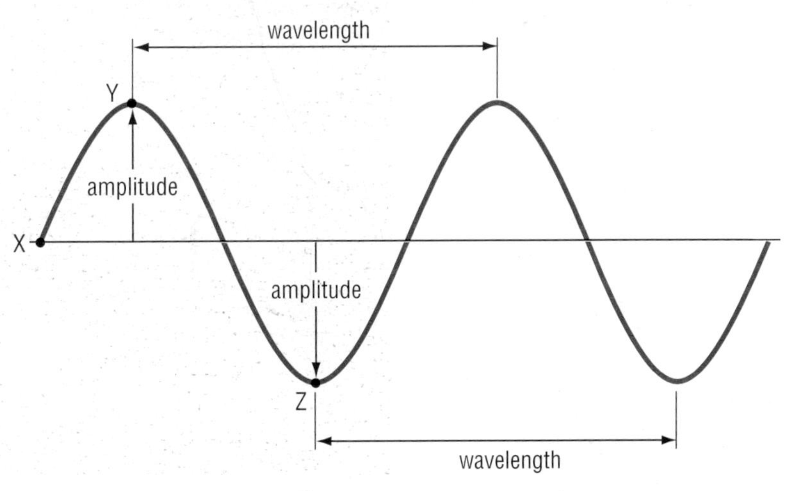

Figure 10.8 Displacement/distance waveform for a sound wave.

A particle at position X (Figure 10.8) is moving through the 'rest' position, a particle at Y has moved the maximum distance in one direction and one at Z has moved the maximum distance in the other direction.

Two characteristics of the wave that can be seen in Figure 10.8 are the amplitude and wavelength. The amplitude is the height of the crest or the depth of the trough and shows the maximum displacement of the particles from their rest position. The wavelength is the distance from the top of one crest to the top of the next crest, or from the bottom of one trough to the bottom of the next trough.

3 Can you think of other ways of describing the wavelength of a wave?

Detecting sound waves

The ear is the organ of the body that detects sound waves. It is divided into three parts – the outer ear, middle ear and inner ear (Figure 10.9).

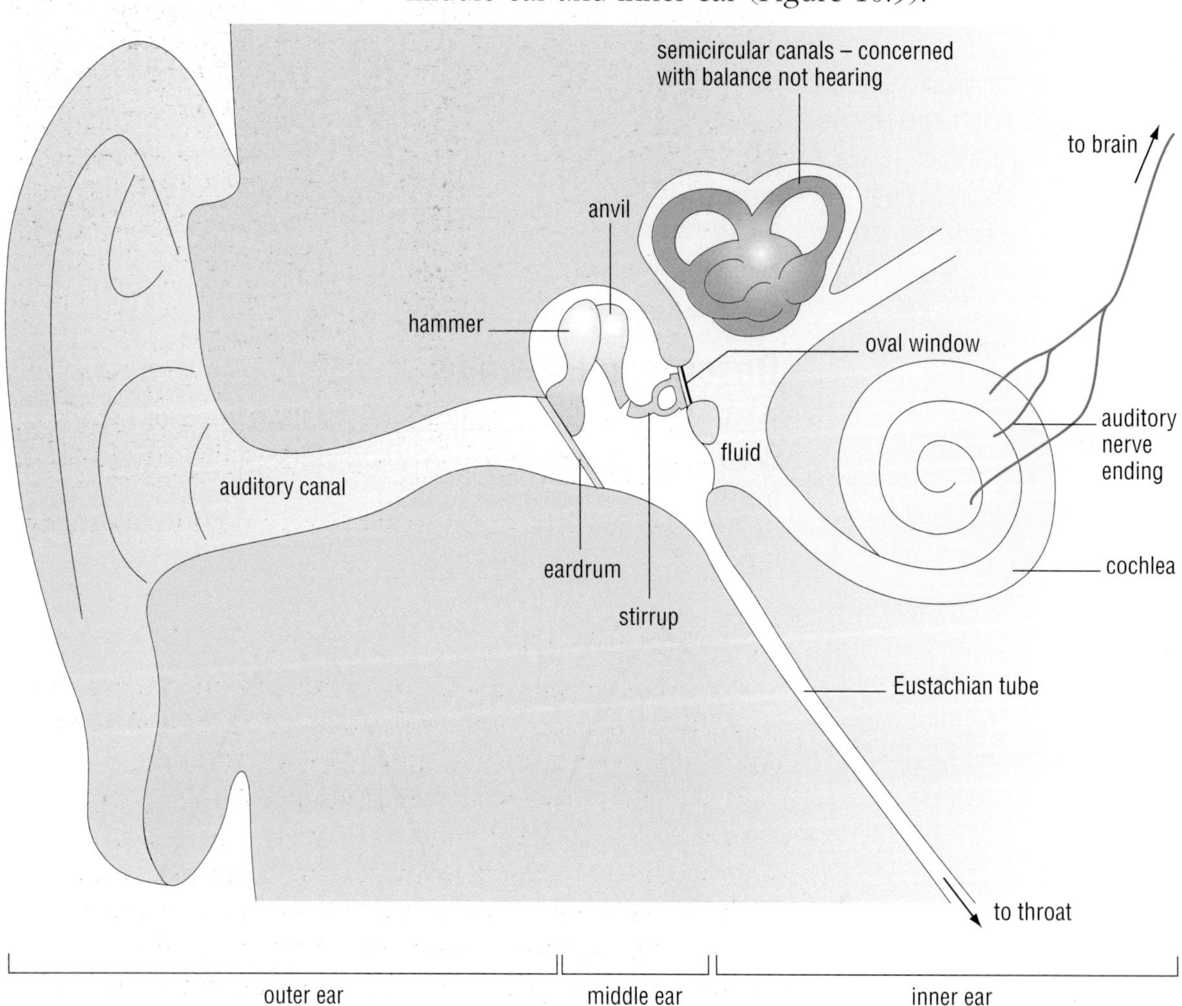

Figure 10.9 Structure of the ear.

4 Why do people put a hand to their ear when they are listening to someone who is whispering?

The outer ear

When sound waves reach the outer ear some pass directly down the middle of the tube called the auditory canal. Some waves which strike the outer part of the ear are reflected into the auditory canal. At the end of the auditory canal is a thin membrane which stretches across it. This is called the eardrum. When sound waves reach the eardrum they push and pull on it and make it vibrate.

Some predatory animals, such as cats, can turn their outer ears forwards to detect sounds from prey in front of them. Some prey animals, such as rabbits, can turn their outer ears in many directions about their head to listen for approaching predators.

Figure 10.10 This rabbit is able to turn its outer ears to capture sound waves from all directions.

The middle ear

In the cavity of the middle ear are three bones. They are called the hammer, anvil and stirrup, after their shapes. The ear bones form a system of levers. When the eardrum vibrates its movements are amplified by the lever system. The oval window on which the stirrup bone vibrates has a much smaller area than that of the eardrum. This difference in area between the eardrum and the oval window causes the vibrations of the eardrum to be amplified as they enter the inner ear and set up vibrations in the fluid there.

5 Why do people go partially deaf when they have a very heavy cold and the Eustachian tubes become blocked?

The middle ear also has a tube, the Eustachian tube, which connects to the throat. When we swallow the tube opens and the air in the middle ear is connected to air outside the body. This brief connection allows the air pressure in the ear to adjust to the air pressure outside the body (see page 52). This balancing of the air pressure allows the eardrum to vibrate as freely as possible.

The inner ear

The inner ear is filled with a fluid. The vibrations of the stirrup set up waves in the fluid. There is a membrane with delicate fibres in the cochlea. Each fibre only vibrates in response to a sound wave with a particular pitch (see page 182). When a fibre vibrates it stimulates a nerve ending and a nerve impulse or message is sent to the brain where we become aware of the sound.

The loudness of sounds

The loudness of a sound is related to the movement of the vibrating object. If an object only moves a short distance to and fro from its rest position, it will produce a sound wave with only a small amplitude and the sound that is heard will be a quiet one.

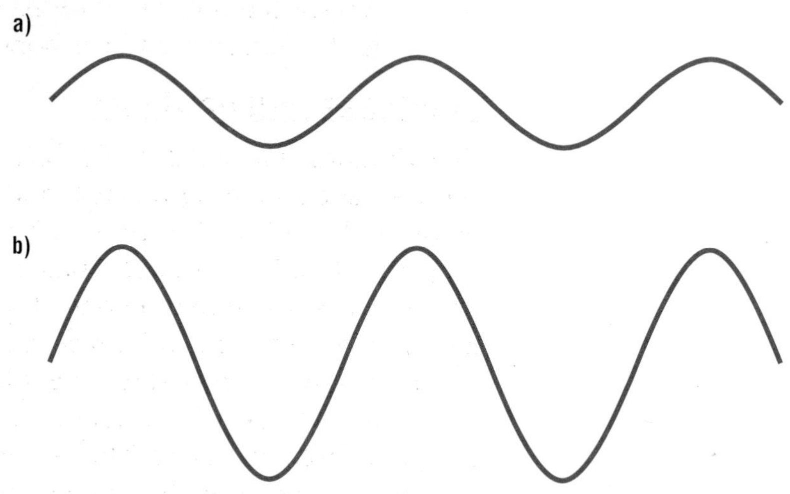

Figure 10.11 Displacement/distance waveform of **a)** a quiet sound and **b)** a loud sound.

If an object moves a large distance to and fro from its rest position, it will produce sound waves with a large amplitude and the sound that is heard will be a loud one. The loudness of sounds is measured in decibels (see Table 10.1).

Table 10.1 Loudness values of sounds.

Sound	Loudness/decibels
The sound hurts	140
A jet aircraft taking off	130
A road drill	110
A jet plane overhead	100
A noisy factory floor	90
A vacuum cleaner	80
A busy street	70
A busy department store	60
Normal speech	55
Voices in a town at night	40
A whisper	20
Rustling leaves	10
Limit of normal hearing	0

Loudness and energy

Sound energy passes through the air as the particles move to and fro. When a wave with a small amplitude is generated, a small amount of energy passes through the air. When a wave with a large amplitude is generated a large amount of energy passes. The energy of a sound wave is converted into other forms such as movement energy in the eardrum and ear bones.

Loudness and deafness

The vibrating air particles of a very loud sound can produce such a strong pushing and pulling force on the eardrum that a hole is torn in it. The eardrum is said to be perforated. It no longer vibrates efficiently and the person loses his or her hearing. The eardrum can heal and normal hearing can be restored.

If a person is exposed to a very loud sound or a particular note for a long period of time he or she will no longer be able to hear it. This is due to permanent damage to a nerve ending in the cochlea. People who perform in pop groups are at risk to this kind of deafness, called nerve deafness. In time they may be unable to hear a range of notes which they frequently used in their music. People who work in noisy surroundings, such as airport workers or metal workers in a factory, wear ear protection in the form of ear muffs which cover the ears and reduce the amount of sound energy entering the ears.

Figure 10.12 Wearing ear protection in a boiler room prevents nerve damage.

6 What kind of ear damage might be caused by a loud explosion? Explain your answer.

For discussion

To prevent ear damage, how should you use earphones on a CD or cassette player? Where should you dance at a disco, and where should you sit or stand at a pop concert?

How far do you follow the advice you have given in answer to the above?

A common form of partial deafness, which is not related to the loudness of a sound, is the development of ear wax in the outer ear. This stops sound waves reaching the eardrum. The wax can be removed with warm water under the medical supervision of a nurse.

Some people have growths of tissues in their middle ears which stop the ear bones moving freely. They may be prescribed with a hearing aid. This contains a microphone and amplifier and compensates for some of the loss of amplification that was provided by the ear bones.

The pitch of a sound

You probably have an idea about the pitch of a sound even if you don't know the word. You might describe a sound as a high or a low sound, which really means a high-pitched or a low-pitched sound. For example, when you say 'bing' you are making a higher-pitched sound than when you say 'bong'.

The pitch of the sound an object makes depends on the number of sound waves it produces in a second as it vibrates. This number of waves per second is called the frequency. The frequency of a sound is measured in hertz. The higher the frequency of the wave, the higher the pitch of the sound.

The graphs in Figure 10.13 show the positions that particles occupy at different times as the wave passes. These graphs are called displacement/time graphs.

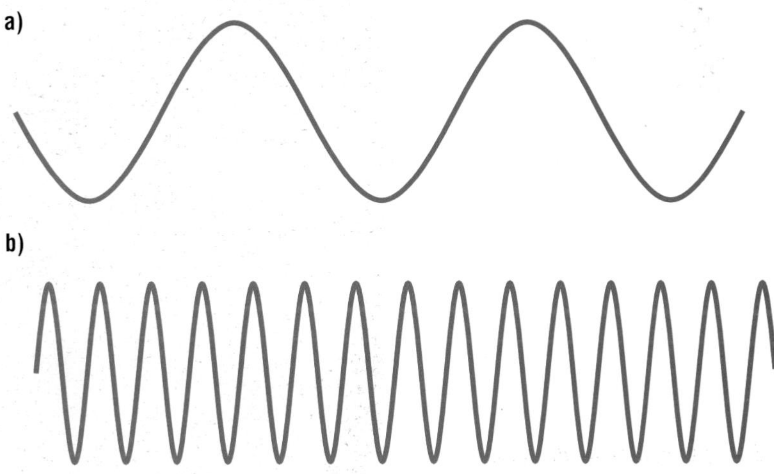

Figure 10.13 Displacement/time waveform of **a)** a low frequency sound and **b)** a high frequency sound.

7 Here are three frequencies of sound waves:

1800 Hz, 50 Hz, 10 000 Hz

a) Which has the highest pitch and which has the lowest pitch?
b) What does Hz stand for?

The higher frequency waves have a shorter wavelength than the lower frequency waves. Sound waves share this property with light waves (see pages 65–66).

The ear of a young person is sensitive to frequencies in the range 20 to 20 000 hertz, but the ability to detect the higher frequencies decreases with age. Some people, such as pop musicians, may have a restricted range of hearing due to nerve damage (see page 181). They may not be able to hear some low-pitched or high-pitched sounds.

Sound energy and electrical energy

If you speak into a microphone some of the energy in the sound waves is converted into electrical energy which drives a current around a circuit.

In the moving-coil microphone the sound waves push and pull on a diaphragm made of thin metal or plastic and make it vibrate. The diaphragm is connected to a coil of wire which forms part of an electrical circuit. The coil is positioned between the circular poles of a magnet (Figure 10.14). As the diaphragm vibrates the coil moves in and out across the magnetic field lines and a current of electricity is generated in the wire. The electric current flows round the circuit. Other electrical components in the circuit may transfer some of the electrical energy to an amplifier and loudspeaker or to the recording components in a tape cassette player.

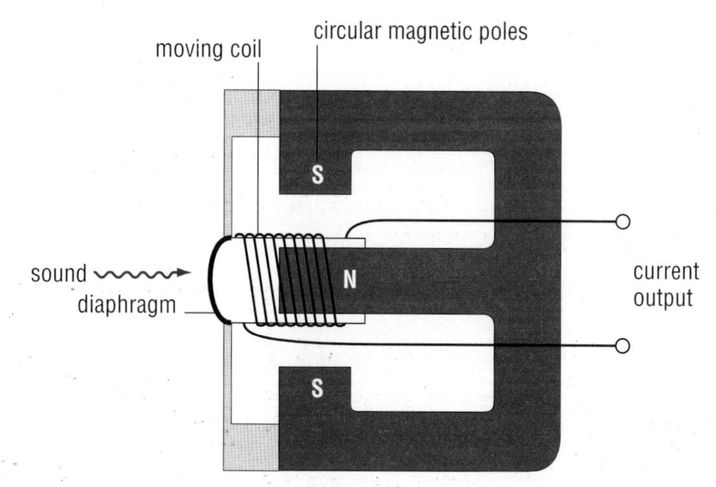

Figure 10.14 Moving-coil microphone.

In a loudspeaker the electrical energy of a current is converted to sound energy. The current supplied to a moving-coil loudspeaker passes through a coil of wire connected to a cone of plastic or paper (Figure 10.15). As the current passes through the coil it generates a magnetic field. As in the moving-coil microphone, the coil is surrounded by the poles of a magnet. The two magnetic fields interact and the coil is pushed and pulled. The coil moves in and out and causes the cone to vibrate. The vibrating cone makes sound waves that pass out into the air in front of the loudspeaker.

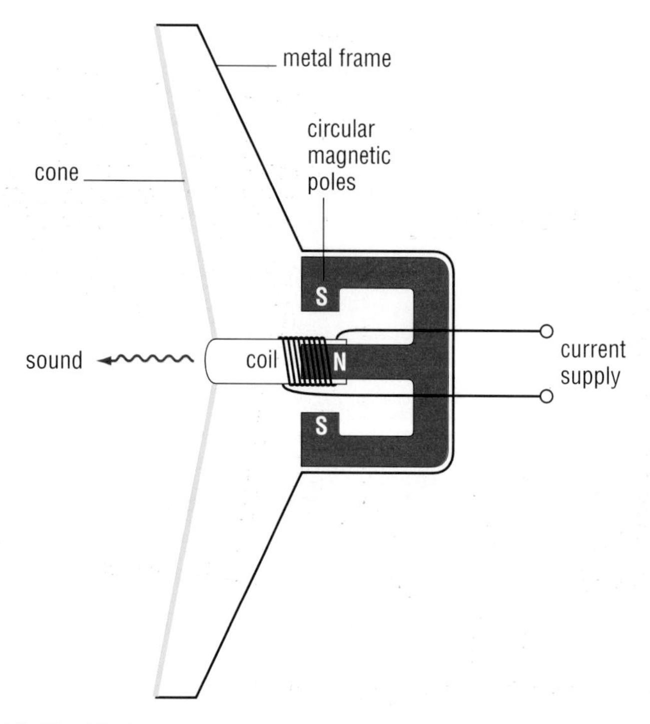

Figure 10.15 Moving-coil loudspeaker.

Experiments on sound

In the past many scientists have performed experiments to find the speed of sound. Isaac Newton (1642–1727) investigated the speed of sound by measuring the time between a sound being made and its echo from a wall being heard. Other scientists measured the time taken between seeing a distant cannon fire and hearing its sound.

Figure A Measuring the speed of sound in air.

The speed of sound in water was investigated using the apparatus shown in Figure B. The experiment was performed at night. When the lever was pulled down both the arm carrying the bell hammer and the device carrying the match moved.

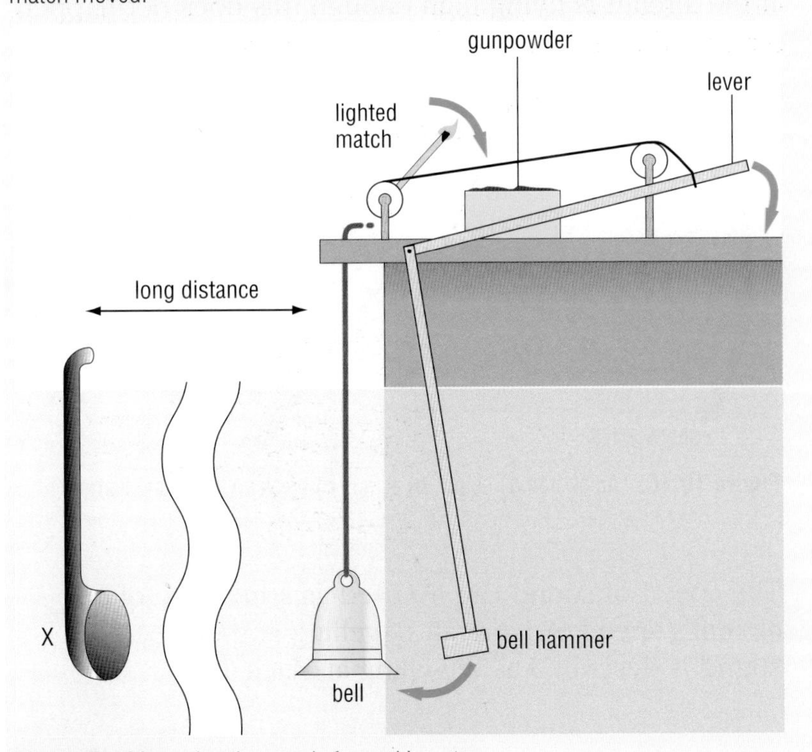

Figure B Measuring the speed of sound in water.

1. What is an echo?
2. What measurement besides time needs to be taken in all the experiments to determine the speed of sound?
3. What is the purpose of **a)** the gunpowder and **b)** the apparatus marked X in Figure B?
4. Why do you think the experiment to find the speed of sound in water was done at night?

8 How is the speed of sound in air related to the air temperature?

For discussion

Why do you think sound travels at different speeds in solids, liquids and gases?

Why do you think there is the relationship you have described in answering question 8?

9 What is the approximate speed of an aircraft travelling at twice the speed of sound in air at −80 °C?

10 Why must aircraft travelling at supersonic speed fly very high?

The speed of sound

Sound travels at 330 m/s in air at 0 °C, at 343 m/s in air at 20 °C and at 277 m/s in air at −80 °C.

It travels through water at 20 °C at 1500 m/s, through glass at 5000 m/s and through steel at 6000 m/s.

Breaking the sound barrier

When an aircraft flies at a speed below that of sound you can hear it approach as the sound from its engines travels in front of the aircraft (Figure 10.16a). When the aircraft reaches the speed of sound, the sound waves form a pressure wave called a shock wave just in front of the aircraft (Figure 10.16b). If the aircraft flies even faster (at what we call supersonic speeds) it pushes through the shock wave (Figure 10.16c) and a smaller shock wave develops at the tail. The pressure in the shock waves is greatest nearest the aircraft and becomes weaker further away. If the aircraft is flying low the shock waves are heard as a loud bang called a sonic boom. The pressure changes produced by the shock waves may be strong enough to shake the walls of buildings on the ground and break the glass in windows. If the aircraft is flying high enough this does not happen.

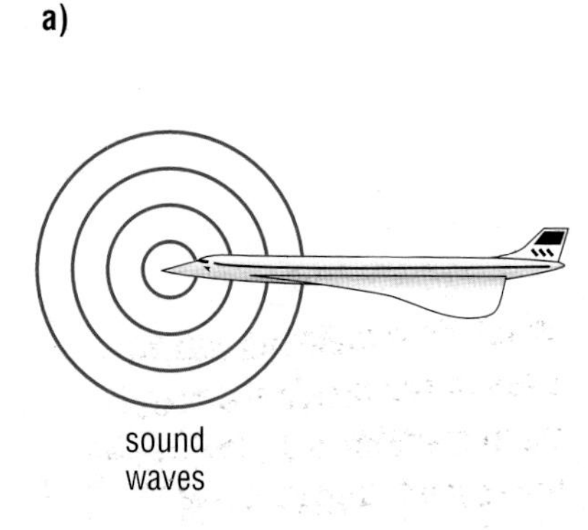

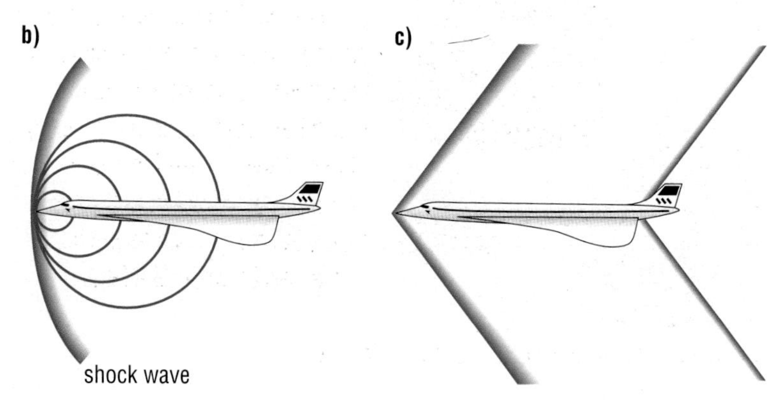

Figure 10.16 An aircraft **a)** below, **b)** at, and **c)** breaking the sound barrier.

11 The temperature of the air falls with an increase in height. How does this affect **a)** the speed of sound and **b)** the value of the Mach number?

The speed of sound can be used as a measure of an aircraft's speed. An aircraft travelling at the speed of sound is described as travelling at Mach 1.

Ultrasound

Ultrasonic waves are sound waves with a frequency above 20 000 Hz. They are beyond the range of human hearing. The bat and the dolphin, however, can both produce and detect them.

Bats use ultrasonic waves to navigate and to detect insects in flight. The bat sends out the waves and listens for waves that are reflected by the insect's body. When a bat detects an insect it can send and receive more waves as it moves towards the insect. These waves and their reflections help the bat to make an accurate attack on the insect.

Dolphins use ultrasound to find fish and to detect sharks that may attack them. They also use ultrasonic waves to communicate with each other.

Figure A This dolphin has discovered a shoal of fish.

1 Why is the method of detecting objects with ultrasound called echo location?

2 How is the way a dolphin uses ultrasound **a)** similar to and **b)** different from the way a bat uses it?

Ultrasonic waves can be made by passing a current of electricity through certain kinds of crystals. The current makes the crystal vibrate very rapidly and produce ultrasonic waves. A device that sends out ultrasonic waves is called a transmitter. The waves are detected by a receiver which contains a crystal. When the waves reach the crystal in the receiver they cause it to vibrate rapidly and produce a current of electricity.

Ultrasonic techniques are used in a wide range of investigative procedures. They are used in the aircraft industry to test for signs of weakness inside metals and on board trawlers to search for shoals of fish. They are used in medicine to examine the condition of tissues inside the body, such as the heart, or the development of a fetus.

Figure B An ultrasound scan of a fetus in a womb.

The principle of the use of ultrasound in these investigative procedures is the same. The waves are directed to the region under investigation from a transmitter. When the waves reach this region they may be reflected from objects there. The reflected waves travel back in the same way that sound waves cause an echo. When the reflected waves reach the receiver the electrical current that is produced is used to make images on a television screen.

For discussion

What other methods can be used to see inside the body? Compare them with the use of ultrasound. What are the advantages and disadvantages of the different methods?

What other ways could be used to try to find shoals of fish? Why is ultrasound more useful?

♦ SUMMARY ♦

- Sounds are made by vibrating objects (*see page 174*).
- Sound travels through materials as waves of vibrating particles (*see page 175*).
- There are three parts to the ear. Each part plays an important role in hearing (*see page 178*).
- The loudness of a sound is related to the amplitude of its waves (*see page 180*).
- The pitch of a sound is related to the frequency of its waves (*see page 182*).
- Sound energy can be converted into electrical energy and electrical energy can be converted into sound energy (*see page 183*).
- Sound travels at different speeds in different materials (*see page 186*).

End of chapter question

1 Describe how the vibration of a ruler is detected in the inner part of your ear.

11 *The Earth and beyond*

Formation of the universe

From studying the universe astronomers believe that it formed about 15000 million years ago. The fact that all galaxies of stars are moving away from one another, and the distribution of 'background' electromagnetic radiation in space, suggest that the universe formed from a tiny point by a huge explosion called the Big Bang.

Figure 11.1 Galaxies of stars as revealed by the Hubble Space Telescope.

In this explosion energy, matter and forces, such as gravity, came into being. As the energy and matter spread out and cooled, the first atoms formed. They were hydrogen and helium atoms. The force of gravity drew them together into huge 'clouds'. In these clouds of gas the force of gravity brought some of the atoms closer together still until they formed huge spheres of hot gas. Inside each sphere the force of gravity drew the atoms closer still until the temperature and pressure became so great that a process called nuclear fusion took place. In this process some of the hydrogen atoms were converted into helium atoms and large amounts of energy were released. The energy escaped from the surface of the gas spheres as light and heat and the spheres became what we now call stars. Groups of stars are known as galaxies.

1 Some scientists believe that the universe may collapse and end in a Big Crunch.

a) How will the galaxies move during the collapse?

b) How could a new universe be created from a Big Crunch?

When a star has used up all its supply of hydrogen to make helium it makes other chemical elements for a while. It may then swell up and form a red giant star, after which it releases its outer layers as a 'nebula' of gas and shrinks to form a white dwarf star. This eventually becomes non-luminous and is called a black dwarf star.

Very large stars do not follow this sequence of events but explode and form a supernova which shoots out stellar material over a wide region of space.

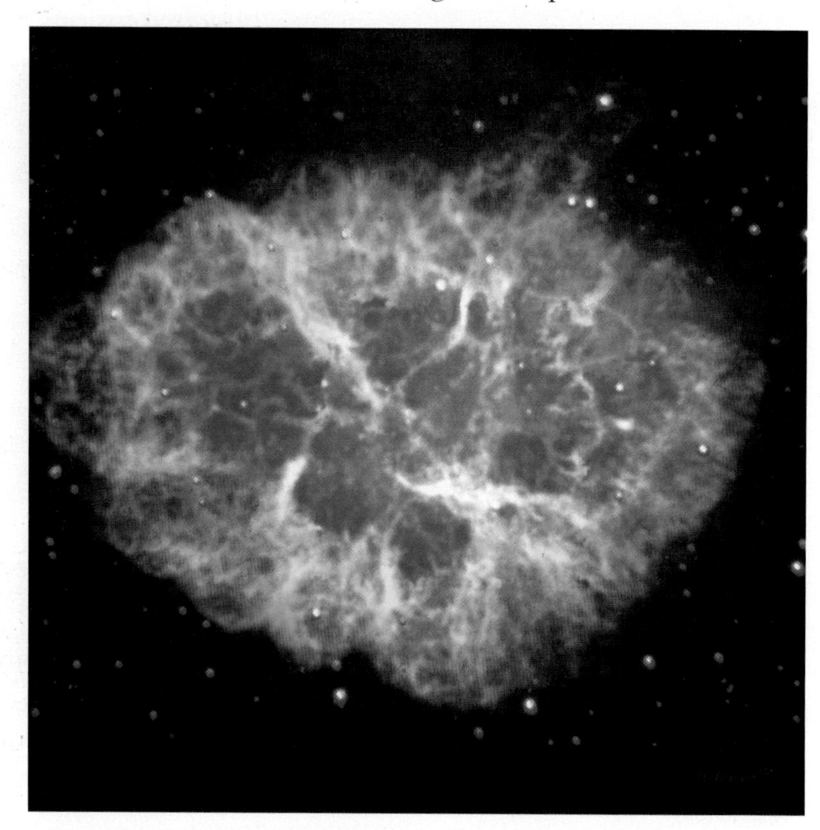

Figure 11.2 The remains of a supernova which exploded nearly 8000 years ago.

Our Solar System

It is thought that about 5000 million years ago the Solar System began to form from a huge cloud of gas and stellar material. An exploding star nearby could have caused the cloud to rotate. As the cloud turned it formed a disc. Hydrogen and helium collected at the centre and formed a star, our Sun. The Sun is a middle-sized star called a yellow dwarf star, powered by the fusion of hydrogen into helium. The material moving round the Sun eventually formed the planets and other bodies of our Solar System.

2 How long after the formation of the universe did the Solar System form?

3 Where did the materials come from to form the Solar System?

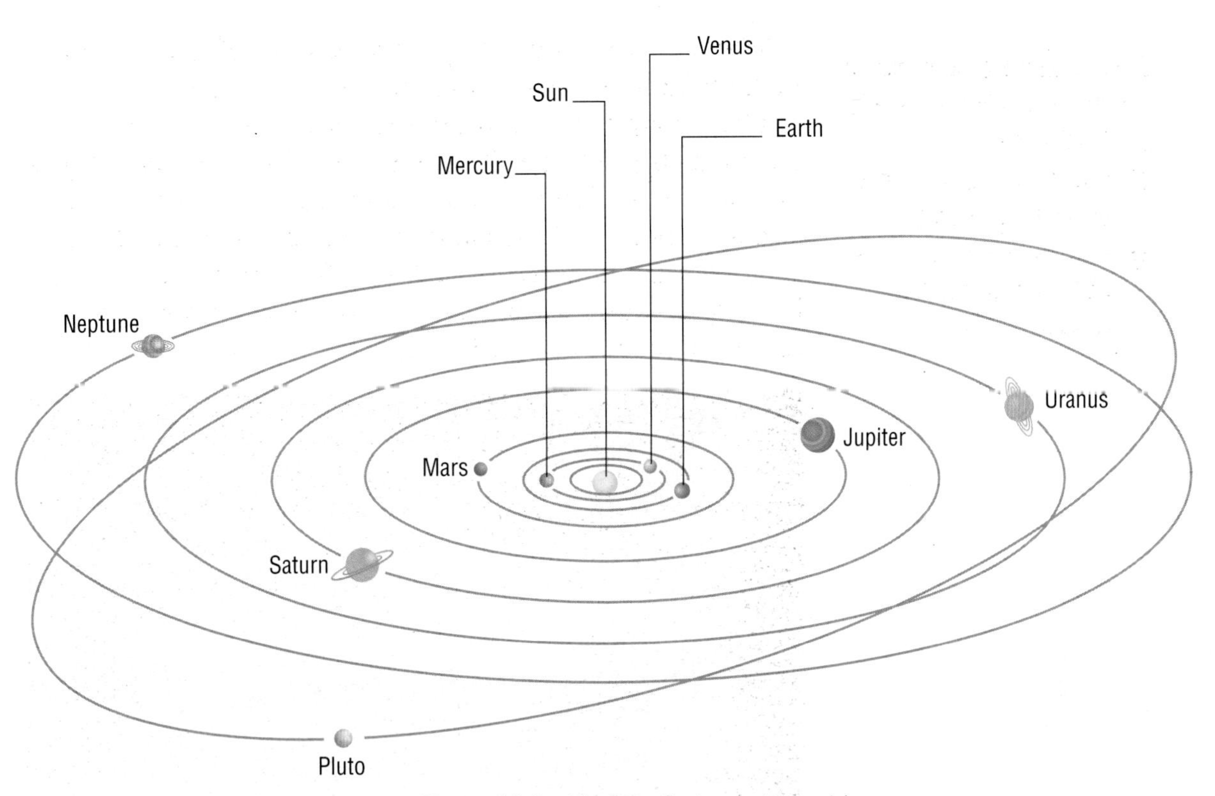

Figure 11.3 The Solar System (not to scale).

> *For discussion*
>
> **Living things use the materials in the Earth and the atmosphere to make their bodies. Can they be described as being made from star dust? Explain your answer.**

The five planets nearest to the Earth can be clearly seen with the naked eye and were known to the people of the ancient civilisations. In 1781 Uranus was discovered by Sir William Herschel (1738–1822), an English astronomer. In 1846 Johann Galle (1812–1910), a German astronomer, discovered Neptune and in 1930 Clyde Tombaugh (1906–1997), an American astronomer, discovered Pluto. Table 11.1 shows some data about the nine planets.

Table 11.1 Planet data.

Planet	Diameter/ km	Distance from Sun/ million km (approx.)	Rotation time days	hr	min	Orbit time/ days
Mercury	4878	58	58	15	30	88
Venus	12100	108	243	0	0	224
Earth	12756	150		23	56	365
Mars	6793	228		24	37	686
Jupiter	142880	778		9	50	4332
Saturn	120000	1427		10	14	10759
Uranus	50800	2871		10	49	30707
Neptune	48600	4497		15	48	60119
Pluto	5500	5914	6	9	17	90777

Comets

Comets are also part of the Solar System. They are not shown in Figure 11.3. They move in orbits round the Sun in the same way as the planets but their orbits are very elliptical (elongated), some stretching out into space well beyond Pluto. It is believed they come from a cloud of ice and rock at the very edge of the Solar System. This cloud is called the Oort cloud.

Measuring with light

The distance between two objects in space can be measured by the time it takes light to travel between them. For example, the time taken for light to travel between the Sun and the Earth is about eight minutes. The time taken for light to travel between the Sun and Pluto is about five and a half hours. The time for light to travel between two stars is much longer and is measured in light years. A light year is the distance travelled by light in a year. This distance is 9.5 million million kilometres.

The nearest star to the Sun is Proxima Centauri which is 4.3 light years away. This star and the Sun are just two of the 500 000 million stars in the Milky Way galaxy. This is a group of stars which is 100 000 light years across. There are about 100 000 million other galaxies in the universe. They are great distances from our own. For example, the Andromeda Galaxy, which can be seen as a fuzzy patch with the naked eye, is 2.2 million light years away.

Figure 11.4 The Andromeda galaxy seen through a telescope.

Lights in the sky

The Sun is the only large luminous body in our Solar System. We see the other large objects, such as the Moon, the planets and comets, by the sunlight they reflect to the Earth. As all these objects are relatively close to the Sun and the Earth they reflect light quite strongly towards the Earth. The other stars are luminous but much further away. Although they generate their own light the beam is very weak by the time it reaches the Earth.

The movement of the gases in the Earth's atmosphere does not significantly affect the strong light beams from the Moon, the planets and comets – they shine steadily in the sky. The weak light beams from the stars, however, are affected and the result is that their light does not shine steadily but appears to flicker or twinkle.

The brightness of a star depends on its size, its temperature and its distance from the Earth. Table 11.2 shows some stars arranged in decreasing order of brightness as seen from Earth.

4 How can you tell a planet from a star in the night sky?

5 a) Look at Table 11.2. Which star is the brighter, Betelgeuse or Spica?

b) Why might you expect Spica to be above Betelgeuse in the table?

c) Betelgeuse is a red giant star. How could this information help you explain its position in the table?

Table 11.2 The features of some bright stars, arranged in decreasing order of brightness.

Star	Temperature/°C	Colour	Distance from Earth
Sun	6000	yellow	8 light minutes
Sirius	11000	white	8.6 light years
Arcturus	4000	orange	36 light years
Betelgeuse	3000	red	520 light years
Spica	25000	blue	220 light years

Constellations and planets

The stars make patterns in the sky. These patterns are called constellations. The arrangement of the stars in a constellation is due to their positions in space which in turn is just due to chance. The stars may seem to be grouped together at the same distance from the Earth but they are not. Some stars in a constellation may be many light years closer to the Earth than others.

While the stars appear to be fixed in their positions, the planets do not. Each night a planet is found in a different position from the previous night. The name planet comes from the Greek word for wanderer. The planets wander across the night sky against the background of constellations. This is due to the orbital motion of the Earth and the planets.

Studies on the Solar System

The movement of the Sun, Moon, stars and planets across the sky was studied by ancient civilisations. They used the movements of the Sun and the Moon to measure time. This helped them with planning when to sow seeds to raise crops.

It seemed to the Ancient Greeks that all the objects in the sky were set in crystal spheres which moved round the Earth (see page 19). However, one Greek philosopher, called Aristarchos (c.320–250BC), suggested that the movements of the planets could be explained by considering them to move round the Sun. The other Greek philosophers were not enthusiastic about his ideas and preferred their model featuring crystal spheres.

The arrangement of the planets in the crystal spheres did not fully fit with the observations made of their movements in the sky. For example, Mercury and Venus did not move so far from the Sun as the crystal sphere arrangement suggested and the apparent backward motion of Mars, Jupiter and Saturn that occasionally occurred could not be explained by this model. The Egyptian astronomer Ptolemy, who lived in the 2nd Century AD, proposed an explanation. If the planets moved around the Earth in a looped circular path (see Figure A), the observed planetary motion would result. This explanation satisfied most people for about 1300 years.

Nicolaus Copernicus (1473–1543), a Polish astronomer, challenged these ideas, and the Earth-centred view of the Church, by suggesting that the Sun was at the centre of the universe and that the planets moved in circular orbits around it. This model supported the observed movements of the planets. For example, the apparent backward motions of Mars, Jupiter and Saturn could be explained by the Earth 'overtaking' them as it moved in its orbit round the Sun.

Tycho Brahe (1546–1601) was a Danish astronomer who made detailed observations of the planets and stars before the invention of the telescope. In 1577 a large comet appeared in the sky. People believed that comets were high clouds in the atmosphere. Brahe measured the position of the comet as it moved across the sky and discovered that it was further away than the Moon and not part of the atmosphere. He also discovered that it moved in an elliptical path, passing through space where the crystal spheres were thought to be without being restricted to movement within one.

Like most people, Brahe could not believe in the Sun-centred model of Copernicus, although his observations suggested that the crystal spheres did not exist. He devised a model of his own. In this model he still placed the Earth at the centre of the universe as the Greeks had done because he was reluctant to give up the ideas he had been taught.

1. How do you think the ancient civilisations used the Sun and the Moon to measure time? (Look back to *Finding a standard* page 4 to help you answer.)
2. How do you think a knowledge of time helped in the production of crops?
3. Why do you think it made sense to the Ancient Greeks to consider the Earth as the centre of the universe?

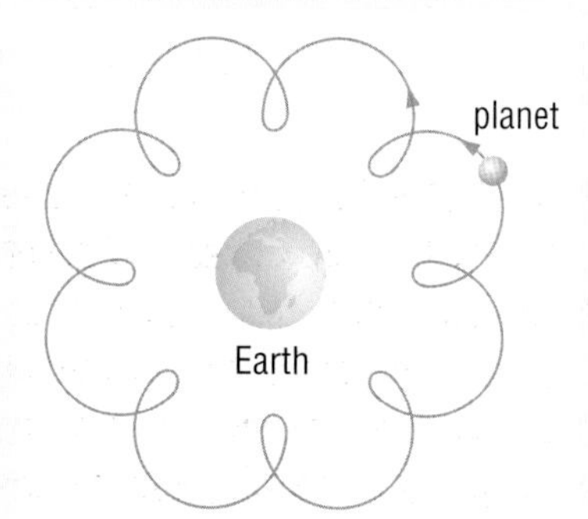

Figure A Planetary motion according to Ptolemy.

(continued)

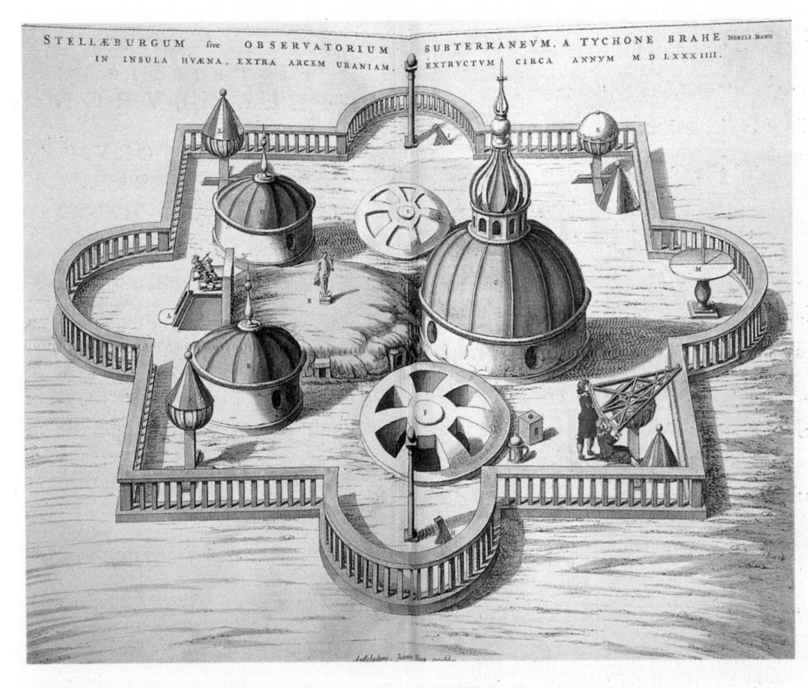

Figure B Brahe's observatory.

Galileo (1564–1642), an Italian scientist, built a telescope and examined the skies with it. He discovered what appeared to be stars around Jupiter and recorded their positions (see Figure C).

Galileo thought that if these stars were like others in the universe then the movement of Jupiter must be unlike that of the other planets. He decided that Jupiter probably moved just as the other planets did and the 'stars' were really moons moving around Jupiter, just as the Moon moves around the Earth. This was proof that some things in the sky did not move around the Earth but moved around other objects.

Johannes Kepler (1571–1630), a German astronomer, worked with Tycho Brahe. When Brahe died Kepler re-examined the vast amount of data Brahe had collected. Kepler studied the orbits of the planets. He found that the data accurately matched orbits of an elliptical shape around the Sun. This discovery provided the final evidence against the Earth-centred universe and established our current knowledge about motion in the Solar System.

At the time that Galileo and Kepler were investigating the Solar System, Gilbert's experiments on magnetism (see page 141) were becoming widely known. Galileo and Kepler thought that a magnetic force might hold the objects in the Solar System in their places, too.

RECENS HABITAE

in tali configuratione. Orientalior diſtabat a ſequenti *min.3.* ſequens a Ioue *min. 1. ſec.50.* Iupiter ab occidentaliſequenti *min.3.* hæc vero ab occi-

Ori. Occ.

dentaliori *min. 7.* erant fere æquales, orientalis tantum Ioui proxima reliquis erat paulo minor: erantque in eadem recta Eclipticæ parallela.

Die 19. Ho. 0. *min.* 40. Stellæ duæ ſolummodo occiduæ a Ioue conſpectæ fuerunt ſatis magnæ, & in eadem recta cum Ioue ad vnguem, ac

Ori. Occ.

ſecundum Eclypticæ ductum diſpoſitæ. Propinquior a Ioue diſtabat *m.7.* hæc vero ab occidentaliori *min. 6.*

Die 20. Nubiloſum fuit cœlum.

Die 21. Ho. 1. *min. 30.* Stellulæ tres ſatis exiguæ cernebantur in hac conſtitutione. Orientalis aberat a Ioue *min.2.* Iupiter ab occidentali ſequente

Ori. Occ.

te. *min. 3.* hæc vero ab occidentaliori *min.7.* erant ad vnguem in eadem recta Eclypticæ parallela

Die 25. Ho. 1. *min.30.* (nam ſuperioribus tribus noctibus cœlum fuit nubibus obductum) tres apparuerunt Stellæ. Orientales duæ, quarũ

Ori. Occ.

diſtantiæ inter ſe, & a Ioue æquales fuerunt, ac *min.4.* Occidentalis vna aberat a Ioue *min.2.* Erãt in eadem recta ad vnguem, ſecundum Eclypticæ ductum.

Figure C Galileo's record of Jupiter's moons. The large 'star' is Jupiter and the small 'stars' are its moons.

(continued)

Isaac Newton (1642–1727) is believed to have begun his investigation on the force that holds objects in the Solar System when he saw an apple fall from a tree.

Figure D Did the same force pull on the Moon?

He reasoned that the force which pulled the small apple down to the Earth may also pull the large Moon, even though the Moon was at a much greater distance from the Earth. He considered the Moon to be falling towards the Earth in its orbit around the Earth. The Moon did not reach the Earth, he thought, because it was at such a great distance and the strength of the force was weaker there. This resulted in the Moon falling around the Earth rather than on to it.

From his calculations on this force of gravity on objects near the Earth, Newton predicted the rate of fall of the Moon needed to give its movement in a curve around the Earth. When Newton made calculations on the actual movement of the Moon he found that they matched his prediction. From this work he showed that the objects in the Solar System moved due to the force of gravity.

4 How did the work of Brahe, Galileo and Kepler destroy the idea of crystal spheres around the Earth?

5 Why was it not unreasonable to believe magnetism might be an important force in holding objects in the Solar System?

6 In what way did chance play a part in the discovery that gravity is the force which acts between objects in the Solar System?

Gravity

Gravity is the force of attraction which exists between any two objects in the universe. If the two objects have small masses the force between them is too small to affect either one noticeably. If the two objects are large, like stars and planets, the force of gravity affects both. If one of the objects is comparatively large (like the Earth) and the other is comparatively small (like you) then the smaller one is more greatly affected by the force of gravity between them than the larger one (see page 30) although the size of the force each experiences is the same.

The force of gravity between two objects that are close together is stronger than the force of gravity between two objects that are far apart.

The Sun is the most massive object in the Solar System. The force of gravity between the Sun and each of the planets holds the planet in its orbit round the Sun. The planets nearer the Sun move faster in their orbits than the planets that are more distant from the Sun

The gravitational forces between a planet and its moons hold the moons in orbit round the planet. Mercury and Venus do not have moons but all the other planets have at least one. More moons around the larger planets may yet be discovered. At present Jupiter is known to have at least 16 moons and Saturn has at least 18.

6 How does the force of gravity vary with the distance between objects?

Our Moon

The Moon moves round the Earth in about 28 days. Only the side of the Moon's surface that is facing the Sun reflects light, so as its orbit progresses the illuminated part that we can see from Earth changes shape. The different shapes are known as phases of the Moon (Figure 11.5).

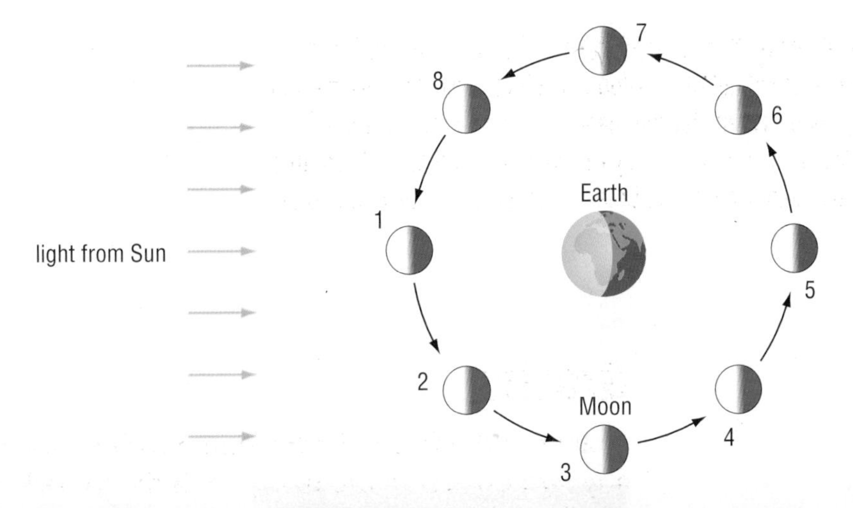

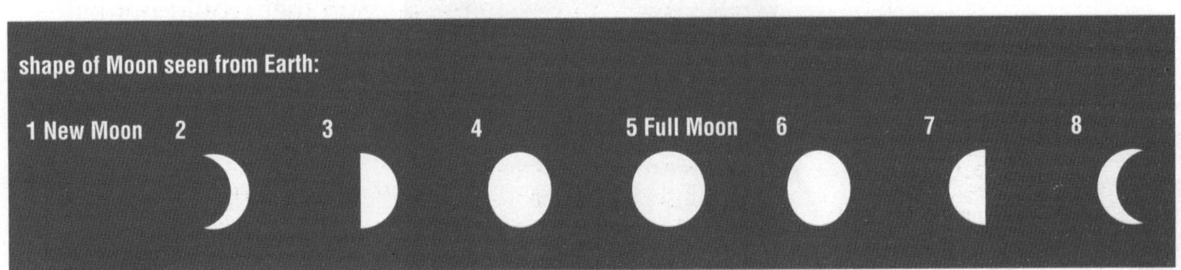

Figure 11.5 Phases of the Moon.

Eclipses of the Sun and the Moon

The imaginary surface in which an orbit lies is called the plane of the orbit. Figure 11.6 shows that the plane of the orbit of the Moon is different from the plane of the orbit of the Earth around the Sun. This means that even when the Moon passes between the Sun and the Earth in its orbit there is not always an eclipse of the Sun. In fact, eclipses of the Sun are very rare.

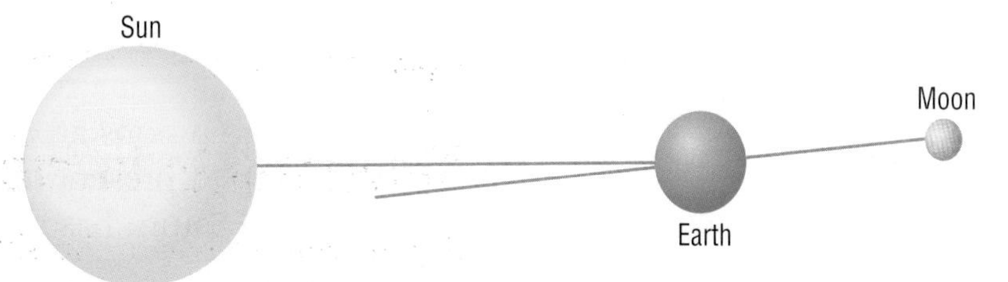

Figure 11.6 Planes of the orbits of the Moon and the Earth.

When the Sun, Moon and Earth do line up exactly a total eclipse of the Sun occurs for viewers on a certain part of the Earth's surface (Figure 11.7). The Moon blocks out the light of the Sun.

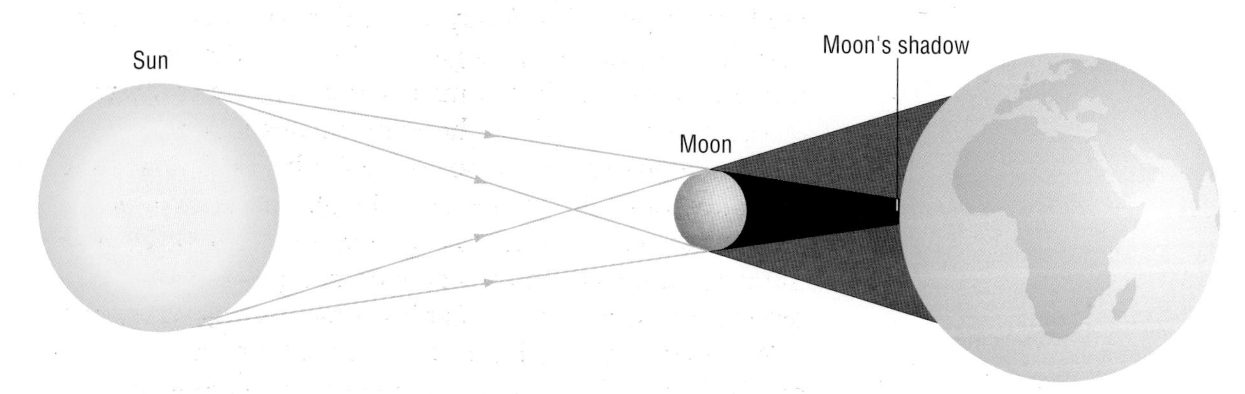

Figure 11.7 An eclipse of the Sun.

Sometimes the Sun, Earth and Moon line up as in Figure 11.9 and an eclipse of the Moon takes place. The Earth blocks out light from the Sun that would normally fall on the Moon at Full Moon phase.

Figure 11.8 The Earth's shadow on the Moon during a partial eclipse of the Moon.

7 How are an eclipse of the Sun and an eclipse of the Moon **a)** similar and **b)** different?

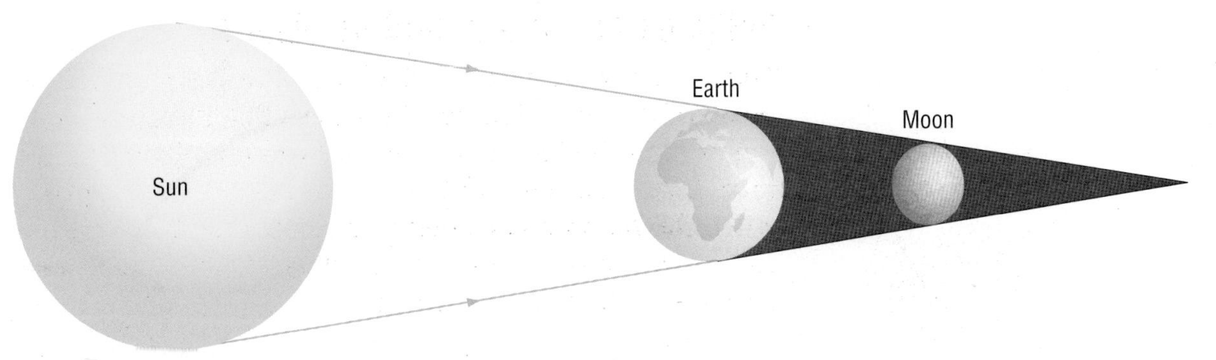

Figure 11.9 An eclipse of the Moon.

Movements in the sky

If you were to watch the sky for a day and a night you would see the Sun rise towards the east at dawn. It would continue to rise in the sky until midday, then it would sink in the sky and set towards the west. As the sunlight faded the sky would darken and other stars would be seen to cross the sky from east to west before they faded as the sunlight appeared again in the sky. People once believed that these movements of the stars really took place but today we understand that the Sun and the stars do not change position. It is the daily rotation of the Earth that makes them appear to move.

The axis about which the Earth rotates is not perpendicular to the plane of the Earth's orbit. If it were, the Sun would rise to the same height in the sky each day of the year. The axis is at an angle of about 23° to the perpendicular and remains pointing in the same direction throughout the Earth's orbit (see Figure 11.10).

We divide the Earth into two half spheres or hemispheres. They meet at the equator which is an imaginary line running around the middle of the planet between the poles. The hemispheres are known as the northern hemisphere and the southern hemisphere.

As the Earth moves in its orbit there is a time of year when the northern hemisphere is tilting towards the Sun and the southern hemisphere is tilting away from it. Six months later the northern hemisphere is tilting away from the Sun and the southern hemisphere is tilting towards it.

These changes in the way each hemisphere tilts towards and away from the Sun cause changes in the length of day and night, and in the strength of the sunlight reaching an area of the Earth's surface. This produces the periods of time called seasons (see *Biology Now! 11–14* pages 177 and 179).

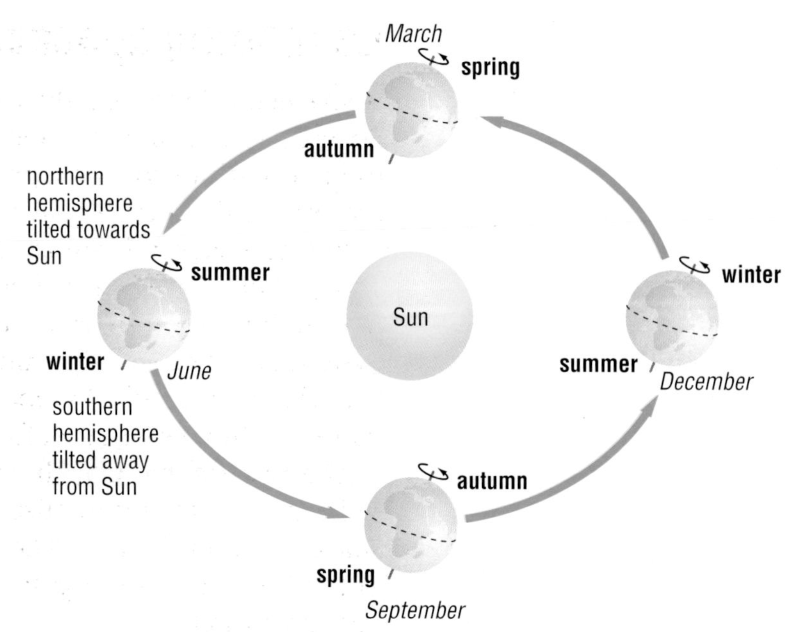

Figure 11.10 The changing seasons in each hemisphere as the Earth progresses in its orbit.

The east to west path of the Sun across the sky changes with the position of the Earth in its orbit. When a hemisphere is tilting towards the Sun, the path of the Sun is different from the path when the hemisphere is tilting away from the Sun. Sunrise is earlier, the Sun rises higher in the sky at midday and sets later in the evening. Figure 11.11 shows the path of the Sun across the sky when the hemisphere is tilted towards the Sun (mid-summer), away from the Sun (mid-winter) and when it is changing from tilting in one direction to the other (at the spring and autumn equinoxes).

8 What is the position of the Earth when it is summer in **a)** the northern hemisphere and **b)** the southern hemisphere?

9 What is the position of the Earth when the Sun rises to its lowest midday position in the sky in **a)** the northern hemisphere and **b)** the southern hemisphere?

10 What is the position of the Earth when **a)** the day is longer than the night in the southern hemisphere, **b)** the day is shorter than the night in the southern hemisphere and **c)** the day and the night are the same length of time?

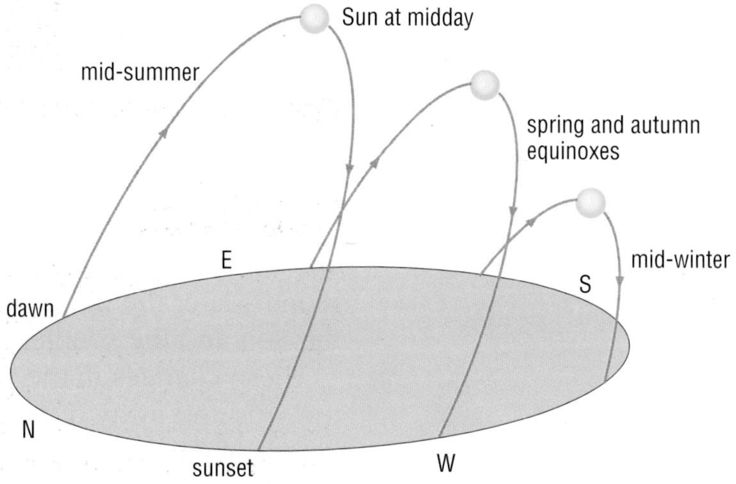

Figure 11.11 The changing path of the Sun across the sky as the seasons change (in the northern hemisphere).

Launching spacecraft

A spacecraft fired directly towards distant parts of the Solar System from the launch pad would have to leave the Earth at the colossal speed of 40 000 km/h to escape the pull of the Earth's gravity.

In fact, spacecraft are launched into space in stages by taking them first on a rocket into orbit around the Earth before they begin their trip to other parts of the Solar System and beyond. By launching a spacecraft in this way the escape velocity does not have to be reached and there is a huge saving on fuel.

The rockets that launch spacecraft into orbit still have to be very powerful to raise the weight of the rocket, the spacecraft and the fuel. The reaction force (see page 36) of the hot combustion gases leaving the rocket engines lifts the rocket.

Figure 11.12 Launch of a space shuttle.

Satellites

Satellites are spacecraft which stay in orbit round the Earth. There are hundreds of them. Some have cameras on board and take pictures of the Earth. These pictures are used for studying and predicting the weather or for monitoring worldwide crop production. Many satellites are communication satellites. They relay telephone messages, television programmes and Internet communications around the Earth.

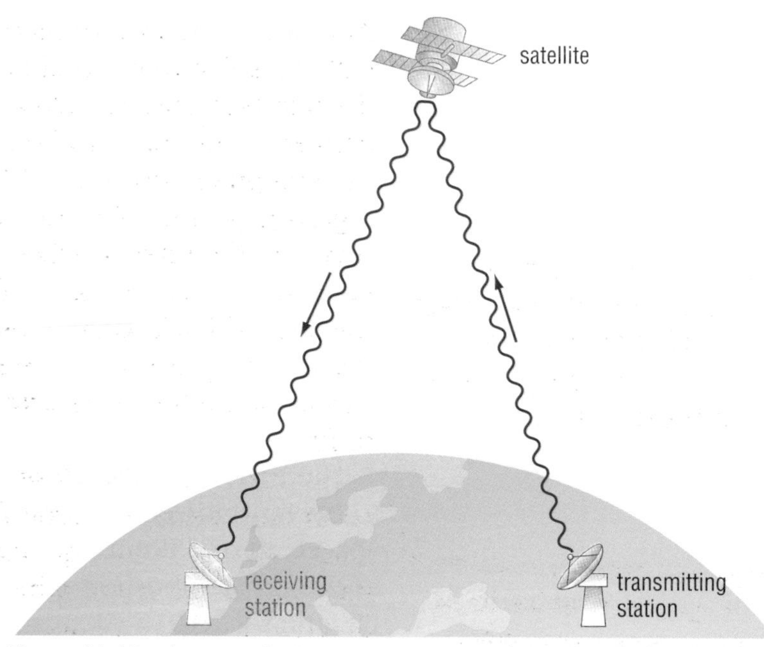

Figure 11.13 A communication satellite link.

Some satellites are used for navigation. The signals they send out are used by the crews of ships and aircraft to keep on course as they travel round the Earth. A few satellites, like the Hubble Space Telescope, investigate space. This telescope is not affected by the atmosphere like telescopes on the Earth's surface so it can obtain clearer pictures of deep space.

Figure 11.14 The Hubble Space Telescope.

After a satellite has reached its orbit, panels of solar cells called a solar array unfold and collect light energy from the Sun (see Figures 4.20 and 11.14). The light energy is converted into electrical energy which is used to work the equipment on board. The satellite is controlled from a ground station. Messages are sent on a beam of radio waves to the satellite where a receiver converts them into electric currents. Messages from the satellite are transmitted back to the ground station also by radio waves. The position of the satellite can be altered by commanding thruster rockets on the side of the satellite to fire.

Satellites that orbit close to the Earth have to travel faster than those that orbit further away because the Earth's gravity is stronger closer to the planet. A satellite must travel at a speed which will prevent it being pulled down to Earth by the force of gravity. A satellite in a low orbit may therefore pass round the planet several times a day.

At a distance of 35 880 km above the equator a satellite can orbit at the same rate as that at which the Earth turns. This makes the satellite stay over a particular place all the time while the Earth rotates. This orbit is called a geostationary orbit and is used by communication and navigation satellites.

11 What is the advantage of a geostationary orbit over a lower orbit for a communication satellite? Look at Figure 11.13 to help you answer.

For discussion

What will happen to a satellite if its speed is a) too low for its orbit, b) correct for its orbit, c) too fast for its orbit?

What are the advantages of setting up a space station in a low orbit rather than a high one?

Space exploration

Robert Goddard (1882–1945) was an American physicist who developed a liquid-fuelled rocket in 1926. It was only about 120 cm high and about 15 cm in diameter and rose to a height of 60 metres. He devised many refinements that allowed his rockets to be steered and carry instruments. By 1935 he had built a rocket that could reach a speed of 800 km/h and rose about 2.4 km into the sky. From his work other scientists developed larger rockets to launch spacecraft.

Figure A Goddard with one of his first rockets in the 1930s.

(continued)

In 1957 the first artificial satellite was launched from the USSR. It was called Sputnik 1 and it travelled in orbit around the Earth at heights of between 220 and 900 km. It remained in orbit for 92 days before it sank into the atmosphere and burnt up due to the heat generated by friction between its sides and the particles in the air.

In 1959 the USA and the USSR sent probes to the Moon. In 1961 Yuri Gagarin (1934–1968), a Russian astronaut, was the first man to enter space. He made one orbit of the Earth in his spacecraft called Vostok 1. In 1962 Mariner 2, launched in the USA, was the first space probe to fly past another planet – Venus. It carried instruments to measure the planet's surface temperature (425 °C) and its magnetic field. In 1963 Valentina Tereshkova (b.1937), a Russian astronaut, was the first woman to enter space. She made 48 orbits of the Earth in her spacecraft, Vostok 6.

Figure B Valentina Tereshkova.

In 1969 Neil Armstrong (b.1930), an American astronaut, was the first person to step onto the Moon. The space programme that had planned the mission was called the Apollo space programme, and the moon-landing itself was Apollo 11. The last Apollo astronauts to visit the Moon as part of this programme did so in 1972, in the Apollo 17 mission.

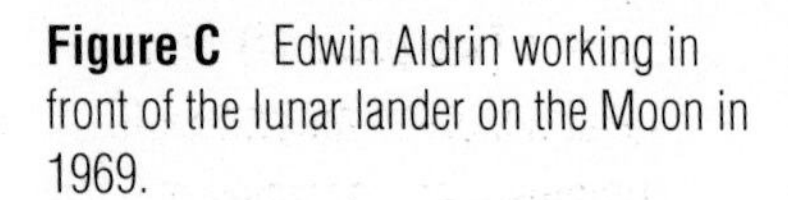

Figure C Edwin Aldrin working in front of the lunar lander on the Moon in 1969.

Since that time there has been the development of space stations, the re-usable shuttle orbiter, and many space probes which have between them visited most of the planets. Some of the probes are sent to their destination planet using a 'sling shot method' – the probe is sent past one planet and uses its gravitational force to redirect it on its way to the next planet (Figure D).

(continued)

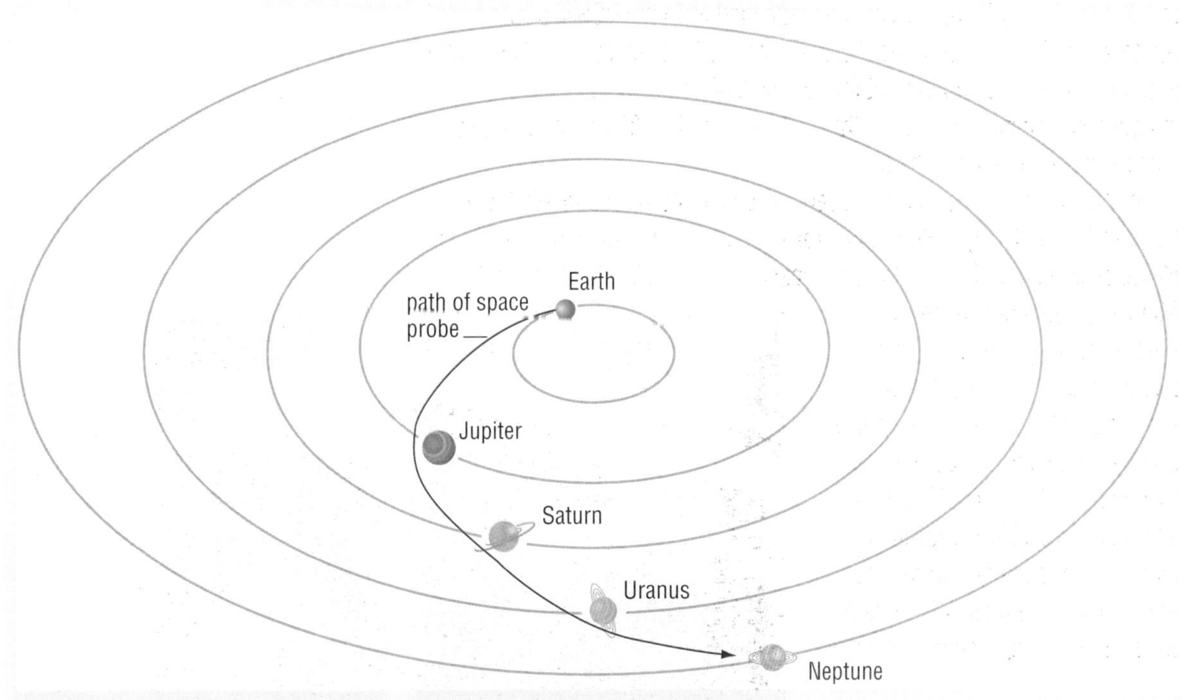

Figure D Sling shot method of sending a probe through the Solar System.

The probes carry a range of instruments which investigate the structure of a planet's atmosphere, the elements that are present, the magnetic field, the temperature and the atmospheric pressure.

Figure E The Magellan space probe being launched from a shuttle at the start of its journey to Venus.

1 Deep space is almost a vacuum (see page 54) whilst the atmosphere around Earth contains many particles of matter. Use this information to explain why friction is not a problem to spacecraft travelling at high speeds in deep space but is a problem to spacecraft returning to Earth through the atmosphere.

Beyond the Solar System

The work of many astronomers has shown that the Sun is not the centre of the Universe as people once believed. It is on an arm of a spiral galaxy called the Milky Way (Figure 11.15). This galaxy received its name from the pale white glow it makes across the sky (Figure 11.16).

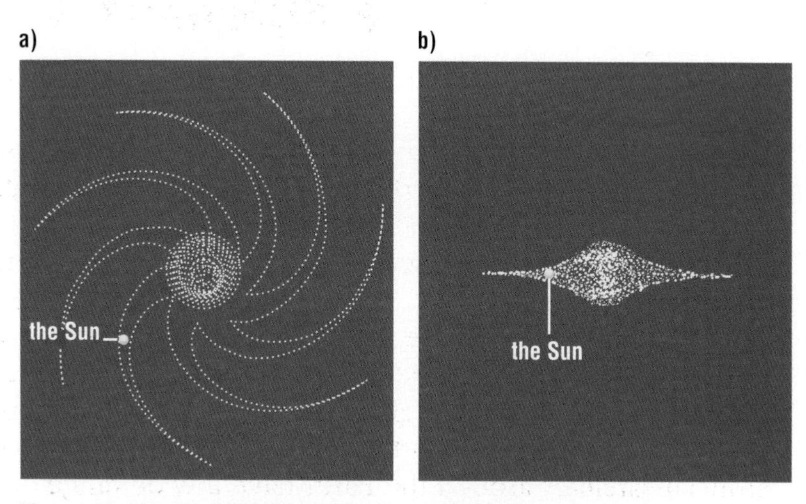

Figure 11.15 The Milky Way: **a)** top view, **b)** side view.

For discussion

Some stars are believed to have planets. What do you think are the chances of simple life forms existing on a planet somewhere in the universe?

How would you rate the chances of discovering the following: a) simple life forms, b) intelligent life forms with a lower technological development than us, c) intelligent life forms with a higher technological development than us? Explain your answers.

How will the vast distances between planets in different parts of the universe hinder communications if we find intelligent life?

Figure 11.16 The Milky Way as seen from Earth.

There are about 30 galaxies relatively close to the Milky Way. They form a group of galaxies called the Local Group. Beyond them in all directions are other groups of galaxies at distances of up to thousands of millions of light years away.

♦ SUMMARY ♦

- It is believed that everything in the universe was produced in an explosion called the Big Bang (*see page 189*).
- Our Solar System formed about 5000 million years ago (*see page 190*).
- Planets can be distinguished from stars by the way that they shine and by their motion across the sky (*see page 193*).
- Gravity is the force of attraction which exists between any two bodies in the universe (*see page 196*).
- The phases of the Moon are due to the Moon's orbit around the Earth (*see page 197*).
- There can be eclipses of the Sun and the Moon (*see page 198*).
- The changes of day and night and the seasons are due to the rotation of the Earth, the tilt of its axis and its path around the Sun (*see page 199*).
- Artificial satellites around the Earth have a wide range of uses (*see page 201*).
- The Solar System is part of the Milky Way galaxy (*see page 206*).

End of chapter questions

There is a unit of measurement called the astronomical unit. It is the average distance of the Earth from the Sun.

Here are the average distances from the Sun in astronomical units of the first six planets in the Solar System:

1.0, 0.4, 9.6, 5.2, 0.7, 1.52

1 Produce a table of these data using Figure 11.3 to name the planets.

Scientists look for patterns in their data. In the 18th Century astronomers looked for a pattern in the orbital distances in the following way.

- Start with the number sequence 0, 3, 6, 12 then continue to double the last number.
- Add 4 to each number then divide the total by 10.
  For example:

$0 + 4 = 4 \quad \frac{4}{10} = 0.4$

$3 + 4 = 7 \quad \frac{7}{10} = 0.7$

The resulting numbers are called Bode numbers after the German astronomer Johann Bode (1747–1826).

(continued)

2 Calculate the first seven Bode numbers in order and write down how they compare with the orbital distances of the planets. What conclusions can you draw from these values?
3 When Uranus was discovered it was found to have a distance from the Sun of 19.2 astronomical units. How did this fit in with the relationship known as Bode's Law?
4 When Neptune was discovered it was found to have an average distance from the Sun of 39.0 astronomical units. How did this fit in with Bode's Law?
5 Between Mars and Jupiter there are large numbers of rocky fragments called asteroids. Does their presence support Bode's Law?
6 When Pluto was discovered it was found to have an average distance from the Sun of 40.4 astronomical units. How did this fit in with Bode's Law?
7 Why do you think Bode's Law is no longer used?

Glossary

A

acceleration The change in velocity of an object in a certain period of time.

air resistance The backward push of the air on an object moving through it.

ammeter An instrument for measuring the size of a current flowing through a circuit, in amperes.

amplitude The maximum displacement of a vibrating object from its rest position.

atom A particle of an element which comprises a central nucleus that is surrounded by electrons.

B

battery Two or more electrical cells joined in series in a circuit.

biconcave lens A lens with opposite surfaces that curve inwards.

biconvex lens A lens with opposite surfaces that curve outwards.

bimetallic strip A strip of material made from two different metals which differ greatly in the way they expand and contract; used in thermostats.

biogas Methane produced by the digestive processes of microorganisms that feed on plant and animal waste.

biomass The amount of matter in a living thing

C

cell A device containing chemicals which react and produce a current of electricity in a closed conducting circuit.

chemical energy The energy stored in the links between atoms of a substance.

conduction The passage of heat energy from one part of a material to another, by vibrating particles passing kinetic energy on to neighbouring particles.

conductor (electrical) A material that allows electricity to pass easily through it.

constellation A pattern of stars in the sky which appear to form a group but may in fact be light years apart.

convection The passage of heat energy through a liquid or a gas, by the particles in the substance changing position and carrying kinetic energy with them.

D

density The mass of unit volume of a substance.

diode An electrical component which allows a current to pass in only one direction through it.

dispersion The spreading out of light of different colours from a beam of sunlight.

domain A tiny region inside a magnet which behaves like a microscopic magnet.

drag A force which acts on a moving body in the opposite direction to which the body is moving, due to air or water resistance.

dynamo A device for generating a current of electricity. There are two kinds: a direct current or d.c. dynamo which produces a current that flows in only one direction, and an alternating current or a.c. dynamo which produces a current that changes direction many times a second. The bicycle dynamo and power station generators are a.c. dynamos.

E

elastic limit The maximum force that can be applied to an elastic material without the material becoming permanently deformed.

elastic material A material that exerts a strain force when deformed, tending to restore it to its original shape.

electromagnet A magnet which is made by coiling a wire around a piece of iron then passing a current through the wire.

electromagnetic waves Waves with electrical and magnetic properties which transfer energy, such as light and radio waves.

electron A tiny particle inside an atom which moves around the nucleus. It has a negative electric charge.

electrostatic charge A charge of electricity which stays in place on the surface of a material; it may be positive (due to a lack of electrons) or negative (due to an excess of electrons).

energy The ability of something to do work.

energy chain The flow of energy through one or more energy converters.

energy converter A material or an object in which energy changes from one form to another as it passes through; also called an energy transducer.

energy level A measure of the amount of energy possessed by an atom, which depends on the arrangement of its electrons.

F

field A region in which a non-contact force acts.
force A push or a pull; it may be a contact force, for example an impact force, or a non-contact force, for example a magnetic force.
fossil fuel A fuel such as coal, oil or gas which is formed from the fossilised remains of plants or animals.
frequency The number of waves passing a point in a certain amount of time.
friction A force that acts against the relative movement of two surfaces in contact.
fuel A substance used to provide energy for heating, producing electricity or working machinery.
fulcrum The point (pivot) on which a lever is supported as it turns.

G

galaxy A large group of stars held together by gravitational forces.
galvanometer A device for measuring small amounts of electrical current; it does not have a scale measuring in amperes.
geothermal energy Energy extracted from hot rocks beneath the surface of the Earth.
gravitational force A force between any two masses in the universe. The force is noticed when the two masses are very large, for example planets, or when one is very large and the other is very small by comparison, for example the Earth and you.
gravitational potential energy The energy stored in an object because of its position above the Earth's surface.

H

heat (thermal) energy The energy transferred to or from a substance by heating, which increases or decreases the internal kinetic energy of the substance.
hydraulic system A machine made from pistons and pipes that contain a liquid. It transmits pressure and converts a small force into a large one.
hydroelectric power Electricity produced from the energy of falling water.

I

image The picture of an object which is produced when light is reflected from a mirror or is focused onto a screen by a lens.
impact force The force exerted by one object on another when they collide.
induced charge An electrical charge which develops on the surface of a material due to the presence of an electrically charged material close by but not in contact.
induced magnetism Temporary magnetism produced in a magnetic material when it is close to a magnet.
infrared radiation Waves of electromagnetic radiation with wavelength between red light and microwaves; they cause warming.
insulator (electrical) A substance which does not allow electricity to pass through it.
internal energy The energy that atoms of a substance possess, partly due to their motion.

K

kinetic energy The energy possessed by a moving object.

L

LDR Light dependent resistor.
LED Light emitting diode.
lens A piece of transparent glass or plastic with two curved surfaces opposite each other; used to change the direction of light rays by refraction.
lever A device that changes the direction in which a force acts, for example a crowbar.
lightning A rapid movement of large amount of electrical charge through air which produces heat and light.
lightning conductor A device on a building which reduces the charge on a storm cloud overhead, and transports the electric charge safely to the ground if lightning strikes the building.
light year The distance travelled by light through space in one year. It is 9.5 million million kilometres.
luminescence The emission of light without heat.
luminous object Any object that releases energy in the form of light.

M

magnetic material A material that is attracted to a magnet and can be made into a magnet.

magnetic pole One of two regions in a magnet where the magnetic force is very strong.
magnetosphere The region around the Earth containing the Earth's magnetic field. Stars and other planets also have magnetospheres.
mass The amount of matter in an object.
moment The turning effect of a force.

N

neutron A particle, in the nucleus of an atom, which has no electric charge.
non-luminous object An object that does not release energy in the form of light but may reflect light from luminous objects.
non-magnetic material A material that is not attracted to a magnet and cannot be made into a magnet.
non-renewable energy source A source of energy, such as fossil fuels and radioactive materials, which cannot be replaced once it has been used.
nuclear energy The energy stored in the nucleus of an atom.
nuclear fission The process in which the nucleus of an atom breaks down into smaller nuclei and releases energy.
nuclear fusion A process in which atomic nuclei join together to form larger nuclei of other elements.
nuclear reactor A device in which nuclear fission is allowed to take place safely so that the energy released can be used to generate electricity.

O

opaque material A material through which light cannot pass.

P

phenomenon Something which can be observed that is due to the way matter behaves; for example when a piece of wood gets very hot it bursts into flame and gives out light.
pitch A measure of the frequency of a sound wave.
potential energy Energy that is stored when work is done moving an object against a force. It is the energy something has due to its position, for example gravitational potential energy: a person who has climbed to the top of a slide has a larger amount of potential energy than someone who has just slid to the bottom.
pressure The term used to describe a force acting over an area of known size.
primary colours (of light) Red, green and blue. They can be used to make all the other colours of light.
prism A piece of transparent glass or plastic which has a triangular cross-section; used to disperse the coloured light in sunlight to form the visible spectrum.

R

radiation A form of energy transfer by electromagnetic waves.
radioactive materials Materials in which nuclear reactions take place and energy is released in the form of nuclear radiation.
reaction force If object A exerts a force on object B, object B exerts an equal and opposite reaction force on object A.
real image An image that can be focused onto a screen.
refinery gases Gases collected by the fractional distillation of oil (see *Chemistry Now! 11–14* page 146).
reflection A process in which light rays striking a surface are turned away from the surface.
refraction The bending of a light ray as it passes from one transparent substance to another.
relay A type of switch used in a low-current circuit to control the current in a second, high-current circuit.
renewable energy source A source of energy such as sunlight, wind and biomass, which can be used again and again.
resistance (electrical) The property of a material which opposes the flow of a current through the material.
resistor A device that offers a certain amount of resistance to a current passing through a circuit.

S

satellite A device that moves in orbit around the Earth (or any moon around any planet).
sliding friction The friction that exists between two objects when one is moving over the other.
solar cell A device that converts the energy in sunlight into electrical energy.
solar panel A device for collecting heat from the Sun to warm water. (Or an array of solar cells).
Solar System The Sun and the planets, moons, asteroids and comets which move around it.
sound energy The energy transferred by a sound wave.
space probe An unmanned spacecraft for exploring space and the objects in the Solar System.

spectrum (electromagnetic) The full range of wavelengths of electromagnetic waves from the shortest gamma rays to the longest radio waves.

spectrum (visible) The bands of coloured light seen when a prism disperses sunlight. The colours are red, orange, yellow, green, blue, indigo and violet.

speed A measure of the distance covered by a moving object in a certain time.

standard form The standard system of recording large numbers, with only one figure in front of the decimal point, for example 3.84×10^8.

static friction The friction that exists between two objects when there is no movement between them. It acts against an applied force, preventing movement.

strain energy The energy stored in an elastic material when it is deformed.

strain force The force exerted by an elastic material when it is deformed; it acts in the opposite direction to the applied force.

streamlined shape A shape that allows an object to move easily through air or water.

T

temperature A measure of the hotness or coldness of a substance; it depends on the average kinetic energy of the particles.

terminal velocity The velocity at which an object falls through air when the air resistance balances the weight of the object.

translucent material A material that allows some light to pass through it but scatters this light in all directions.

transparent material A material that allows light to pass through it without the light being scattered.

U

ultraviolet Electromagnetic waves with wavelength shorter than blue light.

unit A standard for measurements, for example the kilogram.

upthrust The upward force exerted on an object by the liquid or gas around it that it displaces. The force is equal to the weight of the displaced liquid or gas.

V

vacuum A space in which there is no matter; it contains no atomic particles.

velocity The speed of an object or a wave in a particular direction.

vibration The rapid movement of an object to and fro about a rest position, as seen when a guitar string has been plucked.

virtual image An image such as the one seen in a mirror which cannot be focused onto a screen.

voltage The difference in electric potential between two points such as the terminals of a cell, measured in volts.

voltmeter A device that measures the difference in electric potential between two parts of a circuit, in volts.

W

weight The gravitational force between an object on a planet such as the Earth and the Earth itself. The weight pulls the object towards the centre of the Earth.

work The energy expended when a force moves an object through a distance.

X

X-rays Electromagnetic waves with wavelength between ultraviolet light and gamma rays.

Index